Digital Resources for Students

Your new manual provides 12-month access to a digital version which you can view on a compatible computer, tablet, or phone. The Companion Website also includes quizzes you can use to test your comprehension.

Follow the instructions below to register for the Companion Website for *Open Water Lifesaving: The United States Lifesaving Association Manual,* Third Edition.

1. Go to http://www.pearsoncustom.com/usla
2. Follow the on-screen instructions to complete the registration process. You will need the following code during this process:

DSWIZJ-QUIPU-BAUTH-SKEAN-BLUNT-FFLSE

IMPORTANT:

This access code can only be used once. This subscription is valid for 12 months upon activation and is not transferrable.

For technical support go to http://247pearsoned.custhelp.com

D1379135

PEARSON

ALWAYS LEARNING

B. Chris Brewster, Editor

Open Water Lifesaving
The United States Lifesaving Association Manual

Third Edition

Pearson Education, Inc., 330 Hudson Street, New York, New York 10013
A Pearson Education Company
www.pearsoned.com

Printed in the United States of America

2   17

000200010272072521

EEB/JF

ISBN 10: 1-323-58456-0
ISBN 13: 978-1-323-58456-9

Contents

Preface

This manual is intended to be used as a guide in the instruction and training of open water lifesavers, a reference for professional beach lifeguards and aquatic safety managers, and a yardstick against which lifesaving agencies can measure their performance. It is the product of the combined knowledge of the members of the United States Lifesaving Association (USLA), the only national association of open water rescuers at both surf and inland areas.

When the United States Lifesaving Association was established in 1964, an early dream of the founders was to create national standards for beach lifeguarding in the USA. At that time, open water lifesaving standards varied from agency to agency, locally, regionally, and nationally. They had many similarities, but also many differences. There can however, be only one best methodology—one best practice. Agreeing upon it and encouraging all American beach lifeguard agencies to follow it was a great challenge.

In 1980, leaders of national water safety organizations gathered at Texas A&M University in Galveston for what was billed as a *Conference to Develop Guidelines for Establishing Open-Water Recreational Beach Standards*. The USLA was one of the primary sponsors. The conference attendees, after establishing general guidelines, ultimately agreed that the USLA should take the lead in creating national standards within parameters that had been defined by the group.

In 1981 the USLA published our first manual, *Lifesaving and Marine Safety*, edited by Douglas G. D'Arnall. Two years later, in 1983, the USLA published a booklet entitled, *Guidelines for Open Water Lifeguard Training*. These two publications provided the basis for national consistency in open water rescue training, but they were only a start down the road to standardization. There was inevitable resistance to change from lifesaving agencies steeped in decades of individual tradition.

One of the great desires of beach lifeguards and their employing agencies was a system whereby those meeting national standards could be certified. To that end, in 1992 the USLA National Certification Committee amended and added to the existing guidelines to create, *Guidelines for Open Water Lifeguard Training and Standards*. The real breakthrough though, was the creation in 1992 of the national USLA *Lifeguard Agency Certification Program*. For the first time in the USA, this program allowed open water lifeguard agencies in compliance with USLA standards to become nationally certified (accredited). The system relies on training provided by lifesaving agencies in accordance with USLA standards. It was followed, some years later, by the development of

Guidelines for Training & Standards of Aquatic Rescue Response Teams, which opened certification to non-lifeguard aquatic rescue groups.

The original USLA manual needed significant revisions to adjust to advancements in lifesaving and to the updated guidelines. The task of rewriting the text was initially assumed by Tim Hall of New England, who completed a draft update in 1991. In 1992, B. Chris Brewster, who had chaired the National Certification Committee that had most recently updated the guidelines, was appointed to chair a newly formed National Textbook Committee and to edit revisions to the new manual. A team of dedicated members of that group spent thousands of volunteer hours of research and writing, culminating in the 1995 publication of the second USLA manual, *The United States Lifesaving Association Manual of Open Water Lifesaving*. Several years later, that text was updated by another equally dedicated committee, chaired by Brewster, resulting in the 2001 publication of *Open Water Lifesaving—The United States Lifesaving Manual*.

A recurring request of training officers has been a desire for educational materials to assist in their course delivery. That request, along with the need to revise the manual, brought about the creation of a new National Textbook Group in 2016. This resulted not only in the development of the updated version you now read, but also lesson plans, testing resources, skills sheets, and a comprehensive set of computer-based slides. As well, the manual is now available electronically. Each of the members of the group listed in the *Acknowledgements* section of this book spent hundreds of hours on these key tasks.

A profession requires consistent standards to which its members are trained. Until the USLA was formed, there were none. At the time of publication of this manual, over 140 open water USLA certified lifesaving agencies, along with tens of thousands of open water rescuers, follow a single, national standard.

The United States Lifesaving Association brought together beach lifeguards who cared about their profession and sought to make it better. There have been countless efforts of this nature over the years. They are detailed in the history section of this manual and on our website—www.usla.org. As a lifesaver or one soon to be, we hope you might appreciate that our profession is what it is today largely due to these many efforts of volunteer members of the USLA, who gave their time unselfishly. It has been a labor of love and dedication by those who believe, unstintingly, in the nobility of the lifesaving profession.

Editor's Note

- This text represents the collective knowledge of acknowledged leaders associated with the most highly regarded lifesaving agencies in the United States. It is intended to be a comprehensive text essential to the effective training and retraining of those involved in open water lifesaving. Each open water lifesaving agency in America faces unique challenges posed by the local environment and the particular assignments of its personnel. Therefore, this text will only be fully effective when used in conjunction with a training program in compliance with the USLA Lifeguard Agency Certification Program or the USLA Aquatic Rescue Response Team program, and supplemented by appropriate specialized training addressing local conditions.

- This text does not and cannot stand alone as a lifesaving training manual. It has been deliberately written to be used in conjunction with an agency's manual, which must contain the specific policies and procedures pertaining to the information provided in this text.

- The material contained in this text constitutes the considered and expert opinion of the the USLA. The USLA makes no express or implied warranty or guarantee as to the material, opinions, or methods contained in this text.

- The procedures, techniques, and equipment used in open water lifesaving are constantly changing and improving. It has only been through experimentation over the years by innovative lifesavers that improved techniques have been developed. This process must continue if we are to effectively meet the challenge of the future.

About the United States Lifesaving Association

The United States Lifesaving Association is America's nonprofit, professional association of beach lifeguards and open water rescuers. The USLA works to reduce the incidence of death and injury in the aquatic environment through public education, national lifeguard standards, training programs, promotion of high levels of lifeguard readiness, and other means.

Become a Member: We invite anyone who wishes to support the mission of the USLA to become a member. Membership includes discounts on lifesaving gear, a membership card, a USLA decal, a subscription to *American Lifeguard Magazine*, invitations to lifeguard educational conferences, the latest information on open water rescue, and networking opportunities. Our professional and junior lifeguard members are also invited to participate in local, regional, and national lifesaving competitions. Visit: www.usla.org/membership.

Become Certified: The USLA offers certification (accreditation) to open water lifeguard agencies and aquatic response teams. We encourage all open water lifeguard agencies and open water response teams to become USLA certified. Visit: www.usla.org/certification.

Help Us Offer Public Education: We offer educational resources on our website. Visit us at www.usla.org for downloadable public education information that can be shared with anyone.

Donate: The USLA is a 501(c)3 nonprofit. Most donations are tax deductible. We encourage you to donate to the United States Lifesaving Foundation, which is an endowment to ensure the ongoing ability of the USLA to provide services in perpetuity. Visit: www.usla.org/donate.

For further information, visit our website at: www.usla.org.

Acknowledgments

USLA TEXTBOOK PROJECT GROUP

B. Chris Brewster (Chair), Lifeguard Chief (ret.), San Diego Lifeguard Service, California

Adam A. Abajian, Lakefront Coordinator, City of Evanston, Illinois

Julian K. "Duke" Brown, M.Ed., NRAEMT, Horry County Beach Safety Director, South Carolina

Kara D. Harrison, Lieutenant, Galveston Island Beach Patrol, Texas

Bill Humphreys, MPA, Marine Safety Chief, San Clemente, California

Kyle Maxwell, Lieutenant, East Bay Regional Park District, California

James H. McCrady V, Lieutenant, Fort Lauderdale Ocean Rescue, Florida

Robert E. Ogoreuc, M.Ed., EMT-B, Assistant Professor, Slippery Rock University, Pennsylvania

ADDITIONAL CONTRIBUTORS AND REVIEWERS

Rob Brander, Associate Professor, University of New South Wales, Australia

Brian Clark, San Diego Lifeguard Service, California

Rick Gould, USLA National Lifesaving Statistics Coordinator

Bryon Iveson, LCDR, USN

Kenna Kay

Brian Kyle, Lead Forecaster, National Weather Service, Houston/Galveston, Texas

John "Chip" More, USLA Legal Advisor

Daniel A. Nord, BFA, EMT-P, CHT, Director, Divers Alert Network Medical Services

Lt. John Sandmeyer, San Diego Lifeguard Service, California

Peter Wernicki, M.D., FAAOS, USLA Medical Advisor

Betsy A. McKinley, PhD, Curriculum/Instruction, Associate Professor (Ret.), Slippery Rock University, Pennsylvania

FINANCIAL SUPPORT

California Marine Safety Chiefs Association
East Bay Regional Park District, California
Evanston (City of), Illinois
Galveston Island Beach Patrol, Texas
Great Lakes Region, United States Lifesaving Association
Mid-Atlantic Region, United States Lifesaving Association
San Clemente (City of), California
South Atlantic Region, United States Lifesaving Association
Southwest Region, United States Lifesaving Association (California Surf Lifesaving
    Association)
United States Lifesaving Association

Lifesaving History

I n this chapter you will learn how lifesaving began with the rescue of people shipwrecked along coastal shores. It progressed to involve the rescue of swimmers and other recreational water users. The first open water lifeguards were strong swimmers who used their aquatic skills, with little formal training or equipment, to rescue others. Over a period of decades, as you will see, they formed local, national, and international organizations, exchanged knowledge, invented and improved lifesaving equipment, and created standards that have transformed lifesaving in a very short period of time into a highly professional public safety service. The United States Lifesaving Association and its affiliated lifeguard agencies follow the traditions of the first lifesavers to this very day.

CHAPTER EXCERPT

One of the most gallant and skillful crews in the [U.S. Life-Saving] service was lost at Point aux Barques, Lake Huron, in October, 1880, and the heart-rending details of the calamity are known to the world through its sole survivor. These loyal men went out in the surf-boat in prompt response to a signal of distress displayed upon a vessel three miles away. The boat was capsized and righted several times, but finally remained capsized, the men clinging to it; but the cold was such that one after another perished, until six were gone ... These heroic men had during the same year saved nearly a hundred lives.

THE FIRST AMERICAN LIFESAVERS

The first lifesavers in America rarely worked during summer. Most of their work came during fall, winter, and spring, and much of it was accomplished in the dead of night. There were cold and lonely vigils, sometimes in snowstorms, as they met each other on foot patrols along desolate beaches. Consider the following passage from an annual report of the U.S. Life-Saving Service describing one of the scores of dramatic rescues that year. This one took place April 3, 1884 in Wellfleet, Massachusetts on the outer shore of Cape Cod. It involved the schooner Viking, "... on her way from George's Bank with a fare of fish, for Boston."

"At a few minutes after 2 in the morning, the weather being rainy and dark, with a strong northeast wind blowing and a rough sea, Surfman F.H. Daniels, of the

Cahoon's Hollow [Life-Saving] Station ... saw a bright light ahead which he at first supposed to be the station on fire, but which after a moment's reflection he concluded from its bearing must be the distress signal of a stranded vessel. He at once started on a run and in a short time arrived abreast of a schooner aground in the breakers about 50 yards from the beach ... two miles north of the station [and any assistance from other surfmen].

His first thought was to keep on and alarm his comrades, but upon considering the time it would take to get to the station he determined on a bold effort to save the vessel's crew single-handed. The bright light that had attracted his attention was still burning when he arrived, and proved to be some clothing saturated with kerosene oil, which the crew had ignited as a signal for aid.

The whole scene was brilliantly illuminated by it, and the sailors, seeing Daniels arrive, watched their opportunity and threw him the end of a lead line. This he managed to secure by rushing down into the surf, and in a few minutes the end of a larger line was bent to it and drawn ashore. One of the men then secured the bight of the rope around his body, and, with a shout to Daniels to haul away, plunged into the boiling surf.

The gallant surfman was equal to the task, and, with the water waist deep around him, he pulled on the rope and succeeded in landing the man all right, the latter exclaiming, as he staggered to his feet upon reaching the beach, "For God's sake, who are you?" The reply of Daniels was brief and to the point: "I am a life-saving man, and you must lend me a hand to save the rest."

At a signal from Daniels the line was quickly hauled back, and in a short time the entire crew, twelve in all, were safely landed ... It was about 3 o'clock when the last man was drawn ashore and then Daniels, after turning the water out of his hip boots, started with the wrecked crew for the station ...."[1]

After this rescue, the schooner's owner wrote, "The circumstances under which this crew was saved were those of the most extreme peril, not only to themselves but also to the gallant man who, single-handed, attempted and providentially achieved their rescue. His name is not known to us, but we think his deed one worthy to be widely known and well rewarded."[1]

The Early Days

During the late 1700s, much of the American coastline was totally uninhabited. Life was hard and recreational swimming was of little interest. Yet loss of life due to drowning was a serious problem. Shipwrecks were the reason.

With today's modern navigational aids and powered vessels, shipwrecks are relatively uncommon, but prior to these advancements sailing ships were navigated by compass, sextant, and educated guess. They were always at the mercy of nature. Storms and inclement weather, particularly in winter, brought tragedy time and time again as ships foundered along the American coastline. In the mid-1800s on Massachusetts' Cape Cod alone, shipwrecks occurred at an estimated frequency of once every two or three weeks.[2] Few people could swim and the sometimes frigid waters were unmerciful to even the hardiest swimmer. Passengers often died by drowning as their ships broke up a short distance from shore.

The earliest organized lifesaving efforts in the world began with China's Chinkiang Association for the Saving of Life, established in 1708. It eventually came to involve staffed lifesaving stations with specially designed and marked rescue vessels.[3] In the Netherlands, the Maatschappij tot Redding van Drenkelingen (Society to Rescue People from Drowning) was established in Amsterdam in 1767, primarily to address problems of drowning in the numerous, open canals in Amsterdam. In Great Britain, the National Institution for the Preservation of Life from Shipwreck was founded in 1824.[4]

In the United States the first organized efforts at lifesaving began with the founding of the Massachusetts Humane Society in 1786. The Humane Society built houses of refuge along the Massachusetts coast for shipwreck survivors, and in 1807 the Society set up the nation's first lifeboat station on Cape Cod. By the mid-1800s, the Massachusetts Humane Society operated 18 stations with lifeboats and line-throwing equipment.[5]

In 1790, the U.S. Government created the Revenue Cutter Service as an arm of the Department of the Treasury with a goal of protection of revenue by enforcing payment of customs and tonnage duties on ships importing goods to America. Initially the service was not expected to engage in rescue activities, but beginning in 1832 its vessels were assigned to cruise the coast during winter months to assist ships in distress.

House of refuge.

Seal of the Revenue Cutter Service.

It was sometime later though, that they would join forces with shore-based lifesavers.

In 1839 Dr. William A. Newell witnessed a shipwreck near Long Beach, New Jersey and watched as 13 people died while trying to swim to shore. Later, as a U.S. Congressman representing New Jersey, he authored the Newell Act, which was approved in 1848 and appropriated $10,000 to be spent to build and equip eight small lifeboat stations along the New Jersey coast between Sandy Hook and Little Egg Harbor. The Massachusetts Humane Society provided assistance in the endeavor.[5] The next year, $20,000 was appropriated and provided to the Life-Saving Benevolent Association of New York for the purpose of building lifesaving stations on Long Island.

At first, lifesaving stations were simple unstaffed houses of refuge containing basic lifesaving equipment. Keys to the stations were left with local townspeople who, by following a list of printed instructions, were expected to rig and use the equipment to save those stranded aboard foundering ships. While this system resulted in some success and occasionally heroic rescues, without a posted watch from shore many shipwrecks went undetected along uninhabited stretches of the coast. The occupants often perished before any lifesaving efforts could be mounted. In addition, volunteer lifesavers from local towns were sometimes unable to effectively employ the lifesaving equipment due to lack of skill and training. Occasionally lifeboat stations were vandalized and lifesaving equipment stolen. Many became run down and of little use.

By 1854 the magnitude of the problem could no longer be ignored. Congress appropriated additional funds to hire a superintendent for the Long Island and New Jersey coasts and a keeper for each station.[5] The keepers were initially paid an annual salary of $200.[2] Patrols were organized and station keepers were expected to walk the coastline at night, regardless of weather, to detect shipwrecks. Despite these advances however, there were no funds for maintenance, no paid lifesaving staff who could be depended upon to assist the keeper in emergencies, and no regulations to follow. The volunteers had limited time to train for rescues, so they were sometimes poorly prepared when disaster struck.

During the Civil War the system deteriorated even further; but once the war was over, Congress again turned its attention to lifesaving. In 1869 the Revenue Marine Division was established to combine administration of lifesaving stations, the Revenue Cutter Service, steamboat inspection, and marine hospitals.[5] Sumner Increase Kimball was appointed to administrate the Revenue Marine Division in 1871 and eventually came to be the single most important influence in early lifesaving.

Congress appropriated additional funds to staff lifesaving stations on a seasonal basis, but as Kimball toured the stations shortly after his appointment he was disappointed to find many in deplorable condition. Some keepers were not even living at the stations to which they were assigned. Kimball embarked upon a crusade to improve the quality of the service. He enacted regulations, inspected the stations on a regular basis, and discharged those who failed to measure up. He professionalized early lifesaving.

Creation of the U.S. Life-Saving Service

Despite advances, funding continued to be a serious problem. The appropriation for 1877–78 was so low that the lifesaving stations could not open until December. Unfortunately, in late November of that year the steamer Huron grounded along the North Carolina coast and in the absence of lifesavers, 98 people died by drowning. In the wake of this disaster, in 1878 Congress appropriated funds to create a separate organization, the U.S. Life-Saving Service, with Sumner Kimball to be its first and, it turned out, only leader.

During Kimball's tenure, crews were employed to staff each station and the stations' size and comfort facilities were expanded. Most stations were staffed with six surfmen and an Officer in Charge (the station keeper). Professionalism grew too, as strict regulations were set for competence, performance, routine beach patrols, and physical conditioning. The system eventually grew to comprise 189 lifesaving stations—139 on the Atlantic coast from Maine to Florida, 37 on the Great Lakes, seven on the Pacific coast, and one in Ohio.[5]

Like other emergency responders, lifesavers worked long and often tedious shifts, with daily drills and

U.S. Life-Saving Service station and crew.

monotonous foot patrols throughout the night. But once the cry, "Ship Ashore!" was sounded, the boredom was often replaced by heroism in harrowing and exhausting struggles with the sea to save lives. When this happened, the primary tools of the early lifesavers were the breeches buoy apparatus and lifeboats.

LEARN MORE

The U.S. Life-Saving Service Heritage Association keeps history alive: www.uslife-savingservice.org.

Early Lifesaving Apparatus

Lifeboats

The earliest lifeboats used by the lifesavers on the Atlantic coast were made of wood, weighed 700 to 1,000 pounds, and measured twenty-five to thirty feet long. Some had air chambers at either end to help prevent swamping, but they were neither self-righting nor self-bailing. They were generally rowed by a crew of six surfmen, with the station keeper at a sweep oar at the stern that served as a rudder.

The lifeboats were stored inside the lifesaving stations. When duty called, they were rowed by lifesavers wearing primitive lifejackets and water repelling oilskins. Before launching, the Atlantic boats were transported by wagons drawn through the soft sand to a point near the wreck. The distance

Surfboat and crew.

A U.S. Life-Saving Service crew with their surfboat and beach cart.

could be several miles and this effort alone could sap the strength of life-savers, so some stations acquired horses to draw the wagons.[6]

Lifeboats that later came to be used on the Great Lakes and most of the Pacific coast were self-righting and self-bailing with air chambers to prevent capsizing. They weighed about four thousand pounds and were generally launched from safe harbors. In some cases tugs would pull them to the mouth of the harbor, where the lifesavers aboard would take over using eight oars for propulsion. According to an 1880 article in *Scribner's Monthly*, "It is a common occurrence for the life-boats to go under sail and oars ten or twelve miles from their stations to the assistance of vessels in distress."[7]

The Breeches Buoy Apparatus

Most Atlantic coast rescues involved ships aground on sandbars near the beach, driven there by storm surf or through disorientation of the captain. Since the Atlantic coast lifeboats were vulnerable to capsizing, when seas were high and the wrecked vessel near shore, lifesavers turned instead to the breeches buoy apparatus.

The breeches buoy itself was actually a large life ring. Canvas was slung loosely across the center with two holes for the legs of a victim, forming a sort of pants. The victim could hang securely in the breeches buoy with legs through the holes and the life ring under the armpits. It was part of an apparatus that was more complex.

The lifesavers transported the breeches buoy apparatus on a beach cart with large wagon wheels. The main components were a strong, light linen line in a *faking box* (see

Breeches buoy used in training drill.

photo), apparatus to heave or shoot this line to the ship in distress, heavier line on large reels, and a pole with a guide at the top to raise the heavy line above the beach and the water. The lead line was light enough to be thrown or shot through the air to the shipwrecked vessel, but strong enough so that the heavier line could then be fastened to it onshore and then pulled aboard by the shipwreck victims. The faking box had upturned pegs to allow the thread to easily deploy when one end was thrown or shot.

The first step was to get the lead line to the foundering vessel. If the ship was close enough, a *heaving stick* was used. With light lead line attached to this weighted stick, it could

Credit: Brian Feeney, National Park Service

Beach cart with the full breeches buoy apparatus aboard. Lifesavers would pull this cart through the sand to the point of the rescue.

reportedly be thrown up to 50 yards.[8] When the ship was out of reach of a heaving stick, the Lyle gun was employed.

The Lyle gun was a small 163 pound cannon, developed by Captain David A. Lyle of the U.S. Army in 1877. The lifesavers would fire a metal projectile from the gun toward the rigging of the foundering ship. Attached to the projectile was one end of the lead line from the faking box. With the lead line attached, the projectile could reach up to 400 yards.[6] If the shot was a good one, the lead line would become entangled in the rigging or simply drape over the foundering ship. If not,

Credit: B. Chris Brewster

A Lyle gun, faking box, and projectile.

the line was retrieved and another attempt made. Sometimes, repeated attempts were required, and of course sometimes the line didn't make it to the ship in distress.

One hazard of the Lyle gun was its violent recoil. In the interest of keeping the gun light and portable, Lyle eliminated much of the weight normally used to minimize

Credit: Brian Feeney, National Park Service

The Lyle gun is fired during a drill toward a practice target intended to simulate ships rigging. Note heavy projectile with line attached and faking box in the foreground with upturned pegs.

LEARN MORE

You can learn more about the Lyle gun in *The Lifesaving Guns of David Lyle* by J.P. Barnett (1974).

Credit: Dave Foxwell

Lifecar.

a canon's recoil. On the beach, the Lyle gun was positioned so that its recoil was absorbed by the sand itself.

Once a connection was made to the ship with the lead line, the heavier line would be attached to the lead line by the lifesavers ashore and the stranded mariners aboard the ship would pull it aboard. Rudimentary directions on a wooden pallet attached to the line instructed the shipwrecked victims to make the heavy line fast to a high point in the rigging. Meanwhile, the lifesavers erected the wooden pole on the beach to provide a high point for the shore end of the line and anchored it in the sand. Eventually, both ends of the line were made fast and it was drawn taught.

The breeches buoy was hung from the line on a pulley and drawn back and forth by use of a separate line. When it worked properly, victims board the ship could be pulled ashore one at a time sitting in the breeches buoy without touching the water.

Lifecars were also used in some cases. Like the breeches buoy, these devices were hung from the line and pulled back and forth. They were made of copper or iron and enclosed with bolts. Three to four adults could be squeezed inside.

At 2:30 a.m. [in December 1879] the patrol of Station No. 14, Second District, Massachusetts, discovered a vessel at anchor about a mile and a half east-northeast of the station, burning a torch as a signal of distress. He answered the signal and returned to the station for help. The lifesaving crew on reaching the shore found it impossible to launch the boat through the breakers. The keeper then sent to Station No. 13 for assistance, and in the meantime went north abreast of the distressed vessel and showed signals to her and caused fires to be built to show her the deepest water in case her chains should part. The wind was blowing a strong gale with blinding snow squalls, and a heavy sea was running.

When the crew of No. 13 arrived it was evident that the vessel was dragging toward shore. The lifesaving men now brought the mortar cart with the Lyle gun and equipment abreast of the vessel, which was now near the breakers. The first shot took the line across the headstays, but the crew were so exhausted and benumbed that they were unable to get to it. The second shot laid the line over the fore-yard and was happily made fast.

The breeches buoy was then taken aboard, and in thirty minutes the entire crew, eight men, were landed in safety, though five of them were in such a helpless condition that they had to be assisted to the station, where they were furnished with hot drinks, dry clothing, and comfortable beds.[9]

— From the 1880 Annual Report of the U.S. Life-Saving Service

U.S. Life-Saving Service Procedures

Lifesavers patrolled the beaches on foot throughout the night, awakened in turn for their watch. They would walk to a halfway point to the next station, exchange a brass "check" with a lifesaver from the neighboring station, and return to wake up the next lifesaver whose turn it was to patrol. The check proved that the patrol had been completed. If a ship was sighted near shore, the lifesavers would burn a red coston signal (a flare) as a warning to turn away.

Although the lifesaver's work was mostly tedious, when rescues took place they were often harrowing and sometimes lethal. Regulations stated, "You have to go out."[2] Discretion in the face of adversity was not an option. J. H. Merryman, writing in *Scribner's Monthly* quoted a lifesaver as saying, "When I see a man clinging to a wreck, I see nothing else in the world, and I never think of family and friends until I have saved him."[7]

Rescue by breeches buoy circa 1880.

The heroism of the lifesavers became legendary, particularly considering the fear of the sea that many people of the day harbored. *Harpers Monthly* reported the following of one incident, "One of the most gallant and skillful crews in the service was lost at Point aux Barques, Lake Huron, in October, 1880, and the heart-rending details of the calamity are known to the world through its sole survivor. These loyal men went out in the surf-boat in prompt response to a signal of distress displayed upon a vessel three miles away. The boat was capsized and righted several times, but finally remained capsized, the men clinging to it; but the cold was such that one after another perished, until six were gone. The keeper drifted upon the beach, insensible, and was found steadying himself by the trunk of a tree ... These heroic men had during the same year saved nearly a hundred lives."[7]

> **LEARN MORE**
>
> You can learn more in *The U.S. Life-Saving Service* by Ralph Shanks, Wick York, and Lisa Woo Shanks (1998).

Another famous incident was known as the Monomoy disaster. On March 17, 1902 a lifeboat crewed by eight lifesavers picked up five victims from the Wadena, a distressed vessel off Monomoy Point on Cape Cod, Massachusetts. As the lifesavers were making their way back to shore, the victims panicked and the lifeboat was overcome in high seas. All but one of the lifesavers perished, as did all of the victims.

According to the report of the U.S. Life-Saving Service for 1902, "The loss of the 7 lifesaving men who so nobly perished created everywhere a sense of profound sorrow. There was no more skillful or fearless crew on the whole coast, and ... there was a general conviction that the men were practically a sacrifice ... to their own high sense of duty, which would not permit them to turn their backs upon a signal of distress. 'We must go,' said the keeper, 'there is a distress flag in the rigging.'" Over $45,000 was raised to help the widows and orphans of the men and a monument was placed ashore in memory of the victims. It can be found today at the Coast Guard Station in Chatham, Massachusetts.[2]

The Life-Saving Service even performed inland rescues in some circumstances. For example, during serious flooding in the Midwest during early 1913, lifesavers were dispatched with their boats to perform rescues. In an after-action report published by the House of Representatives, Sumner Kimball reported that the Life-Saving Service rescued 3,509 people from flooding in Ohio, Kentucky, Indiana, and Illinois.[10]

Credit: Kenna Kay

Memorial to the Monomoy lifesavers, Chatham, Massachusetts.

To the General Superintendent

United States Life-Saving Service

Dear Sir: The undersigned hereby wish to make known that the keeper and crew of Peaked Hill Bar Life-Saving Station (Cape Cod) have rendered such assistance and exposed themselves to such risk of their own lives during the wreck of the schooner W.H. Mailer, of Calais, Maine, that we cannot go on our way without a word in their praise.

We struck on the inner bar … in a blinding snow-storm and dense fog. Land was scarcely visible at the time, but the patrolman, having good eyes, discovered us and signaled to us, and we answered him. We then saw him start on a run along the beach. In a short time our masts went over the side and then we began to drift over the bar.

We could then see the crew with their apparatus, coming along the beach … The sea made quick work, and in a short time broke us all up, except a small part of the stern, to which, with the captain's wife, we were all hanging. The crew were then three hundred yards distant.

The keeper, seeing there was no time to lose, ran ahead with lines, and, with great daring and terrible risk, succeeded in getting on part of the wreck and passing a line to us. We then made the line fast around the woman, and the keeper, with great pluck, took her off, and both were hauled ashore by the brave men on the beach, through a tremendous sea, the men being at times almost washed off their feet. They then passed the line to us again, and after a lot of courageous work got us all ashore alive, not a minute too soon, as she all broke up just as the last man got ashore …

No human beings could do more for us than the keeper and his men, and they are deserving of great praise.[1]

— A letter reprinted in the 1884 Annual Report of the U.S. Life-Saving Service

In its short lifetime, the U.S. Life-Saving Service amassed a truly extraordinary record—28,121 vessels aided and 178,741 people saved. In 1915, the Life-Saving Service was merged with the Revenue Cutter Service, this time to form the United States Coast Guard. Sumner Kimball retired after 43 years of service, but the lifesavers continued on in their duties as part of the Coast Guard for many years thereafter. As navigational aids improved and powered vessels became the norm, shipwrecks occurred with diminishing frequency. The need for skilled lifesavers to go out through the surf in lifeboats slowly dwindled. The last known use of the breeches buoy apparatus was in 1962.[6] As will become evident to the reader though, the United States Lifesaving Association and its associated lifeguard agencies follow the traditions of the U.S. Life-Saving Service to this very day.

LEARN MORE

U.S. Coast Guard: www.uscg.mil

LEARN MORE

You can learn more about the history of the USLSS and the US Coast Guard in *Guardians of the Sea, History of the United States Coast Guard* by Robert E. Johnson (1987).

ROOTS OF MODERN LIFEGUARDING

During the 1800s, life in America began to change as the country grew. Americans became more prosperous, allowing more free time. Leisure activity was on the rise and Americans discovered that recreational swimming, once widely thought to be a sure cause of death, was an enjoyable pastime. The ocean though, was only a location for the very brave. That was to change.

Some entrepreneurs in Philadelphia had an idea. The city was oppressively hot in summer and of course there was no air conditioning. What if they were to build a railroad to the sea and build a resort there? Certainly many would pay to escape the heat and enjoy the cool sea breezes. They brought investors on board and convinced a railroad to build a line to Abescon Island, then a remote barrier beach. They built the United States Hotel there and named their resort "Atlantic City." The first American seaside resort was born.[11]

Atlantic City opened in June 1854. A major part of its tourism promotion included healthfulness of the sea breezes, said to cure all sorts of diseases, and the extraordinary health benefits of the salt water.[12] Unfortunately, many people had limited swimming skills and even good swimmers were sometimes swept away in rip currents. Without lifeguards, they died. In 1865, for example, there were 13 drowning deaths.[11]

Various efforts to prevent drowning were tried. One was lifelines—ropes to which swimmers could cling—fastened between shore and upright poles driven into the ocean bottom. Then there were the volunteer lifesavers who walked the beaches and rescued people. They provided their services at no cost, but asked for a donation once someone was brought safely to shore.[13]

These volunteers though, were of questionable repute. The writer Gay Talese reports that, "The lifeguard brigade of the mid-1800s was composed of a few petty brigands who received no municipal salary and therefore supported themselves in summer by unsubtly soliciting donations from the proprietors and patrons of bathhouses and the largess of anyone they rescued from drowning. When their funds ran low, they would fake rescues."[12] One regular "victim" was W.C. Fields, who later became a movie actor. He was paid $10 a week to swim out and fake distress, sometimes 12 times a day. He later joked that he had stopped drinking water because he had drunk so much in his Atlantic City days.[14]

Atlantic City was soon joined by other resorts. Down the Jersey Shore, in Cape May, drowning prevention efforts began with rescue rings hung on bathhouses and the provision of dories on the beach that could be used for rescue. In both Cape May and Atlantic City, some hotels hired people to rescue their patrons in distress, typically using dories.[12]

In 1855 the Atlantic City council appointed two men they called, "Constables of the Surf."[13] They were not lifeguards, but performed a similar service. It wasn't enough though, so they hired more and by 1884 there were 25 constables.[13] These constables were actually city police officers who would patrol the town once bathing hours ended. They were a distinct improvement over the volunteers, but the town needed police officers ashore.

The First Lifeguards

Atlantic City decided to end the constables of the surf program and hire specialists to address beach lifesaving. On June 12, 1882, they created a "beach patrol" with two lifeguards employed by the city.[13] It grew rapidly. In 1900 the Atlantic City Beach Patrol had 55 members and by 1910 there were 64. It is regarded as the first official beach lifeguard organization in the world.[15]

This evolution of volunteer lifesavers followed by paid lifeguards occurred elsewhere in the US. One of the more formal efforts was the United States Volunteer Lifesaving Corps (USVLC), created in 1892.[15] Its various local organizations seem to have operated mostly independently. One member, George Freeth, had come to California from Hawaii as a performer to attract people to seaside bathhouses. He was a surfer who was promoted as *the man who walks on water* (on a surfboard). In 1908 off Venice Beach he rescued seven men from drowning in a storm that capsized their fishing boats.[16] He is one of many civilians who was awarded the Gold Lifesaving Medal by the United States Life-Saving Service over the years—a program which continues today under the auspices of the U.S. Coast Guard.[17] (He is also credited with introducing surfing to the U.S. mainland.)[18]

Long Beach, California hired its first municipal lifeguard in 1908, and the city of San Diego began a municipal beach lifeguard operation overseen by the police department in 1914.[18, 19] As was the case on the East Coast, seaside

The first two lifeguards for the Atlantic City Beach Patrol in 1882: Dan Headley and Nick Jefferies. The white belts had a loop at the back which they would fasten to their rescue device.

resorts and bathhouses, serviced by railroads, brought large crowds who ventured into the ocean and occasionally became distressed. In 1918, 13 people died in one day in rip currents off San Diego's Ocean Beach, which brought about significant strengthening of the young lifeguard service.[19] This pattern followed at seaside areas around the U.S.

Public education and the provision of swimming lessons were also promoted by various organizations. The Young Men's Christian Association (YMCA) began building pools at their facilities in 1885, with 17 reported built that year. Mass swim lessons were initiated at the Detroit YMCA in 1907 by George Corsan, who helped promote swimming lessons by providing bronze buttons as rewards for swimming proficiency to any boy who could swim 50 feet. By 1909, his learn-to-swim programs had developed into the first nationwide effort to teach every boy in the U.S. and Canada to swim.

In 1911, lifesaving work and research was established at the YMCA's national college in Springfield, Massachusetts. There, in 1913, the first American work on lifesaving was written (and later published as a lifesaving textbook in 1916) by George Goss as his college thesis. In 1919 the YMCA published the *YMCA Swimming and Lifesaving Manual*.

In 1914, Commodore Wilbert E. Longfellow was charged with developing and forming the Life Saving Corps of the American Red Cross, a corps of volunteers recruited and trained to provide rescues at beaches not regularly patrolled by lifeguards. Not satisfied that this adequately addressed the drowning problem, Commodore Longfellow recruited the strongest swimmers from the corps to teach swimming to beach visitors. He began a program to "Waterproof America," by teaching people to swim and by training lay people in the skills necessary to rescue a drowning person. His slogan, "Everyone a swimmer, every swimmer a lifesaver," became the motto of early Red Cross programs that taught swimming, water safety, and lifesaving to many children and adults.

By the end of the 1930s, publicly employed lifeguards had become a common sight at many beaches across the USA. They were paid professionals, but there was little consistency among these services due to the lack of a national organization charged with setting standards for the new profession. This was quite different from how lifesaving evolved in the British Commonwealth, led by Australia.

For many years there was a ban on daylight ocean bathing in Australia imposed by local and state governments, including Sydney. It was not strictly enforced, but kept ocean swimming to a minimal level. In 1903 the ban in Sydney was lifted due to some high profile protests and ocean swimming soon became popular. But the resort system which had emerged in the USA and the income it generated that could be used to hire lifeguards was not present in Australia. Instead, ocean swimming was practiced mostly by local residents and day trippers. They too needed rescue from time to time.[15]

While there was no income from beach resorts, there were many bathing clubs composed of strong swimmers who competed with each other. In time, the communities came to give them prime oceanfront space for their clubs in exchange for their willingness to rescue those in distress. From this evolved Surf Life Saving Australia, a national system of local volunteer clubs, the first at Bondi Beach in 1907.[15] This system was followed by other countries, like New Zealand and later the United Kingdom. Thus evolved two different lifesaving systems in different countries – one predominately paid professionals and one predominately volunteer. (Most of the countries that started with volunteer systems, including Australia, now have a mix of paid and volunteer lifesavers.)

LEARN MORE

Surf Life Saving Australia: www.slsa.com.au

The U.S. Volunteer Life Saving Corps, founded in 1890, preceded the founding of SLSA by almost 20 years. By 1938 its members are reported to have saved over 17,000 people from drowning.[20] It slowly disappeared however, because professional lifeguards were assigned to meet the increasing volume of activity and local expectation.

Professional open water lifeguards in the U.S. employed techniques that had evolved from the U.S. Life-Saving Service, along with the growing body of knowledge being developed by the lifesaving programs of the American Red Cross and the YMCA. Surfboats, similar to those used by the U.S. Life-Saving Service, were adapted for use by lifeguards to row to swimmers in trouble. They remain in use in a few areas of the U.S. The predominant method of rescue though, was by swimming to the victim.

With open water recreation established as a major national pastime, acquisition of park systems and provision of recreational opportunities came to be seen as an important role of government. Recreation programs and departments were created on a national and local level. During the Great Depression many federal public works projects involved construction of recreation facilities. After the Depression facilities were commonly turned over to local and state recreation agencies and lifeguards were added to operation staffs.

During World War II, the male dominated profession of lifeguarding was impacted by recruitment of men into the armed forces. In some areas of the country, where beach lifeguards were seen as essential public safety providers, draft waivers were issued to keep trained and experienced lifeguards on the beaches. As was the case in other professions, women sometimes filled the vacancies that were created when male lifeguards enlisted in the armed forces.

Credit: Chicago Park District

It was during World War II that the Chicago Park District first employed female lifeguards to work the beaches.

San Diego Lifeguard Captain Spade Burns circa 1923.

Unlike police and fire services with centuries of history, professional lifeguards were new providers of public safety and their place in governmental structures varied greatly. In areas where lifeguards were on duty year-round, some lifeguard services became divisions of other public safety services or were organized into departments unto themselves. These organizational structures gave the lifeguards a stature equivalent to that of police officers and firefighters.

In other areas, open water lifeguard services were administered as part of recreation programs or park systems, and lifeguards were sometimes titled as "recreation assistants" or "program aides." This perception of lifeguards persisted in many areas of the United States well into the 1960s until two events changed the course of professional lifeguarding: 1) the creation of the United States Lifesaving Association; and 2) advances in emergency medical aid.

Credit: San Clemente Lifeguards

San Clemente lifeguards circa 1950.

Birth of the United States Lifesaving Association

Decades after professional lifeguard agencies had been established at beaches throughout America, Australia was chosen to host the 1956 summer Olympics. The volunteer lifesavers of Australia decided to use the occasion to hold the Australian Olympic International Surf Championships at Torquay, outside the city of Melbourne. California lifeguards and a contingent from the Territory of Hawaii agreed to participate. The California lifeguards organized themselves under the banner of the Surf Life Saving Association of America (SLSA), although they were solely from the Los Angeles County, Santa Monica, and Los Angeles City lifeguard agencies.

The event drew a crowd of 115,000 spectators, with "Duke" Kahanamoku as the honorary Chairman. In addition to the Americans and Australians, teams from South Africa, Great Britain, Ceylon, and New Zealand participated.

The U.S. lifeguards brought rescue tubes and rescue buoys along, exposing the Australians to these devices for the first time. They also brought Malibu balsa surfboards to Australia. Until then the Australians had been surfing on boards weighing up to 100 pounds and essentially surfing straight into the beach. Some of the lifeguards were top level surfers in the U.S. and put on quite a show for the Australians. When they departed, the lifeguards left their boards behind. This revolutionized surfing in Australia. The Australians didn't adopt the tubes or buoys though. They were married to their line, belt, and reel, and would be for decades to come.[15]

Just as the Americans introduced new lifesaving equipment to the Australians, the Australians demonstrated the value of a national organization of lifesavers. After they returned, the Surf Life Saving Association of America was maintained, with the strong support of Los Angeles County Lifeguard Chief Bud Stevenson. He appointed one of his lifeguards, Bob Burnside, as president of the organization.

In 1963, efforts were commenced to expand the scope of the SLSA. Burnside called for representatives from as many Southern California lifeguard agencies as possible to attend a concept meeting at the City of Santa Monica Lifeguard Headquarters.

Credit: Surf Life Saving Australia

The cover of the event program for the 1956 lifeguard competition in Australia.

Credit: Surf Life Saving Australia

Australian line, belt, and reel.

Credit: Robert Burnside

A patch designed by Tad Devine and used by the U.S. team during their visit to Australia in 1956.

The group agreed that they should expand the SLSA to a truly national organization, based on the structure of the Australian association. They established a temporary Executive Board to develop a constitution, bylaws, and method of representation and in 1964 the organization was formally launched, with Burnside as the founding president.

Howard Lee of L.A. County designed the SLSA logo, still in use today with minor modifications. His design was influenced by a similar design that Tad Devine of the 1956 Australia team had created for the team uniform. Both are similar to the logo of the U.S. Life-Saving Service.

Many milestones can be traced to these early years. In 1965, the organization changed its name to the National Surf Lifesaving Association (NSLSA). That year, ABC's Wide World of Sports—the iconic sports television show of the era—invited members to participate in an East Coast/West Coast/Australian lifesaving championship at Montauk, New York. A dramatic video clip of a lifeguard surfboat careening down a wave became part of the regular lead-in to the show. Also in 1965, the NSLSA first published the newsletter *Ocean Lifeguard* and also proposed written examinations for beach lifeguards, which were forwarded to civil service departments to encourage standardization.

In 1967, the NSLSA sent a competition team to Ft. Lauderdale, Florida, for the first East Coast vs. West Coast championships. The following year, Lt. Jim Holland of the Miami Beach Patrol was appointed to act as East Coast Liaison.

In 1969, Dade County, Florida requested that the NSLSA representatives journey to Miami and make recommendations for improvements in their lifeguard program. The outcome included suggestions that resulted in installation of a communication system, new vehicles and equipment, new qualification requirements, and increased funding. It was the first demonstration of the potential power of the NSLSA to improve lifesaving standards nationwide.

In 1971, the NSLSA became a founding member of World Lifesaving, which also included the national surf lifesaving federations of Australia, Great Britain, New Zealand, and South Africa. The following year the NSLSA hosted a meeting of World Lifesaving in Huntington Beach, California—the first international lifesaving meeting in the USA. A few years later, in 1976, Vince Moorhouse of Huntington Beach was appointed World Lifesaving's president, and in 1978 the NSLSA hosted a World Lifesaving Educational Congress in Newport Beach, California.

There was much discussion during these times about expanding the reach of the organization to embrace all open water lifeguards, whether at surf or non-surf beaches. President Sheridan Byerly chaired a Board of Directors meeting in Santa Cruz, California in May 1979. It was thick with heated and passionate discussion about the course of the organization's future. Ultimately, the NSLSA Board of Directors voted to change the name of the organization to the United States Lifesaving Association (USLA); and to expand its reach to include any member of an ocean, bay, lake, river, or open water lifesaving or rescue service, including chiefs, directors, and their equivalent.

America's beach lifeguard agencies and professional lifeguards now had a national organization they could use to exchange information on professional techniques, lifesaving equipment, organizational structures, and other issues of concern. The USLA embarked on a goal of reducing the incidence of death and injury in the aquatic environment through public education, national lifeguard standards, training programs, promotion of high levels of lifeguard readiness, and other means.

On the international scene, the USLA had been one of the founding members of World Life Saving, so when it merged to become the International Life Saving Federation in 1993 it was no surprise that the USLA became the United States' full member to this worldwide lifesaving body. USLA members immediately assumed key leadership roles. B. Chris Brewster was appointed president of the ILS Americas Region, including North, Central, and South America—a position he still holds as this book goes to press. Thus, the USLA has helped shape the face of lifesaving internationally, as well as in the USA.

> **LEARN MORE**
>
> International Life Saving Federation:
> www.ilsf.org

Emergency Medical Aid Advances

In 1966, the National Academy of Sciences published a document entitled *Accidental Death and Disability: The Neglected Disease of Modern Society*. This document outlined a poor state of training and service standards for emergency medical care providers in the United States, with many ambulance attendants having little or no training beyond basic first aid. It helped to spur passage of the nation's Highway Safety Act of 1966, which charged the U.S. Department of Transportation with the development and establishment of an Emergency Medical Service Standard. This led to the establishment of standards in emergency medical care now taken for granted in the United States. The document also recommended, "Active exploration of the feasibility of designating a single nationwide telephone number to summon an ambulance." Many now take 9-1-1 for granted, but the 9-1-1 system only gradually came into being over a period of many years after this recommendation.[21]

Recognizing the problems in the nation's emergency medical services also motivated citizen groups and government organizations to carefully evaluate training and service standards for other emergency services, including police, fire, and open water lifeguard services. It became evident that some lifeguard agencies worked with little or no formal training. Others required their lifeguards to undergo only rudimentary training aimed at "drown proofing" the general public, rather than preparing professional rescuers. Many had wrongly considered pool lifesaving training adequate for open water lifeguards, even those assigned to the most treacherous surf beaches. National standards were needed and the USLA was to provide them.

LIFESAVING DEVICES

One of the greatest difficulties for swimming lifesavers was the struggle sometimes required to overpower a panicked victim before the rescue could be completed. The line and reel (landline), was an early solution in the USA (and a mainstay in Australia). A lifeguard would swim out to the victim while attached to the line, clutch the victim, and would be rapidly pulled back to shore by others.

This method had the advantage of quick retrieval, but there were some disadvantages too. The line produced drag, which could slow approach to the victim; it required two or more lifeguards to operate; it was inadequate in cases of multiple rescues simultaneously occurring at different locations; and, it could become tangled. Nevertheless, it was widely used for decades and is still in limited use in a few areas.

As an alternative, Atlantic City lifeguards developed what may be the first *rescue flotation device* (RFD) by fastening an eight-foot line and shoulder harness to a life ring. The lifeguard would swim out with the life ring, throw it to the victim, and tow the victim to a dory or to shore. This avoided contact with the victim, but like the line and reel, the life ring created significant drag in the water.[13]

The Rescue Buoy

Captain T. W. Sheffield, an American with a variety of aquatic accomplishments to his credit, was touring Durban, South Africa in 1897 when he invented another type of RFD, the "Sheffield Life Saving Cylinder." It was made of sheet metal and pointed on both ends, with a line supported by small cork floats and a belt to be attached to the lifesaver.[22] The advantage was that it moved much more smoothly through the water, producing little drag. A disadvantage was that the heavy metal and pointed ends sometimes caused injuries, both to rescuers and those being rescued. Over the years the design was modified in many different ways in the United States, including construction of copper, aluminum, and foam.

Sheffield rescue can patent.

Aluminum rescue buoys, even with their rounded ends, still caused injuries. In the mid-1960s a major advancement in design of these devices occurred. Los Angeles County lifeguard Lieutenant Bob Burnside (the founding president of the USLA) was concerned over the many injuries associated with lifeguards being struck by the aluminum rescue can. He consulted with Professor Ron Rezek at the University of California at Los Angeles (UCLA) to inquire as to the feasibility of designing a buoy from plastic, which appeared possible due to a new process called rotational molding. They created a wood prototype which was submitted for comment to local lifesaving leaders. After favorable reviews, Professor Rezek entered into production with Lt. Burnside for the first plastic rescue buoy. These RFDs are now a basic tool of open water lifeguards and still known to many as *Burnside buoys*, but more commonly referred to as *rescue buoys*.

Credit: Mike Hensler

Some original rescue buoys. They were often known as "can" buoys because of their metal construction.

The Rescue Board

One man seems to have been the primary factor in introducing the surfboard to lifesavers: the swimming and surfing legend Duke Kahanamoku. He visited the West Coast in 1913 and struck up a friendship with Roy 'Dutch' Miller of the Long Beach, California lifeguards. Long Beach lifeguards arranged to have modified surfboards made by the city's maintenance shop and used them for rescue thereafter.[18] Other lifeguard agencies in California used them for rescue as well. (Although he was not a trained lifesaver, Kahanamoku was involved in at least one extraordinary rescue. He and fellow surfers were credited with using their boards to save the lives of 13 people when a motorboat overturned off Corona del Mar, California in June 1925.)[23]

The Rescue Tube

In 1935, based on a design by Reggie Burton and Captain George Watkins, Santa Monica lifeguard Pete Peterson produced an inflatable, bright yellow rescue tube with a snap hook molded onto one end and a 14 inch strap on the other. A line and harness were then attached. This highly visible RFD was used by many lifeguard services into the early 1960s.

In response to the buoyancy problems related to punctures and climatic conditions, Peterson redesigned the tube, constructing it of flexible foam rubber with an orange skin to keep water out of the interior. While this was an improvement, the skin was still subject to piercing and the open cell foam would then act like a sponge, becoming waterlogged. By the late 1960s however, closed cell foam rubber was invented and the tube was manufactured with this material, so that punctures to the skin no longer resulted in water absorption. This device is still known to some as the *Peterson tube*, but is more commonly known as the *rescue tube*. In addition to being a standard item of rescue equipment at beaches, it is also used in a modified version at pools.

Rescue tube.

Credit: Kyle Maxwell

DEVELOPING NATIONAL OPEN WATER LIFEGUARD STANDARDS

It became evident to many that the pool and open water environments are very different for purposes of training or standards. As a result, open water lifeguards began to seek specialized training for their unique environment. None being available, more progressive lifeguard agencies developed their own standards, networking with each other for consistency and validation of their practices. Nevertheless, the open water lifeguard profession suffered greatly for lack of state or national standards.

In 1980, a conference was held at Texas A&M University at Galveston, sponsored in part by the USLA. It brought together all of the major American organizations concerned with promoting public safety in and around the aquatic environment. The intent of the conference was to discuss ways to develop standards for open water lifeguards. The result was a Sea Grant funded publication entitled *Guidelines for Establishing Open-Water Recreational Beach Standards* (McCloy & Dodson, 1981).

LEARN MORE

You can download a copy of *Guidelines for Establishing Open-Water Recreational Beach Standards* from the USLA website at: www.usla.org/library.

In 1981, the first USLA lifesaving text, *Lifesaving and Marine Safety*, was published.[18] In 1983, based on the work accomplished in Galveston, the USLA published a booklet entitled *Guidelines for Open Water Lifeguard Training*, which set the first nationwide standards for open water lifeguards at both inland and surf beaches.

In 1993, the USLA revised the original guidelines as the basis for the first national certification program for both inland and surf lifeguard training programs—the USLA *Lifeguard Agency Certification Program*. Rather than certifying the lifeguards themselves, as did other national organizations, this program acknowledged the reality that open water lifeguard agencies were already conducting their own training in-house, so the USLA program would accredit programs that met the recommended standards.

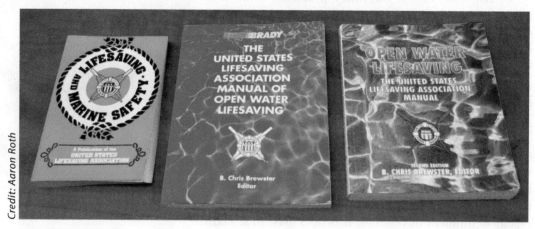

Credit: Aaron Roth

Prior USLA manuals.

This program provides an independent review of open water lifeguard programs and encourages lifeguard agencies across the country to meet the standards recommended by the USLA. It is based on the USLA publication, *Guidelines for Open Water Lifeguard Agency Certification*. By the year 2016, over 140 U.S. lifeguard agencies, large and small, were currently certified by the USLA.

LEARN MORE

You can download a current version of *Guidelines for Open Water Lifeguard Agency Certification* from the USLA website at: www.usla.org/certification.

The first edition of the text you now read was published in 1995 to provide a core reference for the training of America's open water rescuers. It was followed by development of a second certification program for open water rescuers who are not lifeguards, which is known as the *Aquatic Rescue Response Team* (ARRT) certification program.

These publications, along with the USLA website, training videos, and the ongoing work of USLA committees, have greatly added to the body of knowledge used by open water lifeguard agencies and enhanced

LEARN MORE

You can download a current version of *Training and Standards of Aquatic Rescue Response Teams* from the USLA website at: www.usla.org/certification.

development of an image of the lifeguard as a professional emergency provider. Today the USLA is known nationally and internationally as an authoritative body in the field of open water lifeguarding and marine safety. In 2016, the USLA announced that it was a founding member of Water Safety USA, along with 12 other national nonprofit and government organizations with a shared goal of water safety and drowning prevention.

Credit: Nicholas Enns

Avila Beach Lifeguard Department.

MODERN LIFEGUARDING

The profession of lifeguarding will always be unique among emergency services due largely to its seasonal nature. While in Florida, California, and Hawaii hundreds of open water lifeguards work year-round on a career basis, open water lifeguards in most other states work seasonally. Nevertheless, whether year-round or seasonal, professional lifeguard services have perhaps the most direct and profound impact on public safety per employee of any emergency service providers.

Open water lifeguards consistently and continually make the difference between the life and death of otherwise healthy people through timely preventive actions. While other emergency services are largely reactive, responding once an emergency has occurred, alert lifeguards can often prevent the emergencies from developing in the first place or pluck unsuspecting people from harm's way. In fact, far more preventive actions are effected by lifeguards each year than rescues from drowning.

In the warmer states, lifeguards have particularly broad responsibilities. Some American lifeguards are armed police officers serving a dual role of rescue and law enforcement. Others are called upon to perform duties such as marine firefighting, coastal cliff rescue, paramedic services, flood rescue, and scuba search and recovery.

Credit: Volusia County Beach Safety Ocean Rescue. Photo provided by Mark Swanson, Deputy Director of Volusia County Public Protection

Volusia County Beach Safety Officer makes an arrest.

Two American lifeguard agencies (Los Angeles County and San Diego) keep their personnel on duty 24 hours a day to provide immediate response to nighttime aquatic emergencies. In some areas, when a citizen calls 9-1-1 to report an aquatic emergency, the reporting party is connected directly to a lifeguard dispatcher. In other areas, even those lacking regular off-summer lifeguard protection, aquatic emergency response systems are in place to dispatch qualified open water lifeguards whenever the need arises.

Lifesaving equipment continues to evolve as lifeguards experiment and innovate. The inflatable rescue boat (IRB), first employed in Australia and New Zealand, was adopted in many areas for in-surf rescue operations, but personal watercraft (PWC) have now become even more commonly used for this assignment. Hard hull rescue boats up to 38 feet in length, some with firefighting equipment, are also used. The Baywatch vessels of the Los Angeles County lifeguards, after which the popular television show was named, represent perhaps the largest fleet of open water rescue vessels maintained by a local government in the United States. Computer aided dispatching, global positioning, and night vision are a few of the other innovations. Lifeguarding, like other public safety work, is constantly adapting to utilize the benefits of new technology.

Los Angeles County lifeguards aboard a Baywatch rescue boat drill with a U.S. Coast Guard helicopter.

Increasing expectations of the general public for emergency medical care have resulted in dramatic improvements in the quality of emergency medical training. USLA minimum recommended standards require that all lifeguards have emergency medical aid training well beyond the basic levels available to the general public. More advanced open water lifeguard agencies now require their personnel to be certified at the level of Emergency Medical Technician or the equivalent of Department of Transportation Emergency Medical Responder, employing all of the equipment commonly used by people trained at these levels.

Facilities have also improved. Properly designed lifeguard facilities minimize stress and fatigue by providing refuge from the elements. Larger lifeguard stations include areas with private treatment areas for people requiring medical attention. Some include garages, offices, workout rooms, kitchen areas, and other facilities commonly found in the stations of other emergency service providers.

Thus, the period from the 1960s to the present has brought a great change in the scope of roles of the professional lifeguard. Lifeguarding has emerged as a true emergency service with the same charge as that of other emergency services—the protection of lives and property. In a typical year in this country well over 80,000 people are rescued from drowning by open water lifeguards, hundreds of thousands of medical aids performed, and tens of millions of dollars in property rescued.

LEARN MORE

You can view and download the most recent national statistics from America's open water lifeguard agencies from www.usla.org/statistics.

Credit: Robert Martini

Lido Beach on a weekday. Gulf Coast of Florida. Home of the Sarasota County Beach Patrol.

HISTORICAL LESSONS

Despite these advances, not all of today's open water lifeguard agencies can boast of modern equipment and facilities. Many seasonal agencies still operate following years of tradition based on equipment developed for lifesaving more than 100 years ago. Other lifeguard services employ the most basic equipment and training. At some parks and beaches, solitary lifeguards work long hours without assistance; while at others administrators struggle over how, or even if, lifeguards should be employed.

The lessons of the past are hard learned and oft forgotten. For example, on Memorial Day 1994, five people died after drowning at American Beach in northern Florida. No lifeguards were present because they had been eliminated in a cost saving measure. Shortly after the deaths and ensuing nationwide attention, lifeguard protection was restored.

The USLA has led the way in advocating for appropriate levels of lifeguard protection. As recently as 2003, the city of Destin, Florida had no public lifeguard program. USLA representatives were invited by the mayor to make recommendations. The USLA's extensive resulting report culminated in the creation of a new lifeguard agency that exists to this day.

In Pensacola, Florida, between April 2000 and August 2003 there were 21 drowning deaths on beaches controlled by the Santa Rosa Island Authority. The USLA met with decision-makers and issued an extensive report with specific recommendations. In 2005, the Pensacola News Journal reported, "By the close of the 2003 summer season, the Island Authority had doubled its public service budget, and the turn-around began." Drowning deaths had plummeted to zero. The News Journal declared, "Beach lifeguards make a real difference in safety."[24]

The USLA remains ever vigilant. In 2016, the Port Hueneme, California city council considered completely defunding its beach lifeguard program. It was only through strong advocacy that this outcome was avoided. Good thing. On July 4th of that year it was reported that 30 people were rescued from rip currents north of the Port Hueneme pier.

There was a time when the common public perception of lifeguards was that of sun worshippers with little more to offer than directions and suntan lotion. This perception has changed through the efforts of open water lifeguards who understand that recognition of their essential public safety role is directly tied to their own level of professionalism. Lifeguards who willingly accept the old stereotypes directly contribute to their perpetuation, seriously harming not only their own image, but that of their fellow lifeguards. On the other hand, lifeguards who demonstrate respect for their occupation through preparedness, maturity, and dedication help ensure that lifeguards will be recognized, trained, equipped, and compensated at appropriate levels.

The first lifesavers who walked the beaches of America in search of shipwreck victims were not fully respected or funded until they adopted regulations, drilled regularly, and demonstrated an ability to handle the most complex rescues with the ease of professionals. It was through their own actions that their profession became recognized as essential to the safety and well-being of the public. The same is true today. Every open water lifeguard is directly responsible for the professional image of all open water lifeguards.

CHAPTER SUMMARY

In this chapter, we have learned that organized lifesaving efforts began in America in the 1700s to rescue shipwrecked sailors. As the shipwrecks diminished in number, interest in swimming grew, and open water lifeguards were first hired in the U.S. in the late 1800s to rescue swimmers.

Many innovations of training and equipment have taken place since that time. Lifeguards have evolved their skills to include advanced medical aid and a variety of other emergency services. The United States Lifesaving Association was created after American lifeguards visited Australia and saw the benefits of a national lifesaving association. Later, the USLA developed national standards for open water lifeguard training. Today, the USLA is a world leader in lifesaving and, as a result of the efforts of lifeguards throughout the United States, lifeguarding has evolved to become a true emergency service.

DISCUSSION POINTS

- Explain why there was a need for lifesavers in the U.S.
- Explain why the first U.S. lifesavers did not work during summer months.
- Identify three rescue devices used by the U.S. Life-Saving Service.

- Explain the use of lifelines.
- Discuss the impact of World War II on lifesaving.
- Cite the event that promoted the creation of the Surf Lifesaving Association of America.
- Explain the decision to adopt the name United States Lifesaving Association.
- Compare the advantages and disadvantages of the first rescue can.
- Explain how plastic revolutionized the design of the rescue buoy.
- Compare and contrast lifeguards with other emergency service providers.
- Explain the value of lifeguards maintaining a professional image.

Use and Protection of America's Beaches

In this chapter, you will learn that open water beaches are one of the great natural resources of our nation. People have always been drawn to the water, but beaches have experienced an explosion in popularity over the past several decades. In fact, they are the most popular tourist destination in the United States by a wide margin. Some impacts of humans upon the beach environment include pollution and development. Lifeguards play an important role in mitigating negative impacts, protecting both the environment and the people who use it for recreation.

CHAPTER EXCERPT

It is sometimes forgotten that our beaches are a fragile resource that must be carefully protected. In addition to protecting visitors from beach and water hazards, a major role of lifeguards is to protect the beach itself.

BEACH POPULARITY

Beaches are the leading tourist destination in the USA.[1] In fact, their popularity far exceeds other tourist attractions. For example, Trip Advisor reported, "The beach/ ocean is the most popular setting for a vacation rental stay in 2015, as 63 percent of respondents will rent by the shore."[2] Travel Pulse, reporting on a 2012 Expedia survey asserted that, "The beach is the world's most popular vacation destination ... 18 of 22 countries cite the beach as their preferred holiday."[3] One study found that beach tourism contributes $225 billion annually to the U.S. economy, more than seven times that of the National Park Service system.[1]

The beach is a magnet for people from all walks of life. They flock to the shore for myriad reasons. Some come merely to relax, contemplate, or perhaps read a book. Many come to recreate. Most will benefit by the oversight and assistance of a professional lifeguard.

LEARN MORE

Check the latest statistics on beach use in America and the work of open water lifeguards at: www.usla.org/statistics.

Miami Beach, Florida.

Credit: Leslie Schwene

Surfers, bodyboarders, and swimmers mingle at Huntington Beach, California.

Part of the seemingly ever-increasing popularity of the beach stems from the tremendous interest in aquatic recreation. Each year more than 80 million Americans participate in open water swimming and some 77 million participate in boating.[4] There are many other popular aquatic recreational activities, such as surfing, skin and scuba diving, windsurfing, kayaking, stand-up-paddling, and kiteboarding. Beaches are also popular venues for non-aquatic activities like sunbathing, volleyball, walking, running, skating, biking, hiking, backpacking, climbing, and a host of others. Some municipalities even permit vehicle traffic on their beaches. All of these activities have created added demands on the limited recreational space available and on the lifeguards who manage these areas.

The popularity of the beach lends itself to occasional conflicts among users, which lifeguards are often called upon to mediate. For example, lifeguards must be prepared to help resolve the dispute that may arise when a volleyball group sets up next to a group of people practicing yoga, or a visiting college group unaware of the local prohibition of alcohol on the beach arrives with several large coolers of beer. All these problems can be resolved, but require the social, diplomatic, and managerial skills of the professional lifeguard.

THE BEACH ENVIRONMENT

The beach is a complex ecosystem that can be irreparably damaged through misuse. Litter, development, sand loss, and water pollution are just a few examples of potential threats to the beach environment. Each of these can also threaten the safety of visitors. It is sometimes forgotten that our beaches are a fragile resource that must be carefully protected. In addition to protecting visitors from beach and water hazards, a major role of lifeguards is to protect the beach itself.

Litter

Visitors to the beach sometimes seem to think they're visiting an amusement park, and that someone will always pick up after them. Some leave food, paper products, cans, bottles, and other forms of litter. Not only does trash diminish the appearance of the beach, it also threatens the safety of people and animals. People can be injured by stepping on sharp discarded items. Animals may be injured by ingesting or becoming entangled in waste. The problem can be compounded when people use the sand to cover litter, like glass containers that break and create a hidden hazard to other visitors. Many communities ban glass containers or cigarettes, for example, for these reasons. Whether or not regulations exist, lifeguards can play an important role in encouraging people to be responsible and to respect the beach.

Beach litter.

Flotsam

Flotsam is debris floating in the water. It can come in the form of harmless seaweed or large, dangerous objects containing sharp edges or surfaces. Flotsam can include hazardous materials which can pose a health threat to beach visitors. It's typically most evident after a storm or storm surf. At surf beaches, flotsam is particularly dangerous since it can be washed in at high velocity by surf action, injuring swimmers in its path. At both surf and flat water areas flotsam that washes ashore without incident can continue to be dangerous, especially if it becomes buried and therefore hidden. Buried flotsam can later be uncovered by currents or wave action and create new problems. Flotsam can cut, stab, or stick visitors walking along the beach.

Lifeguards should be alert for flotsam and immediately investigate any unexpected floating objects. At surf beaches, it may be necessary to clear a water area until a large

Pollutants washed ashore.

A picnic table caught in storm surge.

object floats in, so that it doesn't strike anyone. Regular patrols of beach areas by lifeguards are important to check for all hazards, including flotsam.

Sand

Sandy beaches are unique environments, ideal for recreation. Sand sometimes seems to be ever-present, but when shorelines are reinforced to protect adjacent structures, the result is sometimes a significant loss of sandy beach frontage. Most sandy beaches are created and regenerated by erosion of coastline by sand that flows to the sea from inland rivers, and by movement of sand along the shoreline. When this natural process is impeded by development, beaches can suffer. At some beaches, jetties and groins have been constructed in an effort to save the beach, although their effectiveness is sometimes questioned. Communities sometimes pay to "renourish" beaches by pumping sand on them—a very expensive process. Although nature will often eventually erode renourished sand, many consider the cost justified by the enjoyment and economic benefit the beach provides.

LEARN MORE

When sand replenishment is conducted at beaches, the Army Corps of Engineers is usually involved: www.usace.army.mil

Blowing sand, thrown sand, and even the natural sand surface itself can all cause injuries. This includes orthopedic injuries from walking on uneven ground and eye injuries from blowing or thrown sand. One of the most serious problems involving sand occurs when visitors dig holes or tunnels in the sand. While digging in the sand may be a common pastime, beachgoers have been buried alive and died when these pits or tunnels have collapsed over them. Lifeguards can reduce the potential for injury by discouraging the digging of holes or tunnels that have any potential to collapse on a beachgoer, or to cause an unseeing beachgoer to fall in. Some areas have ordinances which forbid it. A related problem involves lifeguard emergency vehicles. People sometimes cover each other with sand, but this can camouflage them from a lifeguard driving a beach emergency vehicle. Great caution is essential in all beach driving. (For more on sand holes and sand rescue, see Chapter 15: *Special Rescues*.)

Credit: Jim Jordan

Sand renourishment project on Kiawah Island, South Carolina.

Improper disposal of hot charcoal or ash poses a serious hazard. Visitors may prepare picnics using charcoal grills, then dump hot coals on the sand or bury them. These coals, particularly when buried, can retain their heat for many hours, later causing second and third degree burns to the feet of unsuspecting visitors. This is a particular problem for toddlers who may wander away from their parents and walk on discarded coals, but who may not know how to get away from the burning sensation. Even portable grills positioned above the sand can superheat the sand below and cause injury. Seri-

Credit: Cole Yeatts

Sand holes can cause serious injury and even death, so lifeguards discourage this activity.

ous injuries causing lifelong deformity to children occur this way every year. A solution employed by some agencies is to maintain containers for disposing of hot coals. Lifeguards can assist in prevention of these devastating injuries by educating visitors using grills about the dangers and explaining how to safely dispose of hot coals.

Pressures from Development

As we learned in Chapter 1 (*Lifesaving History*), in a short period of human history the beach has become a very popular place to live, work, and recreate. A home with a view of the water, any open body of water, is often the most sought after in a community. With this popularity comes pressure on the beach. Waterfront property can sometimes obstruct public access to the beach. Development pressure, added to the increasing popularity of beaches and water activities, can threaten the fragile beach environment. One reason sand renourishment is needed is that development impacts the natural erosion process that feeds beaches.

Coastal development encroaches on Waikiki Beach, Hawaii.

To prevent over-development, concerned citizens have pressed for government action. In some cases the result has been public acquisition of oceanfront property. Another method of protection is through coastal zoning laws enacted to protect not only the beach resource, but all aspects of life nearby. This has included protection of the right of people

LEARN MORE

Learn about the California Coastal Act and the California Coastal Commission at: www.coastal.ca.gov

to access public beaches. In California, for example, voters enacted the Coastal Conservation Initiative in 1972 to plan for and regulate land and water uses in the coastal zone in the interests of the public. This resulted in creation of the California Coastal Act and the California Coastal Commission, which wields significant power over coastal development and takes steps to ensure public access to the beach. Its very existence serves to demonstrate public interest in protecting the coastline.

Water Quality

Many things can influence water quality. A malfunctioning sewage treatment plant may cause an inadvertent release of untreated waste. Industrial effluent may be allowed into the water, either accidentally or intentionally. Even natural events can result in significant changes in water quality. Rain and other forms of precipitation can cause pollutants on land to be washed into the water. These include agricultural and lawn fertilizer, pesticides, atmospheric fallout, petroleum products, wild and domestic animal waste, and litter. This is called *nonpoint* pollution because it is not from a single source.

A heavy rain after a dry period can introduce *shock loads* of pollutants, so-called because they have built up over a period of time between rains and can have a sudden, negative impact on water quality. This is why health authorities often caution about human exposure to water quality after rain, particularly in urban areas. Even in the water itself there are various impacts to water quality like waterfowl excrement, tidal mixing, disturbance of sediment, and water temperature. Algae blooms can grow out of control producing harmful or toxic effects on humans and animals. Examples include red tide and cyanobacteria (blue-green algae).

Water pollution threatens both the environment and the health of recreational water users. While swimmers stand a greater risk of contracting disease from polluted water, people who never intended to swim can be affected too. Consider the windsurfer who occasionally falls off the board, the wader, or the person who eats fish from a contaminated body of water. Infectious diseases such as cholera and typhoid fever can be spread by water and food contaminated with fecal waste or sewage.

Many parameters can be used to evaluate the quality of a body of water. The most commonly used indicators in determining risk to human health are bacteria levels. Bacteria called coliforms and enterococcus are specific microorganisms whose elevated densities can cause human health hazards for water users. They should be frequently monitored at aquatic recreation areas.

Red tide.

Government agencies responsible for protecting public and environmental health have implemented laws and procedures to reduce the level of pollutants entering the water. When a body of water declines below levels considered safe, responsible health authorities typically direct that the area be closed to water contact. In some cases, decisions are based on predictive modeling.

The quality and frequency of recreational water quality testing varies in the U.S., and even within states. Swimmers can be unknowingly exposed to pathogens (disease causing agents), incorrectly assuming testing is taking place and the public is being notified. Not surprisingly, according to the Environmental Protection Agency, "You are less likely to be exposed to polluted water at beaches that are monitored regularly and posted for health hazards."[5]

Federal legislation aimed at ensuring a more consistent level of testing and public notification was signed into law in 2000. Known as the Beaches Environmental Assessment and Coastal Health (B.E.A.C.H.) Act, it amended the federal Clean Water Act. The BEACH Act was coauthored by Member of Congress Brian Bilbray, a former ocean lifeguard. It requires the Environmental Protection Agency to ensure that a minimum national water quality testing standard is met or exceeded by the coastal states and to ensure that the public is notified.

Lifeguard agencies should have established procedures in effect for recognizing and reporting possible contamination events. They should also have procedures for helping ensure that the public is notified and protected from exposure. Normally, once the local department of health determines that water is unsafe for human contact, the beach will be officially closed by public notice, including verbal warnings, signs, media advisories, etc. Lifeguard agencies should have a relationship with local health authorities to ensure that they are notified immediately when the public health authority issues an advisory.

Some incidents may cause a lifeguard agency to close a beach to public contact before the local health authority makes a determination of severity. For example, evidence of petroleum, medical waste, or sewage may cause a preemptive closure. In more serious cases, even aquatic areas not designated for recreation may be closed.

When a beach is closed due to contamination, everyone suffers. Those who enjoy water recreation are prevented from recreating. The economy of the local community may be negatively impacted because of lessened tourism. Lifeguard staff may be reduced. There are therefore many reasons for lifeguards and the communities they serve to be very concerned about maintaining the highest possible levels of water quality.

LEARN MORE

Both the National Resources Defense Council (www.nrdc.org) and the Environmental Protection Agency (epa.gov) publish annual reports on water quality monitoring results.

NOTICE
NO SWIMMING!

Toxic Algae Present In Water

• No bodily contact with the water. Supervise children and pets at all times—they are particularly vulnerable.

• Keep pets, especially dogs, out of the water.

• Skin in contact with algae should be rinsed with tap water.

• Fish may be consumed after removing guts and liver, and rinsing fillets in tap water.

• For the latest water quality conditions please visit: www.ebparks.org/activities/swimming/facilities

For more information contact East Bay Regional Park District at (510) 544-2328 or visit the California Department of Public Health online: www.cdph.ca.gov/healthinfo/environhealth/water/pages/bluegreenalgae.aspx

East Bay
Regional Park District
www.ebparks.org

A temporary sign warning of toxic algae bloom.

CHAPTER SUMMARY

In this chapter we have learned that beach popularity seems to be constantly on the rise, with new beach and water activities ever expanding. We have learned that our beaches are a fragile resource which needs protection. Various laws and regulations discourage water and beach pollution; and regular water testing, combined with public notification, can reduce negative impacts on public health. Lifeguards can be protectors and advocates for the beach environment by encouraging people to recognize the beach as an irreplaceable natural resource of great value. In doing so, lifeguards help protect the future enjoyment of generations of beach visitors and even their own jobs.

DISCUSSION POINTS

- Describe some conflicts among patrons that you have observed at the beach.
- Identify three activities that have a negative impact on the beach environment.
- List three ways lifeguards can encourage the public to keep the beach clean.
- Identify the main reason flotsam should be removed from the beach.
- List the three dangers to beachgoers when digging holes in the sand.
- Explain why hot coals are a concern at the beach.
- Identify the agencies in your area that are responsible for water quality testing in your area.
- List five regulations that help protect the beaches in your area.
- Identify three reasons why beaches lose sand.
- List five ways lifeguards are impacted by water quality.

CHAPTER

3

The Role of the Professional Lifeguard

In this chapter you will learn that the professional lifeguard has many responsibilities. Primarily they involve lifesaving and other forms of public safety, but they include providing many other public services to beach users, like finding lost people and acting as a local information resource. The professional lifeguard serves as a manager of both public safety and general activities. Professional lifeguards should always perform their duties ethically. By performing their duties both professionally and ethically, lifeguards can expect to enjoy extraordinary rewards.

CHAPTER EXCERPT

The stress of a lifeguard's responsibilities can sometimes be immense. The challenges however, make lifeguarding one of the most diverse and rewarding professions. How many people can go home after work with the satisfaction of knowing that they have performed the most important act of all in our society—the saving of human life?

THE USLA CODE OF ETHICS

In recognition of the fundamental responsibilities of a professional open water lifeguard, the trust and confidence placed in the lifeguard, the unwavering devotion to duty required of the lifeguard, and the dignity commensurate with the lifeguard's position, the United States Lifesaving Association recognizes ethical principles.

Lifeguards will:

- Maintain an unwavering dedication to the safety of those they are assigned to protect.
- Recognize and accept that heightened personal dangers are an unavoidable aspect of the job.
- Maintain high standards of fitness, recognizing that their strength, stamina, and physical skill may mean the difference between life and death.
- Make every reasonable effort to prevent accidents before they occur.
- Avoid any undue distraction which may deter them from their primary responsibility.

- Proudly carry out the duties they are assigned, providing the highest possible levels of courtesy, respect and assistance to those whom they watch over.
- Take proactive steps to educate the public about the hazards of the aquatic environment and ways to safely enjoy aquatic recreation.
- Promote their profession through personal actions which serve to demonstrate that lifeguards everywhere are deserving of the trust placed in them by the public they serve.
- Diligently follow established policies and procedures set forth by their employing agency to promote the best possible public service.

RESPONSIBILITIES AND EXPECTATIONS

Unlike untrained citizens who may bravely or impulsively respond to an unexpected emergency, lifeguards are uniquely trained and prepared to anticipate, prevent, and respond to emergencies in and around the aquatic environment. Most lifeguards who spend any significant time in the profession will perform many lifesaving acts with little recognition nor expectation thereof. It is, after all, the basic job of a lifeguard to help ensure that those who visit the nation's beaches, waterways, adjacent parks, and campgrounds return home safe. Not all accidents can be prevented, but well trained professional open water lifeguards rescue tens of thousands of people from drowning in America each year and perform many times that number of preventive actions to intercede before emergencies develop.

Accomplishing these core tasks of prevention and rescue has a significant impact, not only on the individual who is saved from injury or death, but also on the families of those rescued, and even on the nation's economy. A study commissioned by the Centers for Disease Control and Prevention found that for every 10,000 beach visitors there is a national monetary savings of between $705,000 and $16,000,000 as a result of professional lifeguards doing their job.[1] This figure includes not only the direct economic cost of preventing accidental death or injury, but also measures the value of lost quality of life associated with death or injuries. In other words, it assesses what society would be willing to pay to prevent such a loss. These numbers rise to astounding levels when multiplied by the hundreds of millions of people who visit beaches each year and very clearly demonstrate the value of open water lifeguards as emergency service professionals.

LEARN MORE

You can review the latest statistics on lifeguard rescues, beach attendance, and related information in the Statistics section of the USLA website at: www.usla.org/statistics.

Credit: San Clemente Lifeguards

Lifeguard entering the water for a rescue.

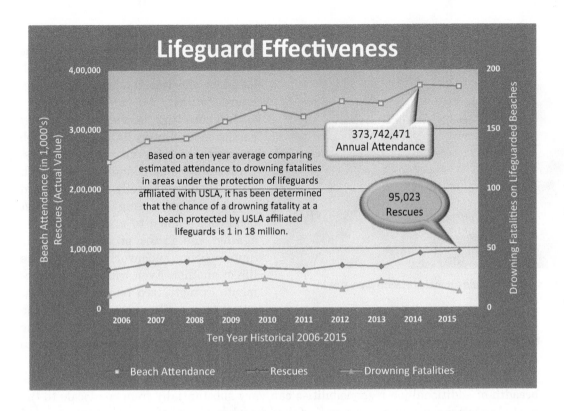

In 2001, the Centers for Disease Control and Prevention's National Center for Injury Prevention issued a report entitled *Lifeguard Effectiveness: A Report of the Working Group.* This extensive report covered many topics and included numerous findings. Among them: "Most [drowning deaths] are preventable through a wide variety of strategies, one of which is to provide lifeguards in public areas where people are known to swim and to encourage people to swim in those protected areas ... There is no doubt that trained, professional lifeguards have had a positive effect on drowning prevention in the United States."[2]

> **LEARN MORE**
>
> You can download and read a copy of *Lifeguard Effectiveness: A Report of the Working Group* at: www.usla.org/library.

In the U.S., open water lifeguards have worked hard to be recognized as equals to other emergency services professionals, such as police officers, firefighters, and emergency medical personnel. This has been accomplished through a steady process of improving the quality of the services provided and a constant dedication to public safety. As a result, Americans have come to expect professional lifeguards on their beaches, just as they have come to expect professional police, fire, and emergency medical services in their communities. In many areas the incidence of drowning has prompted enhancements to lifeguard services, just as increased crime has prompted augmentation of police services.

> **LEARN MORE**
>
> The USLA offers the Medal of Valor to lifeguards and its Heroic Act Award to non-lifeguards whose actions meet extraordinary criteria. For a list of recipients, visit the USLA website at: www.usla.org/heroic.

Credit: Drasko Bogdanovic

Lifeguards from multiple agencies attend an event in uniform.

Conversely, in some cases reduction or elimination of lifeguard services has resulted in serious loss of life, often followed by the reinstatement of the lifeguard staffing.

Lifeguarding is viewed by many as the most physically demanding job among the various emergency services. Unlike other emergency services, which are able to rely heavily on mechanized support, lifeguarding in its purest form comes down to a simple struggle against the forces of nature by one human being endeavoring to save the life of another. Even with new developments in motorized rescue equipment, many rescue situations depend on the sheer strength, physical endurance, running ability, and swimming skills of the lifeguard. It is why physical fitness and superior swimming skills are so critical to effective lifeguarding.

While the primary job of a professional open water lifeguard is public safety, the breadth of additional job responsibilities can vary substantially from one locale to the next. At one agency a lifeguard may find that the job is a blend of several aquatic related public safety responsibilities, such as law enforcement, flood rescue, and firefighting. At another, the job may be defined more narrowly, emphasizing the more traditional aspects of lifeguarding.

Professional lifeguards are typically intimately familiar with all facets of the aquatic environment and adjacent land areas they serve. This familiarity leaves them uniquely prepared to handle a variety of functions that serve to protect public safety, such as emergency medical services, scuba search and recovery, cliff rescue, boat rescue, marine firefighting, swiftwater rescue, and flood rescue. Many open water lifeguards are given law enforcement powers and responsibilities to help maintain public safety within their jurisdiction.

Lifeguards have additional functions. Among these are the responsibilities to provide public information and education, complete required documentation, and locate missing persons. Lifeguards should never be assigned or assume duties beyond those directly related to their public safety role. Such

Credit: California State Parks Lifeguards

A California State Parks lifeguard gives a talk to junior lifeguards.

assignments only serve to diminish attention to safety and can result in serious, life-threatening consequences.

Professional lifeguards are reliable, mature, consistent, and prepared to demonstrate an expert knowledge of the area served. They maintain a professional appearance and readiness to respond to instill public confidence in their reliability. They train diligently in order to preserve their skills and readiness.

THE LIFEGUARD AS MANAGER

Lifeguarding includes more than just watching the water and responding to emergencies. Lifeguards act as managers for the areas they oversee. Each day of work, the pressure is on, the public is watching, and lifeguards hold the lives and welfare of the people they watch over in their hands. This means managing safety and the interactions of people—both with the environment and with each other. High levels of coordination with other emergency service providers can help lifeguards accomplish these goals. Constant vigilance is imperative—a momentary distraction may mean that a person whose distress is unnoticed could die or be seriously injured.

Managing Safety

Water is not a natural environment for humans. With proper skills, people can recreate safely in water, but they are ill-equipped for surviving in some water conditions. Many beach visitors have never experienced the variety of challenges of the open water environment. Others simply forget. Many emergencies occur because people visiting an area wrongly presume that conditions will be similar to those near their home or the same as the last time they visited the beach.

Lifeguards should never assume that visitors are familiar with a beach's particular hazards or energy conditions, such as waves, currents, or dams. Considering the large number of new visitors in most beach crowds, lifeguards must assume, until it is demonstrated otherwise, that patrons have no knowledge of their beach.

Lifeguards must also be cognizant of the demographics of their beach crowds. People often behave differently in groups and some may push themselves beyond their capability just to impress one another. For example, drowning statistics indicate that teenage boys are inclined to risk-taking behavior, which can lead to emergency situations for lifeguards.

Lifeguards are sometimes drawn away from the water to handle problems or emergencies involving medical aid, rule enforcement, and so on. Good managers will be sure adequate backup is available to maintain watch over the water and that lifeguards are trained to conclude any contact which diverts attention from the water as soon as

A lifeguard warns of the danger of sand collapse.

Credit: California State Parks Lifeguards

possible. Attention directed away from the water, even for short periods of time, can create a situation where simple problems become serious ones, including drowning.

Managing Conflict

Wherever people gather, particularly as crowd sizes increase, there can be conflicts. Problems of human interaction at the beach may be as simple as verbal disputes or more serious, like theft or fights. A major aspect of effective beach management is people management. This means protecting people from themselves and each other, in addition to protecting them from the hazards of the aquatic environment.

Beach users sometimes feel liberated to act in ways they might not usually behave. They may unintentionally or even intentionally anger others. They may intrude on the personal space of other beachgoers. The use of alcohol and drugs can exacerbate these problems.

Effective beach management includes preventing conflicts by separating incompatible activities whenever possible. For example, participants in a game of horseshoes being set up near an area where small children are playing might be asked to move, or the Frisbee player who inadvertently, but consistently allows his disc to strike others might similarly be relocated. This is a part of the lifeguard's preventive role. It not only helps promote respectful behavior, but minimizes the need to intervene later, when tempers may flare.

When disputes do arise, lifeguards, as the most prominent and available source of authority, are often expected to mediate. Before intervening, a lifeguard must evaluate the safest approach for the lifeguard and other lifeguards. This may mean avoiding intervention until law enforcement has been summoned and has arrived on-scene. Knowing when to avoid intervention is as important as knowing when to intervene. Personal safety is paramount. The best approach in conflict situations is a calm demeanor, complete objectivity, and a goal of finding a way for both parties to feel that they have been heard. Experienced lifeguards become experts at beach diplomacy.

Sometimes it's a good idea to separate the parties in dispute, out of earshot of each other, so that the conflict doesn't intensify as each tells their side of the story. First, tell the parties you will hear them out, but that you want to talk to them privately. Listen patiently to both parties. Don't provide suggestions until you have heard from each. If there's a large group involved, avoid conversing in front of all of them. Ask first who the group leader or representative is and take that person aside. Otherwise, a very real sense of group resistance may arise with many members of the group yelling out their opinions and inciting each other further. The ideal resolution is one which allows both parties to continue their activity, perhaps in some modified manner. Can you find a resolution like this?

Sometimes, one party or the other (or both) will need to be told that they must discontinue what they're doing, perhaps because it violates a beach rule or regulation. Disputes involve ego and a resolution that requires someone to change their behavior may cause them to "lose face." Minimizing this outcome will help greatly. Talk to the person or the group representative quietly, to avoid drawing a crowd or undue attention. A patient and calm lifeguard can resolve most disputes without the need for summoning police (although in some cases, there may be no choice).

Managing conflict between two parties is quite similar to enforcing regulations. Similar principles are involved including prioritizing the safety of lifeguards, maintaining a professional demeanor, and ensuring that other responsibilities of lifeguards are not compromised. We discuss further considerations in the *Rules and Regulations* section of Chapter 9 (*Preventive Lifeguarding*).

LIFEGUARD REWARDS

A lifeguard's stress and challenges can sometimes be immense; but lifeguarding is also one of the most diverse and rewarding jobs available. There are innumerable opportunities to interact with the public, to gain special training, to learn leadership, to advance in the profession, to learn to manage people. Simply helping people can be a reward in and of itself. There is one very special reward though: How many people can go home after work with the satisfaction of knowing that they have performed the most important act of all—the saving of human life? Lifeguards have many opportunities to experience that very feeling, so long as they are always prepared to respond professionally when the need arises.

Lifesaving is a family. There are lifeguards around the world performing much the same services, experiencing many of the same challenges. You will find, as a lifeguard, that when you meet lifeguards from other places you have a common bond. It's a bond that will last a lifetime, providing friendship and hospitality wherever you travel. This spirit has been embodied in a phrase used often and even trademarked by the USLA: *Lifeguards for Life*®.

Credit: Cole Yeatts

A lifeguard assists a victim from the surf.

CHAPTER SUMMARY

In this chapter we have learned that lifeguards have a wide variety of responsibilities that extend beyond water safety, but that they must ensure that public safety is never compromised, whatever they may be doing. We have learned that lifeguarding is a physically demanding job, with responsibilities similar to those of police or firefighters; and that lifeguards must work hard to maintain their readiness and demonstrate their professionalism. As beach managers, lifeguards must be prepared to handle both safety and conflict. They must behave ethically at all times. In performing to these expectations, lifeguards can expect lifelong rewards from their job that extend well beyond financial compensation.

DISCUSSION POINTS

- Identify the value of having a USLA Code of Ethics for lifeguards.
- Identify what separates lifeguards from other people who attempt a rescue of a person who is drowning.
- Identify the value of having a lifeguard on duty.
- Identify common factors that make lifeguards similar to police and firefighters.
- Identify the importance of professional appearance when working as a lifeguard.
- Explain the need for backup in managing safety.
- List five ways to mediate conflicts among beach users.
- Identify the rewards of being a lifeguard.

Open Water Lifeguard Qualifications and Training

I n this chapter, you will learn that lifeguards work in a variety of environments. Open water lifeguards require specialized skills and training for the many different environments and circumstances in which they work. The USLA training system addresses these needs through a core curriculum, along with specialized training components. This chapter provides an overview of USLA recommended training standards for open water lifeguards and the various ways training can be provided. It explains how lifeguard agencies which adhere to these standards can become nationally certified under the USLA *Lifeguard Agency Certification Program*.

CHAPTER EXCERPT

The USLA has set a minimum swimming proficiency standard of 500 meters in 10 minutes or less for open water lifeguards since 1980. The USLA based this minimum standard on consensus input from representatives of the major aquatic safety organizations of the United States.

THE USLA LIFEGUARD TRAINING SYSTEM

There are many different aquatic environments requiring lifeguard protection. The USLA believes they fall into two general categories: (1) the controlled environment of pools and waterparks, and (2) the natural environment of open water. Because of the fundamental differences between these environments, we recognize two corresponding categories of lifeguards—pool/waterpark lifeguards and open water lifeguards.

In comparison to open water lifeguard training, pool and waterpark lifeguard training is highly standardized. Under various existing training systems, if a candidate successfully completes training as a pool lifeguard in Michigan, for example, the training is likely to be accepted by a pool manager in Arizona as adequate for employment. This is possible because of the inherent similarity in the pool and waterpark environment regardless of where the facility may be located.

Conversely, the open water environment varies greatly from place to place, and open water is a more challenging environment for lifeguards. Additionally, open water lifeguards often have more wide-ranging responsibilities. For these reasons, open water lifesaving requires markedly differing physical conditioning, training, and skills. Open water lifeguard training must therefore be more intensive and adapted appropriately to local conditions. The following table provides some examples of the different challenges faced by lifeguards safeguarding these two types of environments.

COMPARISON OF AQUATIC ENVIRONMENTS

Condition	Pool/Waterpark	Open Water
Water Temperature	Can be controlled	Subject to natural conditions
Water Clarity	Can be controlled	Subject to natural conditions
Difficulty of Rescue	Accomplished by jumping into pool and wading, swimming, or paddling a short distance	May require long distance swimming in adverse conditions
Natural Hazards	None	May be extensive and may not be readily apparent
Wave Action and Currents	None or fully controlled	Surf and currents may present the most significant source of swimmer distress and difficulty of rescue
Attendance Levels and Hours	Can be controlled	Generally not controllable
Weather Conditions	Little effect	Possible severe effect

Open water lifeguards must deal with a variety of natural hazards which cannot be controlled. Some of these hazards are surf, currents, and underwater obstacles. Rescues may take place far from shore. Open water facilities are sometimes located in remote areas which can increase the amount of time it takes EMS to respond. In these locations lifeguards must be prepared to support victims with medical emergencies for extended periods.

While open water lifeguard operations share many similarities with each other, they can differ in a variety of ways. A surf beach in Maine, for example, has a different climate, water conditions, and even a different clientele than a similar surf beach in Florida. An intensely populated surf beach on the urban Chicago lakefront requires different lifeguarding approaches from a camp waterfront in rural Kentucky. The warm water conditions, large surf, and reefs on the North Shore of Oahu present markedly different challenges from the colder waters, sand bars, and longshore currents of the outer shore of Cape Cod.

Hanauma Bay, Hawaii.

Misquamicut Beach, Rhode Island.

North Shore, Oahu, Hawaii.

Credit: Kyle Maxwell

North Avenue Beach, Chicago.

Ocean Beach, San Diego, California.

Credit: San Diego Lifeguard Service

In addition to variables in environmental conditions, open water lifeguards have varying responsibilities, organizational structures, authority, and lifesaving equipment. Open water lifeguards are assigned many different tasks, such as boat rescue, law enforcement, cliff rescue, flood rescue, marine firefighting, and scuba search and rescue. Open water lifeguards may be expected to operate emergency vehicles with lights and siren, rescue boats, and other technical equipment. They may work for lifeguard departments, recreation departments, harbor departments, police departments, fire departments, state or national park systems, or private businesses, to name some examples.

To address these many variables, in developing training text, curriculum elements, and our *Lifeguard Agency Certification Program*, the USLA has taken into account the unique aspects of open water lifeguard operations across the country. The USLA publication entitled *Guidelines for Open Water Lifeguard Agency Certification* provides a training curriculum and recommended standards flexible enough to meet the training needs of all agencies employing open water lifeguards, while recognizing the many differences among them. Lifeguard agencies which provide training and maintain standards in accordance with USLA recommendations can achieve national certification under the USLA *Lifeguard Agency Certification Program*. Agencies which are certified by the USLA have demonstrated their adherence to these guidelines and standards. The USLA also offers course completion cards that can be issued by USLA certified agencies to the lifeguards they train.

LEARN MORE

You can download *Guidelines for Open Water Lifeguard Agency Certification* from the USLA website at: www.usla.org/certification.

Under the USLA training system, open water lifeguard training in Colorado need not provide information on effecting surf rescues, just as a lifeguard training program for surf lifeguards in California need not discuss issues unique to rescues in reservoirs. This allows open water lifeguard training programs to focus on tasks specific to each local agency's geography and mission. Because of this specialization however, open water lifeguard training conducted under the USLA system is not interchangeable from one agency to another. Retraining is required if the lifeguard moves to an agency other than that which provided the training.

Credit: California State Parks Lifeguards

Lifeguard training at Lake Perris, California.

Despite the local training variables offered under the USLA system, central elements are consistent nationwide. This manual provides information both on the core aspects of open water lifeguarding, in which all open water lifeguards should be skilled, as well as the specialized information needed to assist in training that is unique to particular geographic locations. It is the responsibility of lifeguard agencies to select portions of the text for trainees which are appropriate to the areas where the trainee will work.

The USLA also offers *Training & Standards of Aquatic Rescue Response Teams* for the training of open water rescuers who are not lifeguards. These guidelines allow specialized aquatic rescue teams to achieve national certification under the USLA *Aquatic Rescue Response Team* certification program.

LEARN MORE

You can find out which agencies are currently certified by the USLA on the USLA websites at: www.usla.org/certified.

LEARN MORE

You can download *Training & Standards of Aquatic Rescue Response Teams* from the USLA website at: www.usla.org/certification.

TRAINING MODES

In establishing guidelines for open water lifeguard training, the USLA recognizes three major modes of training—prerequisite, pre-service, and in-service.

Prerequisite Training

Employers in many fields of work require prospective employees to have a minimum level of training before they can apply for a job. This is sometimes true in lifeguarding. In the pool environment, for example, those seeking employment as lifeguards are often expected to have completed basic training prior to application. In the open water environment however, this is less typical.

Some open water lifeguard employers may require pre-employment completion of a medical aid or CPR course, or both. Since the USLA recommended standards include training in medical aid and CPR that is recognized by the Federal Government or the state government in the state of employment, nationally recognized courses like Department of Transportation Emergency Medical Responder or Emergency Medical Technician might be accepted as a prerequisite by an employer regardless of where the training was provided.

In some areas of the U.S., open water lifeguard agencies have joined with local colleges to develop open water lifeguard courses consistent with USLA recommended standards. Completion of these courses may be required as a prerequisite to application for local employment.

Some open water lifeguard employers require pool lifeguard training as a prerequisite to undergoing open water lifeguard training. While experience working as a pool lifeguard may well be of value for someone interested in working as an open water lifeguard, requiring pool lifeguard training as a prerequisite for open water lifeguard training is not encouraged by the USLA. There are fundamental differences between the training approaches for each environment that are, in some cases, contradictory. Thus, requiring pool lifeguard training prior to open water lifeguard training can create confusion and uncertainty.

Credit: Eric Nurse

Lifeguards practice CPR during pre-service training.

Credit: Kathrine Osiecki

Explaining the details of an ocean swim test to trainees on Long Island, New York.

Pre-Service Training

Pre-service training is the training provided before assignment to lifeguard duties. It is a fundamental principle of USLA guidelines that no one should be assigned to the duties of an open water lifeguard prior to receiving the minimum training needed to perform the function assigned. This training may take place before or after hire.

The preferred method of pre-service training is to provide all training prior to assignment as a lifeguard. The USLA lifeguard agency certification system allows an exception to this approach for agencies which elect to spread their training over a period of time. Under USLA guidelines, pre-service training, with the exception of medical aid and CPR training, which must always be taught prior to deployment, may be integrated into the first 30 days of actual lifeguard beach work. This is permissible only if trainees work under the direct and immediate supervision (side-by-side in the same station or area) of a lifeguard with at least 1,000 hours of experience. The ratio of experienced lifeguards to such trainees may be no greater than one to one. Minimum pre-service training is detailed in the USLA *Guidelines for Open Water Lifeguard Agency Certification*.

In-Service Training

The third type of lifeguard training is in-service training. This is used to develop and maintain the skills and knowledge of lifeguards. Subsequent to their initial training, USLA guidelines call for lifeguard agencies to provide a minimum of 16 hours per year in formal training. As well, agencies are expected to provide daily opportunities, conditions permitting, for activities such as swimming, rescue board training, and running. This promotes physical fitness and hones lifeguard skills.

Required in-service training may include daily physical conditioning or regular reviews of rescue procedures. Drills, such as mock rescues and other simulated emergencies, are also encouraged. Programs to train and certify lifeguards in the operation of special rescue equipment, advanced rescue techniques, supervision, management, and other operational areas that lie outside the scope of basic lifeguard operations are highly recommended. Lifeguards may be encouraged or required to pursue higher levels of training in areas such as special equipment operation, emergency medical care, or emergency management. Some agencies, for example, require lifeguards to acquire Emergency Medical Technician training after hire.

Lifeguard efforts to garner continuing education by taking courses and attending conferences aimed at improving their knowledge and skills should be both encouraged and supported by their employers. The USLA includes an educational conference as part of each

Credit: Kekai Brown

In-service rescue board training.

biannual Board of Directors meeting, and occasionally sponsors special conferences for open water lifeguards. These conferences present excellent opportunities to garner nationally recognized training.

MINIMUM STANDARDS

The USLA has developed minimum standards to be met *and maintained*. While recommended for all open water lifeguard agencies, in order for a lifeguard agency to be USLA certified its policies, equipment, training program, trainees, and lifeguards must meet these standards. The USLA has established higher standards for agencies wishing to be certified as providing an advanced level of service. The USLA standards are detailed in the USLA booklet *Guidelines for Open Water Lifeguard Agency Certification.*

USLA guidelines establish *minimum* recommended standards only, whether at the regular or advanced level. To address local needs and conditions, lifeguard agencies are encouraged to establish standards that exceed them. The following is a brief synopsis of USLA training and employment standards current at the time of publishing this manual. (Equipment standards are discussed in Chapter 24: *Lifeguard Facilities and Equipment*.) For the most recent information, visit the Certification section of the USLA's website at www.usla.org/certification where current standards and certification applications can be found.

The USLA recognizes three classes of open water lifeguards: *Open Water Lifeguard Trainee*, *Seasonal Open Water Lifeguard*, and *Full Time Open Water Lifeguard* (these classes are defined in the USLA certification guidelines). The USLA also sets recommended standards for *Open Water Lifeguard Instructor*. (The USLA does not designate or accredit lifeguard instructors. It is up to lifeguard agencies to appoint their instructors.) All USLA standards are subject to regular review and revision to address the most current needs in lifesaving.

- **Minimum Age—16 for Hourly Lifeguards and 18 for Full Time Lifeguards**—The USLA recognizes that a lifeguard must be physically and mentally mature to handle the responsibilities of professional lifeguarding. The USLA set this standard following

LEARN MORE

To read about the national consensus conference which formed the basis for the USLA's recommended standards, training, and certification program, visit the Lifeguard Library section of the USLA website at www.usla.org/library and select, *Guidelines for Establishing Open-Water Recreational Beach Standards—Proceedings of a Conference.*

the consensus agreement of national experts at a conference cosponsored by the USLA in 1980.[1] Beginning in 2010, the U.S. Department of Labor prohibited the employment of people under the age of 16 as beach lifeguards.[2] Many professional open water lifeguard agencies have established higher minimum ages commensurate with more complex responsibilities. Full time lifeguards are typically assigned to broader responsibilities and may lead the work of hourly lifeguards. For this reason, the USLA has determined that 18 should be the minimum age for full time open water lifeguard employment.

- **Advanced Training in Emergency Medical Care**—The USLA has determined that all open water lifeguards should be trained to a level appropriate for professional providers of medical aid. Medical aid training for lifeguards employed on an hourly basis should be at least 21 hours in length, not including CPR training. For lifeguards employed full time, a course equivalent to U.S. Department of Transportation Emergency Medical Responder is the minimum recommended standard.[3] The USLA strongly encourages agencies to train all lifeguards employed on an hourly basis in a course equivalent to Emergency Medical Responder, with Emergency Medical Technician highly recommended, especially for full time lifeguards.[3]

LEARN MORE

You can find the National Standard Curriculum for Emergency Medical Responder and Emergency Medical Technician on the U.S. Department of Transportation's website at: www.ems.gov

- **Advanced Training in CPR**—Prolonged submersion results in respiratory distress and, ultimately, respiratory failure, leading to cardiac failure. (This is different from sudden cardiac arrest.) Therefore, cardio-pulmonary resuscitation training is absolutely essential. The USLA minimum recommended standards call for up-to-date successful completion of a course in providing one person adult, two person adult, child, and infant CPR including obstructed airway training, accepted by the Federal Government or by the state government in the state of employment. This is also referred to as *basic life support* (BLS).

- **A Thorough Course In Open Water Lifesaving**—USLA recommended standards call for a course of not less than 40 hours, covering all curriculum elements delineated by the USLA. This is *in addition to* training in medical aid and CPR. More advanced agencies are required to provide at least 48 hours of this training, as well as training for all hourly personnel as Emergency Medical Responders and all full time personnel as Emergency Medical Technicians.

- **Minimum Swimming Requirement**—The USLA has set a minimum swimming proficiency standard of 500 meters in 10 minutes or less for open water lifeguards since 1980. The USLA based this minimum standard on consensus input from representatives of the major aquatic safety organizations of the United States.[1] Strong swimming skills are critical in open water lifesaving. While few rescues occur 250 meters offshore, the 500 meter (550 yard) timed swim is a well-established minimum standard which should be met and maintained at all times by all open water lifeguards. It ensures that open water lifeguards will have adequate stamina to swim themselves and the victims they rescue to shore in adverse conditions, such as strong currents or surf. It also helps to ensure the stamina necessary to

Miami-Dade Fire Rescue lifeguard corps.

perform repeated rescues in a short period of time, as well as rescues of multiple victims. Agencies are encouraged to set higher standards for swimming proficiency to address local needs and conditions, so long as the minimum guideline is met.

- **Health and Fitness Adequate for the Stresses of Lifesaving**—Lifeguards must possess adequate vision, hearing acuity, physical ability, and stamina to perform the duties of an open water lifeguard as documented by a medical doctor, or the doctor's designated physician's assistant or advanced registered nurse practitioner (ARNP).

- **Scuba Training**—Any open water lifeguard who will be required to utilize scuba in the course of employment must, at a minimum, be certified as a scuba diver at the basic level by a nationally recognized certifying organization. Higher levels of certification and training are encouraged. In addition to preparing lifeguards to use scuba, this training provides information regarding the physiology of scuba diving, which can be invaluable in treating victims of scuba related injuries.

CHAPTER SUMMARY

In this chapter we have learned that open water lifeguards require a higher level of training and preparedness than pool or waterpark lifeguards. To address variables in local conditions, this training must occur in the area where the lifeguard will be assigned. We have learned about three modes of training—prerequisite, pre-service, and in-service. We have learned that the minimum recommended standards for open water lifeguards include an age of 16 (18 for full time lifeguards), advanced training in emergency medical care and CPR, a course in lifesaving of at least 40 hours, and the ability to swim 500 meters in 10 minutes or less.

DISCUSSION POINTS

- List the differences between open water lifeguards and pool lifeguards.
- Compare and contrast the various beaches you have visited citing the uniqueness of each.
- List five types of in service trainings the lifeguards might participate in.
- List three reasons open water lifeguards need to be mature.
- Identify why lifeguards must be strong swimmers.
- Explain why lifeguards need to be trained to high levels of emergency care.
- Explain the need for lifeguards to have advanced CPR training.

CHAPTER

5

The Flatwater Beach

I n this chapter, you will learn about the unique features of flatwater beaches and the special hazards they present. These can include lack of surf, reduced buoyancy, currents, drop-offs, plant life, and turbidity. You will learn about beach topography and an unusual phenomenon called a seiche. A thorough understanding of these factors is critical to lifeguards seeking to maintain safety in flatwater areas.

CHAPTER EXCERPT

At flatwater beaches swimmer distress can develop immediately and unpredictably, requiring an instant reaction by the lifeguard prior to submersion of the victim. This presents a major challenge for lifeguards.

LACK OF SURF

Given a choice, many people select flatwater beaches over surf beaches because they consider the conditions to be safer, particularly for non-swimmers and those with weak swimming ability. Lack of surf seems to lessen the fear of drowning. Parents may let their guard down and lower their vigilance over children. Adults who are non-swimmers or weak swimmers may be lulled into a false sense of safety. Despite the absence of surf related hazards, fatal drownings and other accidents happen with surprising regularity at flatwater beaches. A major contributing factor is that people underestimate the hazards, some of which are hidden beneath the surface.

At surf beaches, most rescues develop as a result of observable surf and rip current conditions, which you will learn about in the next chapter. Beach patrons at surf beaches with weak swimming ability are generally intimidated by surf and attempt to stay in shallow water, or stay out of the water altogether. Those venturing into the surf typically have moderate or even strong swimming abilities, enabling those in distress to maintain buoyancy for a time. These factors allow surf lifeguards to focus particular attention on known hazard areas. They also provide time for lifeguards to anticipate problems and react. Not so in the flatwater environment.

At flatwater beaches swimmer distress can develop immediately and unpredictably, requiring an instant reaction by the lifeguard prior to disappearance of the victim. This presents a major challenge to lifeguards. A person standing in neck deep water playing with a ball, for example, may appear quite comfortable, but may be a complete non-swimmer. One step in the wrong direction can leave this person submerged and out of sight in the blink of an eye, with no observable sign of struggle. As a result, high levels of vigilance and the ability to quickly distinguish between play and struggle are essential for effective flatwater lifeguarding. Constant scanning, timely and effective preventive actions, adequate breaks, and immediate, decisive action, when needed, are critical. A key preventive action is to work to counter the sense of overconfidence flatwater may engender among beachgoers, helping them take prudent steps to avoid accidents.

BUOYANCY

Many flatwater environments are fresh water, rather than saltwater. Because fresh water is less dense than saltwater, swimmers are less buoyant in fresh water. This lessened buoyancy affects people in several ways. In fresh water people cannot stay afloat as long as they might in saltwater. Weak swimmers will tire more quickly in fresh water because they must expend more energy to stay afloat. If they sink, they will sink faster. The lifeguard will thus have less time to identify and respond to signs of distress, if any.

FLOTATION DEVICES

Surf generally prevents poor swimmers with flotation devices from venturing out, since the surf pushes them back toward shore, but no such impediment is present at flatwater beaches. Many people visiting flatwater areas use flotation devices such as inflatable rafts, swim noodles, or bodyboards to move away from shore into deep water. These devices make it difficult or impossible for the lifeguard to assess swimming ability. The person using a flotation device may be an Olympic swimmer, or may be a non-swimmer.

When poor swimmers and non-swimmers become separated from a flotation device they may quickly disappear, sometimes at a significant distance from shore, making effective rescue extremely difficult (assuming the lifeguard sees this happen). This is one reason that some areas ban flotation devices. Prudent lifeguards assume that all people using flotation devices are non-swimmers, unless they are able to determine otherwise.

Credit: Eric Nurse.

Prudent lifeguards assume that all people using flotation devices are non-swimmers, unless they are able to determine otherwise.

OFFSHORE ATTRACTIONS

Offshore floating attractions such as rafts, diving platforms, inflatable slides, and obstacle courses are sometimes added at flatwater beaches. They create a goal to which people try to swim, and some inevitably overestimate their ability. They also create offshore activity, adding to the areas lifeguards must watch over. Depending on their size, they can create a visual block to lifeguard observation. For these reasons, many areas ban these attractions or elect not to provide them.

Where offshore attractions are in place, lifeguards must maintain a high level of vigilance over the areas in, around, and even under them. Some areas will station a lifeguard on or near attractions of this nature. Additional lifeguard staff is prudent in these cases to cover all blind spots and offshore areas.

Offshore attractions can also include natural features, like the opposite shore or a sandbar, for example. As is the case with floating attractions, these may entice people to swim beyond their limits. Managing flatwater beaches includes deciding whether swimming beyond a given distance from shore will be permitted and determining how lifeguards will respond when the need arises.

Buoyed lines are sometimes placed to mark the boundaries of the swimming area and provide separation from boating or other use areas. While there may be benefits to these lines, weak swimmers and non-swimmers sometimes cling to them as a means of staying afloat and venturing into deep water. As is the case with flotation devices, a non-swimmer may suddenly become separated from the lines, which is why many areas prohibit clinging to them.

Credit: Seattle Parks and Recreation

Where offshore attractions are in place, lifeguards must maintain a high level of vigilance over the areas in, around, and even under them.

CROWD DENSITY

Crowd density presents another challenge for lifeguards. During heat spells or when large groups hit the beach, crowd density can skyrocket. Large crowds increase the visual workload of the scanning lifeguard and can even block the lifeguard's vision. As well, increased activity levels make it statistically more likely that an incident could occur. One strategy, if possible, is to assign additional lifeguards when unusually high crowds overwhelm a beach area.

Credit: Eric Nurse

Crowd density creates a challenge for lifeguards.

CURRENTS

Although the water may appear calm, many flatwater areas experience significant currents. In saltwater bays, tides can create inflow and outflow currents which are much stronger than rip currents. People caught in such currents can rapidly be drawn to deep water, where serious problems can develop. Wind and waves also create currents in flatwater areas.

The currents of rivers can be even more dangerous than the currents at surf beaches, because river currents are relentless. There is no lull or pulse—the force of the current continues without interruption. River currents are influenced by such factors as the channel width, grade, and depth, but also upstream barriers and water volume. Currents in deeper water of rivers are often faster than in shallower water. In addition to rivers, currents are also prevalent at some lakes and reservoirs, particularly at areas close to inflows or outflows.

Strong river currents moving over obstacles in the river, including low dams, can create reverse currents (reversals) just below them, trapping the victim in an inescapable cycle. Logs and other debris may form strainers, allowing water to move through, but not large objects, like human bodies. Even a strong person caught in a strainer may be pinned underwater, unable to escape. River currents can also carry weak or non-swimmers offshore, drive them into stationary objects, or pull them over falls.

Credit: San Diego Lifeguard Service

Specialized training and equipment are necessary to safely perform rescues in river currents.

People caught in a current often react by swimming against the current pulling them or they try to swim toward a specific point, taking an upstream angle. Little if any progress may be made, with the effort draining the energy and strength of the victim. Swimmers caught in flatwater surface currents should normally be instructed to swim with and diagonally across the current toward the nearest safe spot ashore.

It takes very little moving water to cause a strong current. When water appears calm, current speed and direction can be identified by watching for movement of the water, or of material in the water. Lifeguards working flatwater areas with currents must be thoroughly familiar with the dynamics of the environment, both for the safety of those they protect and themselves.

BEACH TOPOGRAPHY

Currents, tides, natural configuration, and even human engineering can affect the topography of the beach at flatwater areas. Where water is moving swiftly, the topography of the land under the water can change quickly and often. Drop-offs, where the bottom suddenly falls away to cause deep water very close to relatively shallow water, are the greatest concern. Currents, dredging, or other forces may cause them. The calm and even surface of the water hides this hazard from the unsuspecting wader, who may

suddenly be in deep water without the skills necessary to deal with it. Non-swimmers who step into the drop-off may simply disappear, submerging instantly.

To complicate matters for the lifeguard at a tidal beach, the distance from shore and depth of drop-offs change constantly as the tide rises and falls. A drop-off which threatens adults at high tide may be an equal threat to young children at a lower tide. The ideal beach design, particularly in a lake or similar aquatic environment, is a gradually sloping beach with no drop-off, but this is not always possible to control.

People walking on an uneven bottom or in a current can easily lose their balance and fall. Toddlers trying to walk in water can trip. Once face down, their lack of body control can make it impossible for them to right themselves and they can drown in very shallow water.

Rock outcroppings, cliffs, and rocky shores present additional safety hazards at flatwater beaches. The water just off a rocky shoreline can be quite deep. The unsuspecting person who jumps or falls into the water

Credit: East Bay Regional Park District

A drop-off exposed during water draw-down at a reservoir beach.

Credit: Kyle Maxwell

An aerial view shows the dramatic drop off at this swimming area.

from shore may suddenly need immediate assistance. Changing water conditions, reservoir heights, and tides may alter the water depth at popular spots, making them even more hazardous. Submerged obstacles are a related problem, especially where water bodies and beaches have been created by planned flooding, such as in reservoirs. Tree stumps, rocks, and other objects can lie hidden just below the water's surface. Other submerged objects may be washed in with currents and deposited beneath swimming areas. Non-swimmers may stand on submerged objects, then step off into deep water, resulting in problems similar to drop-off.

A severe trauma hazard posed by submerged objects involves diving. The unexpected striking of an underwater hazard or shallow bottom is a prime cause of the most tragic of non-lethal injuries—permanent spinal cord damage resulting in paralysis.

Where feasible, extraordinary hazards which are not normal features of the area should be removed or marked. This is not to suggest that every stump or outcropping of rock must be signed or eliminated, but this may be appropriate for hazards of an unusual nature or those easily removed. Common examples are logs and other floating debris that wash up on a beach. Regular patrols to check for beach hazards are prudent, particularly during and after storms.

WEEDS AND PLANT LIFE

Calm water areas may have weeds and other plant life. While the obvious problem may seem that people will become entangled in weeds, this is very rare. Rather, swimmers often panic when they contact unseen substances. While swimming through heavy plant life, slow deliberate movements should prevent entanglement. If entanglement does occur, slow shaking motions as the swimmer moves away should cause the plant to slide off. When feasible, swimmers should be kept out of areas with heavy plant life.

TURBIDITY

Turbidity is a cloudiness of water caused by suspended particles of sediment. Currents, where they exist, may churn up debris. In areas with no current, sediment may build up on the bottom only to be disturbed when people enter the water, causing it to become cloudy. Turbidity can also be exacerbated by dredging operations, floods, channelization, and even bottom feeding fish. Depth perception is affected when the water is turbid, while drop-offs and other underwater hazards are obscured. This poses a particular problem for lifeguards conducting an underwater search.

SEICHES

A seiche (pronounced say-sh) is a rare condition that typically occurs in a landlocked body of water, though seiches also occur in bays and harbors. It involves oscillation of the water surface. A seiche can be created by the same events that cause a tsunami (discussed in Chapter 6: *The Surf Beach*), such as seismic activity, but seiches are more commonly generated when a very strong wind combined with variations in atmospheric pressure pushes water on the surface to one side, then subsides.

You can simulate a seiche in a bucket of water by placing it on a flat surface and shoving it. The water sloshes back and forth until the water surface eventually flattens again. In a similar manner, water in a lake or bay may move alternately higher and lower on either side until well after the forces that created the seiche subside. In Chicago, in June 1954, a Lake Michigan seiche generated a ten foot wall of water that killed eight people. Most seiches are imperceptible, but seiches have been recorded to levels over 20 feet and have caused deaths.

> **LEARN MORE**
>
> You can see a diagram of a seiche in action in the seiche section of: www.seagrant.wisc.edu.

CHAPTER SUMMARY

In this chapter we have learned that flatwater presents unique challenges for the lifeguard. The lack of surf creates a particularly inviting environment for weak swimmers. The tranquility though can be deceptive, as it may hide many hazards and lull people into a false sense of security. We have learned that decreased buoyancy in fresh water can shorten the length of time the lifeguard has to recognize and respond to distressed swimmers.

We have also learned that dense swimming crowds or sudden separation from a flotation device can make it extremely difficult for the lifeguard to spot a victim in distress before submersion. Currents can be relentless and sweep swimmers from safety. Beach topography creates a variety of hazards. Rock outcroppings, cliffs and rocky shores may also attract diving that is unsafe due to submerged objects lying hidden below the surface. Changing water levels from tides or other causes can alter the location of hazardous areas, such as drop-offs. Swimmer contact with underwater plant life can cause panic, though the risk of entanglement is low. Each of these factors creates specific challenges for flatwater lifeguards to keep their beaches safe.

Credit: Eric Nurse

DISCUSSION POINTS

- List five hazards that can be found at a flatwater beach.
- Compare similar hazards found at surf and flatwater beaches.
- Describe the effects of buoyancy in fresh water versus saltwater.
- Explain how underwater objects are a safety concern for swimmers.
- Identify concerns that lifeguards have with patrons using inflatable rafts in the flatwater environment.
- Describe the effects of turbidity in lifeguard observation.
- List three factors that cause a seiche condition.

The Surf Beach

In this chapter you will learn about the characteristics of surf beaches, including their attractions and dangers. We will explain how waves are formed in the open sea, how they change as they approach shore, and what causes them to become breaking waves. Here we describe rip currents, which cause the vast majority of distress and rescues at surf beaches, and identify the various types of these currents. You will also learn about other aspects of surf beaches that pose hazards for beach users, including uprush, backrush, lateral currents, shorebreak, inshore holes, storm surge, and tsunamis.

CHAPTER EXCERPT

The USLA has determined that *rip currents* are the primary source of distress in over 80% of swimmer rescues at ocean beaches. This is based on annual reports provided by over 140 U.S. lifeguard agencies. Rip currents are probably responsible for a comparable proportion of surf beach drowning deaths in cases where lifeguards are not present.

At sea, powerful forces are continuously at work. The nearshore surf can change from calm to rough and dangerous in a short period of time. Seemingly gently sloping beaches can hide deep channels that produce strong currents. Although big surf may appear to create the greatest demand for lifeguards, life-threatening currents can occur even in low and moderate surf conditions, and it's in those conditions that more people tend to swim.

Lifeguards who have charge of surf beaches must be intimately familiar with waves and wave action so that they can effectively intervene when the power of the surf overwhelms swimmers, surfers, boaters, and others. The USLA strongly recommends that all surf beach lifeguards spend extensive periods in activities such as board surfing, bodysurfing, and paddling rescue boards. Lifeguard employers should encourage and make time for this training. It allows lifeguards to learn to read waves, anticipate when they will break, and use the same forces that endanger swimmers to quickly rescue them. Lifeguard familiarity with surf and how surf impacts their beach will help ensure that they can successfully effect rescues with necessary confidence and safety.

WAVES

Waves are an extraordinary phenomenon of nature. They are a hypnotic, calming influence for those gazing seaward. They are an endless source of pleasure for

all sorts of recreation. Surfing, whether through use of a surfboard, a bodyboard, bodysurfing, or a stand up paddleboard, attracts millions of people each year. Millions more who don't surf at all enjoy swimming in the surf. While it provides great pleasure, surf can be a powerful force capable of killing or injuring even experienced water users. Understanding the forces that create waves and surf is therefore of vital concern to every surf beach lifeguard.

Wave Formation

Waves are normally formed by the force of wind on the water. They are also formed in unusual cases by seismic activity and volcanoes, for example, but we will discuss these events later in the chapter. Even the casual observer has seen ripples form on calm water as a breeze blows across it. As wind blows over water there is a transfer of energy

Credit: Mark Holtzman

As waves approach shore, surf forms differently based on the direction of the shoreline, bottom conditions, and other factors.

from the wind to the water—the wind essentially grabs the bumps on the ocean surface. The faster the wind blows and the longer it blows, the bigger the bumps get and the greater the transfer of energy, until proper waves are formed.

Stronger, more continual winds create progressively larger ripples and ultimately form waves. Large waves can occasionally be created by strong local winds very nearshore, but most waves are formed by storms well offshore. These waves may travel across great expanses of water—sometimes thousands of miles of open sea—before the energy, initially created by the wind, is diffused as the waves strike the shoreline.

Waves get their shape from the movement of this energy through the water. The water contained within waves moves in circles underneath the passage of a wave. Water at the crest (top) of a wave will move forward, then as the trough (bottom) of the wave moves through, the water will move backward. Even if the wind stops blowing, once waves are moving with energy, they can travel for long distances.

Many people observing waves assume that the water in them moves forward at the speed of the wave itself. This is not the case. When offshore, these waves of energy mostly cause the water surface to move up and down on a vertical plane, with hardly any forward movement, except in the most tempestuous conditions. Perhaps what confuses people in understanding wave energy is the end of the wave's life, as it breaks onshore, pushing water forward, up the beach. Offshore though, wave energy can be compared to a mouse running under a rug—the rug rises as the mouse runs along, but then falls back to the floor when the mouse has passed, moving forward little if at all.

Wave Propagation

Each wave contains a crest and a trough. They can be measured in a number of ways such as:

- **Wave Period**—The time it takes two consecutive wave crests to pass a given point
- **Wave Length**—The horizontal distance between two wave crests (or troughs)
- **Wave Height**—The vertical distance between the crest and trough of a wave
- **Wave Velocity**—The speed at which the incoming set of waves advances

There are different types of waves and they are normally distinguished based on their wave period. Waves that are formed locally by wind events such as an afternoon sea breeze or an offshore storm are often short and choppy with periods less than eight seconds. Waves that have travelled a significant distance from the wind source that formed them tend to spread out and become more organized with periods greater than eight seconds. These are what are called *swells*.

The speed of individual surface waves can be roughly calculated by multiplying wave period by 3.5, with the result expressed in miles per hour.[1] For example, a wave with a period of ten seconds is traveling about thirty-five miles per hour.

Three major factors contribute to the size and power of wind-generated waves: (1) wind velocity at the generating point; (2) duration of the blow; and (3) the distance of open water over which the wind blows (*fetch*).[1] Generally, increases in any of these factors produce progressively larger waves. As waves form, moving out and away from the wind that creates them, their crests become more rounded and take on a similar period and height, becoming more uniform the farther they travel. A succession of waves from a single source, with a consistent direction is known as a *wave train*.

Set Waves

If all waves arriving at a beach came from a single wave train, the waves would tend to be quite similar in appearance and therefore of a fairly consistent period, length, height, and velocity. This is rarely, if ever the case, because many different storms can contribute to the wave energy that ultimately arrives at a beach at any given point in time.

Waves can be unpredictable and may surprise beachgoers.

Credit: Cole Yeats

LEARN MORE

You can learn more about rogue waves and related phenomena at:
www.oceanservice.noaa.gov.

As two or more wave trains collide and intermingle, their behavior and appearance also changes. When waves from different wave trains merge trough to crest, they tend to cancel each other out and disperse the energy they carried, reducing wave height. On the other hand, when these waves match each other trough to trough, crest to crest, the ultimate height of the combined wave may be greatly increased over the individual height of the waves.

The intermingling of different wave trains often results in *set waves*. These are occasional groups of larger waves interspersed among a greater number of smaller waves. As the wave trains come into phase, matching each other's pattern, the waves increase in size. At other times when out of phase, the waves are smaller and irregular. Surfers will sometimes wait for long periods of time, well outside the point where most waves are breaking (the surf break), for these larger set waves.

Set waves can have substantial impacts on beach safety. When waves of a higher than average height reach shore they can send water much higher up the slope of the beach or adjacent rock areas than usual. Pedestrians can be surprised and swept into the sea, as may those lying on the beach. Set waves can also magnify the strength of dangerous currents. The number of waves in a set will vary, as will the time between sets. It's totally unpredictable, which adds to the hazard sets waves can create.

In the open ocean, far from the beach, the same intermingling of wave trains, sometimes combined with open ocean currents, is believed to be responsible for what are known as *rogue waves*—waves that form suddenly in open water and are far higher than any other waves in the area. The *Ramapo*, a 478 foot U.S. Navy tanker survived a trip from Manila to San Diego despite encountering a wave estimated at 112 feet.[2] Many ships encountering rogue waves have not been so lucky. Rogue waves can be double the size of the normal wave height. In April 2005, the *Norwegian Dawn* cruise ship was traveling in waves averaging 25 to 30 feet high when it was suddenly hit by a 70 foot wave.[2]

Wave Characteristics

The character of waves can change predictably with the seasons. For example, in most areas, winter waves tend to be larger, more violent, and less regular. The prevailing direction of waves can also vary seasonally. For example, on the West Coast of the U.S., the predominant swell direction from late April to early October comes from storms as far south as 40 degrees latitude in the southern Pacific (the Southern Hemisphere). From late October to mid-April, the swell direction changes and most larger wave trains originate in the Gulf of Alaska near the Aleutian Islands.

Depending on swell direction, some beaches are protected by the direction they face or by offshore islands. For example, according to National Weather Service Senior Meteorologist Randy Lascody, "The southeast Florida coastline is protected from most long period swells. This is due to: 1) the north northeast to south southwest orientation of the shoreline, which prevents north swells from reaching the coast, and 2) the shallow waters around the Bahama Islands which block most of the effects of northeast, east and southeast swells."[3] Therefore, in this area, most waves are due to nearshore storms.

When standing at a beach and watching waves break, it often seems as though the waves are coming from a source directly perpendicular (or nearly so) to the beach. Actually, this is rarely the case. Instead, wave *refraction* causes wave trains to bend as they approach the shore. Refraction is an important concept for surfers because for them an acute angle of approach of breaking waves is generally better. When waves are fully refracted their crests essentially parallel the shoreline, so on a long, even sand beach they will normally break all at once. On the other hand, when waves strike a beach diagonally, the break moves laterally along the shoreline allowing long rides. Breaks caused by offshore reefs and peninsulas are often prized because the effects of refraction are muted and the break tends to peel off these geographic barriers.

Credit: Mark Holtzman

Santa Monica, California point break.

Breaking Waves

As an open water wave approaches the shoreline it becomes a *shallow water wave.* Wavelength decreases, wave height increases, and velocity slows, but the period remains unchanged. As water depth lessens, the wave steepens, becoming higher and higher. Finally, upon reaching a depth approximately 1.3 times its height, the wave can no longer support itself and the crest falls forward, forming a *breaking wave,* which is commonly known as surf.[1] Breaking waves cause an *uprush* of water, running up the slope of the beach. Once the uprush reaches its peak, gravity takes over and causes a *backrush* of water returning to the sea. Backrush, also known as *runback* or *backwash,* occurs wherever there is surf, but it is most powerful on steeply inclined beaches.

Contour of the sea floor has a decisive influence on the manner in which a wave breaks. When a large swell is forced to expend its energy rapidly upon colliding with a steep underwater slope or reef, the crest of the wave tends to plunge or peak quickly, causing the water to mix with air and form foam or *whitewater.* A bottom that slopes gradually forms a wave that spills more gradually, with the small froth of whitewater being pushed ahead of the broken wave on its journey up the beach. These gentle waves create less sound than plunging waves that spray into the sky as air and water are compressed together.

Anyone who has sat by the shore and surveyed the sea understands that no two waves are ever alike—similar, but never identical. Breaking waves can however, be classified into three primary forms:

- **Spilling Waves**—These are formed by swells as they move over flatter, wider beaches where the sea floor ascends gradually beneath them, with the crest of the wave spilling onto the wave face until the wave itself is engulfed by foam.

Credit: California State Parks Lifeguards

Breaking wave.

- **Plunging Waves**—These are also known as *shorebreak,* formed when a swell suddenly strikes a steep beach, reef, or other obstacle and breaks with flying spray, both expending most of its energy and transforming it into a spilling wave for its remaining distance to shore.
- **Surging Waves**—These are created where water is deep adjacent to shoreline cliffs, reef, or steep beaches, with the waves keeping their rounded form until they crash against the shoreline barrier with very strong uprush and backwash.

Wave Measurement

Waves are measured in different ways for different purposes. The heights of waves are of vital interest to lifeguards, who use this information to assess the turbulence of the surf and its potential effect on those in, on, or near the water.

Methods of estimating surf size include measuring against a nearby structure of known size or by comparison to the body of a surfer standing erect on a surfboard. Regardless of methodology, it's crucial that lifeguards learn to assess wave height consistently and objectively. This information is used to inform beach users about the relative hazard, to report observations to the media, and to create a historical record. If lifeguards report the same conditions differently from day to day, credibility suffers and there is little value in the reporting.

Wave height is typically reported in a range, since occasional set waves will be larger than the usual waves. Thus, for example, reporting that waves are three to five feet in height would suggest that most of the waves are in the three foot range, but the waves occasionally reach five feet. Considering that sets are, by their nature, infrequent, estimating wave height requires watching the waves for a long enough period to take into account the normal height and the highest height.

A surfer can be used to estimate surf size.

Wave Hazards

Waves cause problems for beach visitors because of their tremendous power and energy. Wave energy is proportional to the square of the wave height, so small increases in wave height signal disproportionately greater increases in wave energy. People often underestimate this power and may be injured by the forward motion of the wave. As an example, consider an imaginary experiment in which one fills a gallon jug (about eight pounds) with water and tosses it to a friend. Most people would be concerned with such

Credit: Desi Stoyanova

Shorebreak is sudden and violent.

a weight being thrown to them. A single wave though, may represent the equivalent of thousands of such containers approaching at a similar velocity. While a swimmer in the water moves with the wave, unlike a person standing in the shallows who may take a direct hit, the force is still very substantial.

Breaking waves can violently thrust swimmers and surfers to the bottom, causing serious trauma to the head, neck, back, and other parts of the body. They can throw people into rocks or other fixed structures. Uprush and backrush may knock visitors down and injure them, or pull them into deep water. When surf is rough, backrush may be met by a second, forceful uprush, creating violent turbulence that is dangerous to young and old, especially those who lack the strength to maintain their footing when caught up in this force.

The combined force of strong surf, uprush, and backrush is a particular hazard on steep beaches with shorebreak. On these beaches large waves can break in knee deep water, suddenly and violently. When this occurs, a vigorous suction is caused both by the breaking wave and by the backrush from previous waves. A standing person can be knocked down and caught up in the next wave. Pedestrians and swimmers can be seriously injured by the sheer force of incoming waves. Lifeguards typically enter shorebreak by running and diving toward the middle of an incoming wave just before it breaks, swimming out on the seaward side. Returning to a beach with shorebreak requires timing and speed to get safely ashore before being hit by the next incoming wave.

Heavy surf may intimidate swimmers, keeping them close to shore, if not completely out of the water. Unfortunately, the relative calm period between set waves, known as a *lull,* can fool beachgoers. Inexperienced swimmers may go out during the lull and then be unexpectedly caught in the next group of set waves. People walking near the shoreline, perhaps to observe larger than usual surf, are sometimes surprised and overcome by the uprush and backrush of set waves. People fishing near the shoreline may suffer a similar fate. This is why it is prudent to attempt to keep people well back from large surf.

SHORELINE TOPOGRAPHY

The beach environment includes not only the exposed shoreline and water surface, but also the nearshore bottom of the sea. Beaches enlarge and contract in size based on many factors. The shoreline, combined with wave action, helps create forces that can both enthrall and endanger beachgoers.

The types of sediments that make up beaches can greatly influence the shape of the beach. Beaches with very fine sand tend to be flat, so there are usually more spilling waves and the surf zones are wider. Beaches with very coarse sand or gravel tend to be steeper, producing more shorebreak (and backrush). So hazards vary based on the beach composition, as well as the wave energy.

Sandbars

Ridges of sand of varying height and contour, called *sandbars*, exist off most surf beaches. They are normally submerged, but may emerge at low tide. They are created and modified by surf and related currents. Sandbars may run parallel to shore for many miles, one outside the other. They can also be quite irregular, depending upon surf conditions and currents. Usually, sandbars maintain regularity when surf size and direction are consistent, but as these influences change, so do the underlying sandbars. Sandbars can be completely separated from the beach by a deep trough, but they can also be connected to the beach in places, with holes or channels in between.

Winter storm surf typically moves sand from the beach offshore to sandbars. Calmer surf conditions, usually evident in summer, result in a sand transport from offshore to the beach. This is why many exposed surf beaches are wider in summer, narrower in winter.[1] In areas that experience seasonal swell direction changes, the ocean bottom can become very uneven during these times.

Sandbars can be attractive deceptions to poor swimmers. Seeing others standing in shallow water far offshore, poor swimmers may try to wade out, but deep water may lie between themselves and their goal, and they may quickly find themselves beyond their capacity to swim or to cope with currents. Another problem arises when a poor swimmer wades successfully to the sandbar at a low tide, only to become entrapped by a rising tide and forced to attempt to swim ashore. It's a common misperception that sandbars can suddenly collapse, causing a current outflow at a low point that didn't previously exist. This is not the case, but what can happen is that a large set of waves arriving at the beach can quickly increase the water level, causing people to lose their footing and to be pulled offshore by outgoing currents.

Serious, life-threatening spinal injuries can be caused when swimmers unfamiliar with a beach attempt a surface dive from a standing position, believing the water is deeper farther out. If the diver strikes the bottom, particularly headfirst, the head can be snapped back and the spinal cord compromised. Complete and incomplete spinal cord injuries (SCI) are possible results. Even people who don't experience an immediate SCI may experience tingling in the extremities, short-term blackout, or simple neck pain.

These concerns notwithstanding, the role of sandbars in creating and magnifying the effects of currents, is the greatest hazard they pose. This hazard is explained in detail later in this chapter.

Inshore Holes

Inshore holes are depressions in the sea floor dug into the sand by wave action and currents. They are, in effect, the opposite of sandbars and may be part of a sandbar system. Non-swimmers and small children can easily step from very shallow water into depths over their heads or be swept into them by currents or waves, causing immediate distress. They are also a significant hazard to lifeguards, who can seriously injure a knee or ankle while running to make a rescue. Lifeguards at surf beaches tend to focus their attention toward the surf zone, but inshore holes can create distress much closer to shore.

Credit: Leslie Schwene

Just above the four waders at the bottom of this photo is a large inshore hole that can be identified by darker water color.

Rocks, Reefs, and Other Obstacles

Underwater rocks, reefs, and other obstacles also pose hazards at surf beaches. Since they are usually hidden from beach visitors, they are difficult to avoid. They can cause surf to break unexpectedly and swimmers may be thrown against them by the surf. Submerged objects in shallow water are particularly dangerous to surfers, bodysurfers, and bodyboarders, who are moving quickly through the surfline.

Above water, rock outcroppings, piers, groins, and cliffs can also present hazards. They tend to focus wave energy, creating larger waves, reflection of wave energy, and turbulence. This can be very irregular and unpredictable. Lifeguards normally discourage people from swimming near these features.

As is the case with underwater obstacles, a person forced upon them by waves and currents can suffer serious injury. Pedestrians may venture out onto these structures to be close to the water with no intention of swimming, perhaps to fish, for example. Waves can sweep them into the water, which is usually deeper than water just off the beach, or slippery surfaces may cause them to fall, sustaining trauma injuries. Rescues of such victims can be arduous and dangerous because the lifeguard may also be injured by the hard surface during the rescue attempt. The intersection between powerful, incoming waves and immovable objects is a very dangerous place.

Jetties present significant hazards for beachgoers.

Credit: California State Parks Lifeguards

Cliffs and rock promontories often seem to invite people to dive, though they may be unaware of dangerously shallow water below. Wave surges and tides alter water depth from one moment to the next and improper timing of a dive can then leave the diver in water shallow enough to cause serious injury. In light of this, some areas prohibit these types of activities. Lifeguards should be aware of the dangers and can prevent injuries by issuing appropriate warnings.

It's not unusual for flotsam to appear at surf beaches, pushed ashore by waves and surf action. When feasible, dangerous pieces of flotsam should be removed immediately. It may also be necessary to close a beach area until large floating objects make it to shore so that people in the surf zone are not harmed. One of the values of regular patrols by lifeguards is to check for the presence of beach and water hazards that can be removed or marked to protect beachgoers.

RIP CURRENTS AND LATERAL CURRENTS

When waves break in shallow water, the structure of the wave breaks down and the whitewater you see associated with breaking waves physically moves towards the shore on the surface. The water level rises due to addition of the incoming water. It is this wave breaking and moving water that ultimately creates strong currents in the surf zone and along the shoreline. Because underlying topography is typically irregular, wave breaking is uneven along a beach.

Some places have greater amounts of wave breaking than others. There is a tendency of water pushed up the beach by waves that have broken to move from areas of intense wave breaking (higher water levels) to areas where waves are not breaking as much (lower water levels). This is what primarily drives currents that can seriously threaten the safety of swimmers and other water users. Any body of water where breaking waves of significant size are present, whether the ocean or a very large lake, can experience these currents. The most serious of these by far are rip currents, but to best understand rip currents one must first understand lateral currents.

Lateral Currents

A *lateral current*, also known as a longshore current or lateral drift, runs roughly parallel to the beach. These currents are often caused by waves coming from an angle diagonal to the beach, thus pushing water along the beach as the waves break. They can be channeled by sandbars. They may also be fed by tidal inflows and outflows from nearby entrances to harbors and bays. They can sweep swimmers along at a rapid rate. Most swimmers caught in a lateral current will naturally swim toward the safety of shore, and since this involves swimming across, rather than against the current, they can normally reach shore relatively easily. Non-swimmers however, may be seriously endangered by a longshore current, and even strong swimmers may experience difficulty if the current pulls them away from safety or into a hazardous area, such as rocks or a pier. Many rescues on northerly reaches of the outer shore of Cape Cod, Massachusetts are caused by complications related to sandbars and longshore currents. A particularly hazardous role of a lateral current however, is to act as the feeder to a rip current, which can endanger the safety of even strong swimmers.

Rip Currents

The USLA has determined that *rip currents* are the primary source of distress in over 80% of swimmer rescues at ocean beaches. This is based on annual reports provided by over 140 U.S. lifeguard agencies. Rip currents are probably responsible for a comparable proportion of surf beach drowning deaths in cases where lifeguards are not present. The USLA has estimated that in a typical year there are more than 100 deaths from rip currents nationwide. According to Lascody, "Rip currents, on average, result in more deaths in Florida than hurricanes, tropical storms, tornadoes, severe thunderstorms, and lightning *combined*."[3] A 2015 review of weather related deaths by the National Weather Service found more deaths nationally from rip currents than from lightning, tornadoes, or hurricanes.[4]

In some areas of the country, rip currents are referred to by colloquial, local terms. The USLA encourages exclusive use of the term "rip current" because it helps to educate the public through consistent and scientifically recognized nomenclature. The USLA has worked closely with the National Oceanic and Atmospheric Administration (NOAA) since 2003 to educate the public about rip currents and to encourage proper, consistent terminology. Use of other terms may confuse the public and thus adversely impact safety. The term *riptide* is a misnomer sometimes used interchangeably with rip current, but this is incorrect.[5] Rip currents can be influenced by tide level, but that is not their source of energy.

Rip currents can move at speeds over four miles per hour.[6] They vary greatly in size, width, depth, shape, and power. They are created primarily by the force of incoming waves, combined with the force of gravity. As previously described, once the force of uprush is expended, gravity creates a backrush of water to the sea.

LEARN MORE

Read more about rip currents on the United States Lifesaving Association website at: www.usla.org.

Credit: Leslie Schwene

Multiple victim rip current rescue.

That backrush of water may be diffused fairly evenly along the shoreline, in which case currents will be minimal. It may also flow from areas where waves are breaking to areas where they aren't breaking as much. When the returning water concentrates in an offshore flow it forms a rip current. Some rip currents dissipate very close to shore, while others can continue for hundreds of yards offshore.

Components of Rip Currents

Rip currents have three major components:

- **Feeder**—This is the main source of supply for the rip. Water that has been pushed up the beach and is being pulled back by gravity, follows the path of least resistance—the rip current channel. To get there, the water may have to travel laterally along the beach some distance. Once the water finds a channel or an obstacle in its lateral movement, it will turn seaward. A rip current may have one or two feeders. For example, waves breaking on both sides of a deeper water channel can create two feeders. Single feeder rip currents are however, much more common. There may sometimes be no feeder at all if the rip is squeezed between transverse sandbars.

- **Neck**—This is the river of water running away from the beach. The neck can vary in width from a few yards to many tens of yards. The majority of both rescues and drownings occur in the neck. This is where the rip current has its strongest offshore flow.

- **Head**—This is the area where the offshore current from the neck ends, dispersing broadly. The current's momentum, which was initially caused by waves pushing water up the slope of the beach and then by gravity pulling the water back from whence it came, has now been exhausted.

Rip Currents Form in Different Ways

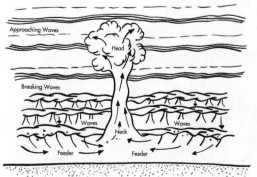

Multi-feeder

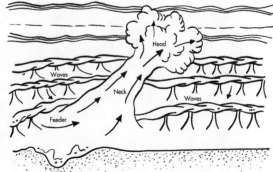

One Feeder

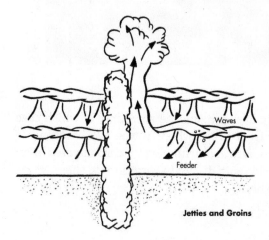

Jetties and Groins

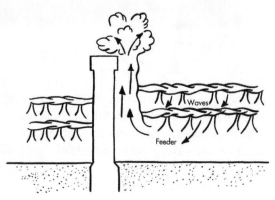

Piers

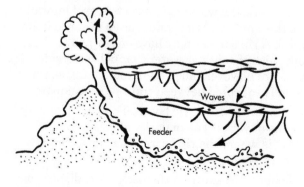

Rocky Points

Types of Rip Currents

There are four types of rip currents:

- **Fixed Rip Currents**—These are found only on sand beaches. They pull offshore in one location because the depth directly underneath is greater than surrounding depths. These rips are usually created when the water transported by incoming surf "piles up" between the shore and offshore sandbars, as well as incoming surf. Eventually, the water returns to the sea, following the path of least resistance, which is normally a low point in the sandbar system. This return flow further erodes the underlying sand bottom, creating a rip current channel, which remains fixed in the same location so long as sand and surf conditions remain stable.[1] When these surf conditions change, fixed rips may also change if wave action moves underlying sand. Therefore, a fixed rip may lie in a given spot for an extended period of hours, days, or even months, or change or even disappear within a matter of hours.

- **Permanent Rip Currents**—These rip currents are stationary year-round, though they may vary in intensity. They are usually found on coastlines with rocks or reefs, and exist due to undulations in the bottom that do not change. The speed and power of these rips depend entirely on the size of the surf. These rip currents usually pull harder than sand beach rips because water moves more forcefully over solid, stationary obstacles, and the excess flow of water may be more concentrated in pronounced, fixed channels.

Purple dye released at Australian beaches shows variation in the direction of rip currents.

Credit: Surf Life Saving Australia

Piers, rock jetties, drain pipes, projecting points of land, and some beach contours may also force lateral currents to turn seaward, creating permanent rip currents. In many areas, permanent or fixed rips are given names that relate to nearby landmarks or streets. Such identification can be helpful when lifeguard teams answer emergency calls because they pinpoint where assistance is needed.

Credit: Dr. Tom Herrington, Stevens Institute of Technology

Permanent rip adjacent to a jetty.

- **Flash Rip Currents**—Temporary rips generated by increased volumes of water brought to shore from concentrated sets of waves are called flash rip currents. Flash rips do not typically accompany depressions in the bottom. Flash rips, like flash floods on land, occur unexpectedly and without warning. When they strike an otherwise safe swimming area suddenly, part of the crowd can be quickly swept from shallow water. Since flash rips usually subside rapidly, many people caught in them can return to shore without assistance, but those who are non-swimmers or who have panicked require expeditious rescue. It's not easy to determine from the beach which of those pulled suddenly offshore is in danger due to lack of swimming ability, so rescue operations must begin immediately and usually several lifeguards are needed. In some cases, crowds of waders actually create an effect similar to that of a jetty or pier, obstructing the flow of a lateral current and causing it to turn seaward, forming a flash rip. In these cases, part of the group may be drawn seaward with the rip current.

- **Traveling Rip Currents**—Like other types of rip currents, traveling rip currents pull away from the beach, but these rip currents do not accompany depressions in sand or reef formations. They move along the beach pushed by the prevailing direction of the waves. Traveling rips usually occur in a strong, one-direction swell movement with long, well-defined periods. The wave action moves the rip away from the set of waves that feeds it. A traveling rip usually continues moving and pulling well into the lull period until the excess water has dissipated. The next set of waves starts the process all over again. Traveling rips can be pushed 200 or 300 yards and farther along the beach, depending on the size of the surf or the number of waves in a set. They are similar in all respects to flash rips except that their movement is predictable once their sequence has begun and the established pattern repeats itself. Like flash rip currents, traveling rips can wreak havoc on a swimming crowd as they move along the beach pulling large numbers of people offshore.

Credit: Mark Holtzman

Rip currents can move in various directions.

Characteristics of Rip Currents

Although rip currents can vary greatly in appearance, as a general rule they look somewhat different from the surrounding surf. A rip may seem especially rough or choppy, may have the dark color of deeper water, and may or may not have foam. Rips sometimes pick up debris, seaweed particles, or sand, giving the water a dirty or muddy quality. At other times the seaward current shows clear evidence that the water at the surface is running in the opposite direction from incoming waves—either flowing perpendicular to them or at another angle from the shore. Rips moving through calm, level surf are easily detected, but rips are harder to spot when the sea is rough and conditions are windy. Under most conditions, rips can be readily identified by a trained lifeguard.

Rip currents may look very different from different angles.

Credit: B. Chris Brewster

Fixed and permanent rips typically pull harder when the tide recedes. Rip channels are more defined compared to the surrounding areas, which become progressively shallower. There will normally be a darker gap of water with less breaking waves than surrounding areas. Consequently, the excess water is considerably more concentrated into the rip current channels while returning seaward. Of course, if a rip current channel is fully exposed by an outgoing tide, coming all the way out of the water, its effect will be negated by the tide. Rips may characteristically stop pulling at high tide, only to begin again as the tide recedes, although the reverse situation is also possible depending on water depth and other factors.

Rips can move far offshore beyond the breaking waves.

Credit: B. Chris Brewster

The power of rip currents typically relaxes when set waves arrive onshore, as the successive large waves create a damming effect between themselves and the shoreline. As soon as the set waves expend their energy by breaking onshore however, the transient damming effect quickly subsides and rip currents can become particularly intense. Lifeguards observing set waves arrive should of course watch for distress that may be caused by the waves themselves, including from rising water levels, but as soon as they subside, great attention must be paid to the inevitable increase in the intensity of rip currents. The ever changing condition of rip currents is one reason lifeguards must constantly read the surf in order to safeguard the assigned area.

On steeper beaches, where shorebreak is present, rip currents tend to pull only a short distance offshore, but the combination of backrush and a rip current can both knock a beachgoer down and pull the person quickly into deep water. For many years, the term *undertow* has been used, perhaps to describe this phenomenon. However, this term is a misnomer and should not be used by lifeguards. It suggests a condition which can actually suck a person under the water. Backrush, particularly on a steep beach, can knock a person down and, along with a rip, may pull a person offshore, but it does not pull the victim underwater. Similarly, the offshore flow of rip currents will not pull a person under the water. Of course, if a non-swimmer or poor swimmer is carried into deep water, the person may submerge, but this is due to gravity and the loss of buoyancy, not a downward sucking action of current.

Although there are constant problems with rip currents at surf beaches in the U.S., some areas report seasons when rips are particularly hazardous. For example, spring and early summer are the most hazardous times on the West Coast as the prevailing swell direction swings from its northerly origin to a southerly origin. This change of swell direction causes holes and channels in the sand that foster rip current formation. Other areas report more serious problems with rip currents in late summer, or at other particular times of the year.

Effects of Rip Currents on People

The hazard presented by rip currents is magnified by the fact that they often appear to be the calmest water area along the beach. This is because the underwater channels that can cause rip currents are deeper than areas on either side. Since waves break as the bottom depth becomes shallow, there are often breaking waves on both sides of a rip current channel, with little or no apparent wave activity in the rip current itself. In addition, the force of a rip current moving away from the beach tends to counter the power of incoming waves. This results in a relatively calm appearance that often attracts unsuspecting beachgoers to swim in a rip current. What may appear to them to be the safest place to swim is typically the most dangerous.

Credit: B. Chris Brewster

A rip current channel (dark water with no surf) may seem like the calmest and safest area to beachgoers.

Credit: Rob Brander

Rips can form in small surf and be very subtle in appearance, but the current can still move well offshore.

Effects of rip currents on swimmers and surfers vary with water skills. Those caught in a rip current are usually pulled away from shore, which for non-swimmers can be fatal. People with a basic ability to tread water may be able to stay afloat for a short time, but may be overcome by panic if they are pulled any significant distance offshore and start to be impacted by breaking waves. Those with moderate to strong water skills may at first be completely unconcerned about being in water over their head and oblivious to any danger. Noticing that they are farther from shore than they expected, they may attempt to swim directly back, but notice that they are making no progress or going backwards. At this point, even good swimmers can panic. Once swimmers panic, their stroke becomes less effective and their energy is quickly expended. There is a characteristic desperation of people in rip currents fed by their loss of control.

Credit: California State Parks Lifeguards

The head of a rip current far from shore with the sand it has stirred up.

Credit: Huntington Beach Marine Safety

A rip current's sinuous path far offshore.

Every rip current is different in size, strength, direction, and configuration. At water level it's very difficult for a swimmer to see the boundaries of the rip current. And of course the skill levels of swimmers vary tremendously. Therefore, no one escape strategy is universally effective in all rips.

The simplest way for a capable and competent swimmer to escape from the seaward pull in the neck of a rip current is to swim across the current, rather than against it. Since rip currents normally pull away from the beach at a roughly perpendicular or slightly diagonal angle, the best direction to swim is typically (though not always) parallel to the beach, or toward a region of whitewater and breaking waves which would indicate a shallower area outside the rip current channel. Once there, the swimmer can turn and swim to shore, often aided by shoreward wave action which borders the rip current.

Credit: B. Chris Brewster

Rip currents can be very concentrated or diffuse.

RIP CURRENTS
Break the Grip of the Rip!®

ESCAPE   ESCAPE

ESCAPE   ESCAPE

CURRENT   **RIP CURRENT**   CURRENT

Rip currents are powerful currents of water moving away from shore.
They can sweep even the strongest swimmer out to sea.

www.ripcurrents.noaa.gov

IF CAUGHT IN A RIP CURRENT

◆ Don't fight the current

◆ Swim out of the current, then to shore

◆ If you can't escape, float or tread water

◆ If you need help, call or wave for assistance

SAFETY

◆ Know how to swim

◆ Never Swim alone

◆ If in doubt, don't go out

More information about rip currents can be found at the following web sites:

www.ripcurrents.noaa.gov
www.usla.org

The United States Lifesaving Association and the U.S. National Oceanic and Atmospheric Administration created a national campaign in 2003 to educate people about rip currents. Signs from the campaign can be seen at beaches throughout the USA and the world. The artwork can be downloaded for free from www.usla.org.

Credit: B. Chris Brewster

Rips can be very large. Note the two people standing in the shallows of this rip.

This maneuver is relatively easy if the rip current is a stationary one, but if it is a traveling rip moving in the same direction as the swimmer, an attempt to escape the force by swimming to the side may be futile. Another danger is that swimmers may escape from the neck of the rip current and swim toward shore only to enter the broader feeder and be sucked back into the neck. Lifeguards sometimes refer to this as being recirculated by the rip.

Another way to escape from a rip current is to relax and allow oneself to be carried to its outermost limit—the head—which is sometimes not far beyond the breaking surf. After judging the width of the rip current, the swimmer can then swim parallel to the beach outside the break, reenter the surf, and swim safely to shore. This strategy is perhaps easier said than done. Even good swimmers with surf experience can become panicked when pulled away from the beach and some rip currents pull hundreds of yards offshore before expending their energy. Swimming out of the neck, if possible, is usually the best option. However, for poor swimmers, attempting to relax and stay afloat may be the only viable option.

A third possibility, which is observed in some rip currents, is a circulation back toward shore. Some rips have been shown

Credit: Mark Holtzman

Rips can sometimes turn back towards shore.

to actually move in something of a circle, in which case a swimmer treading water may be returned to safety if able to patiently tread water. However, there is no certainty of this strategy and panic can worsen as a person is pulled further from shore, so understanding the various options is useful.

TIDES

Tides are rises and falls in the level of the ocean caused by gravitational attraction of the sun and moon. While tides can occur in large lakes, their effect is virtually unnoticeable. Knowledge of tides and a daily awareness of the times of the tides is essential to effective lifesaving at beaches influenced by them.

Normally, there are two high tides and two low tides each day. They are based on a lunar day, which is 24 hours and 50 minutes, so the time of day of tides advances each day on our 24 hour solar clock. The high and low of tides varies from day to day with spring tides (greater range) roughly every two weeks around the new and full moon, and neap tides (smaller range) in between. Generally, beaches near the equator have the least tidal variation. Beaches near the poles have the greatest.

Wave action, currents, boating traffic, and many other elements of the daily life of a beach are impacted by tides. One of the most obvious impacts on beach users is that there is more beach available at low tide. On beaches with significant tidal change, an incoming tide causes crowds of people onshore who have spread out at low tide to move ever closer together, which can sometimes cause interpersonal tension and will make it more difficult for lifeguards to respond to emergencies.

LEARN MORE

You can learn more about tides at:
www.tidesandcurrents.noaa.gov

As explained in the previous section, tides can exaggerate or minimize the effects of currents, depending on a variety of factors. Since tides can be reliably predicted through a variety of means, there is no need for complex calculations by lifeguards to predict tidal changes. Tide charts, tide watches, and computer apps are widely available.

East Rockaway inlet, New York.

Tidal Currents

Unlike rip currents, which are primarily caused by wave energy, some currents are caused by tidal action. These typically occur as water rushes through entrances to bays and estuaries during tidal changes. The Bay of Fundy's legendary tidal change, including currents up to eight knots, is an excellent example, but currents will occur during tidal changes wherever a tidal basin is separated from the ocean by an inlet or channel, for example.

One tragic example of the power of tidal currents occurred in East Rockaway Inlet off New York City. In this inlet, tidal currents can reach 2.9 knots. On July 23, 2001, three girls wading off the beach were swept into deep water by the current and died. Tidal currents vary with the tide height (spring versus neap). They can be just as strong as a fast flowing river and the current is relentless. There are no short term variations in the intensity of the flow, as is typically the case with rip currents.

EXTRAORDINARY SEA STATES

Waves and currents are normal sea states. They exist continually, though their intensity can vary significantly. There are however, extraordinary ocean conditions which, while rare, can seriously endanger beachgoers.

Tsunamis

Earthquakes, volcanoes, landslides, calving glaciers, or even the unlikely crash of a meteorite into the sea can cause very large sea waves. These are tsunamis. They were once called tidal waves, but tsunamis are not caused by tides.

To better understand the effect of a tsunami, consider this analogy: Most young swimmers have had the experience of themselves or others doing a "cannonball" dive into the water, by jumping into a pool while making their body into a ball. This causes a great splash

LEARN MORE

Learn more about tsunamis at:
www.tsunami.noaa.gov

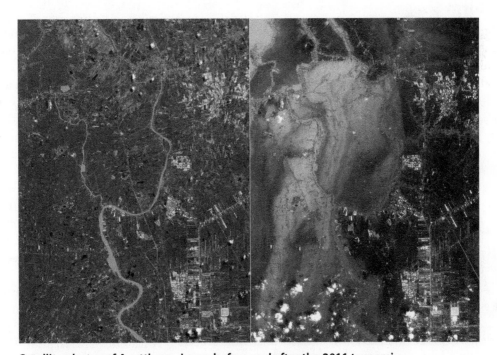

Satellite photos of Ayutthaya, Japan before and after the 2011 tsunami.

and waves moving out in all directions. Imagine then, a similarly dramatic event on an exponentially larger scale in the ocean, or even in a lake. Unlike normal wind generated waves, this creates large, fast-moving waves that can quickly travel great distances and cause tremendous destruction.

Tsunamis can travel over 500 miles per hour. Because of their very long wave length, they may be hardly noticed in the open sea, but upon striking land they can cause tremendous destruction, primarily by temporarily, dramatically lifting the sea height and pushing water much farther ashore than normal. In many ways they are analogous to surging waves, except they are much bigger. One reason they do so much damage is that they have so much energy. That energy can push water much farther inland than normal during the uprush, and the backrush of water can also do enormous damage. People may be swept far offshore. The threat of a tsunami is usually announced by disaster preparedness officials, but there is limited protection available, with the exception of evacuating to high ground.[7]

Historically, some tsunamis have had devastating consequences. An 1896 tsunami killed some 27,000 people in Northern Japan. A 1946 tsunami which struck Hilo, Hawaii, caused 159 deaths and extensive destruction. It is notable that in this case it is believed that many deaths occurred due to curious people noticing an initial, dramatic drawdown of the water level in the harbor and walking out to observe, only to be inundated when the wave arrived, submerging them and the town itself. A dramatic drawdown of water level is a sign of a deadly wave (or waves) to come. More recently, in 2004 a tsunami in the Indian Ocean killed well over 100,000 people. A 2011 a tsunami in Japan caused more than 15,000 deaths and the meltdown of a nuclear generating station.

Storm Surge

Storm surge occurs during violent storms near the shoreline, such as hurricanes. According to the National Hurricane Center, "Along the coast, storm surge is often the greatest threat to life and property from a hurricane."[8] Storm surge can be magnified by a high tide, creating a *storm tide* of up to 20 feet in elevation or more. The effects are often accentuated by high waves, caused by wind associated with the same weather conditions that create increased sea level. The fact that these storm waves come one after another mutes the normal backrush effect. Incoming waves then continue to push water ahead of them. The result can be very serious coastal flooding.

Storm surge figured greatly in the devastation from Hurricane Katrina (2005). The National Hurricane Center reports that, "At least 1,500

Credit: Leslie Schwene

Storm surge.

persons lost their lives during Katrina and many of those deaths occurred directly, or indirectly, as a result of storm surge."[9] In 1900, storm surge inundated Galveston, Texas, where it is estimated that some 6,000 people died in storm tides of 8–15 feet. Lakes can be impacted by storm surge as well. In 1928, Florida's Lake Okeechobee was influenced by surge associated with a hurricane that caused 6–9 foot flooding and the deaths of over 1,800 people.

Coastlines with flat terrain, many structures near sea level, and a gradual off-shore drop-off toward the ocean are the most susceptible to the ravages of storm surge. Those with a steep drop-off and a more hilly coastline are less likely to sustain serious damage. The factors that influence the strength and height of storm surge are complex. Using the National Hurricane Center's Sea, Lake and Overland Surges from Hurricanes (SLOSH) computerized model, disaster preparedness officials typically arrange evacuations, sometimes of very broad areas.

> **LEARN MORE**
>
> You can read about storm surge and even run a computerized model of how it might impact a given coastal area on the National Hurricane Center's website at: www.nhc.noaa.gov/surge/

> **LEARN MORE**
>
> Read about the devastating storm surge that inundated Galveston, Texas in the bestselling book: *Isaac's Storm: A Man, a Time, and the Deadliest Hurricane in History* (September 1999 - Crown; ISBN: 0609602330)

Storm surge in Galveston, Texas from Hurricane Ike in 2008.

CHAPTER SUMMARY

In this chapter, we have learned about how waves form and what factors impact their size, shape, and speed. We have learned what happens as surface waves approach a beach and become shallow water waves, then breaking waves. We have reviewed a variety of ways in which waves can provide enjoyment, fascination, and great danger to beach users. We have garnered an understanding of the manner in which shoreline topography both changes and is itself changed by the power of the surf.

This chapter has described the hazard presented by longshore currents and rip currents, and how rip currents are the primary cause of rescue and drowning at surf beaches. We have learned about the components, types, and characteristics of these currents. We have also learned about tides and the currents they produce, as well as the unusual and extraordinary threat to safety posed by tsunamis and storm surge.

DISCUSSION POINTS

- Identify three weather conditions that produce waves.
- List three conditions in combination that would produce the largest waves.
- Describe how a mouse running under a carpet is similar to a wave in the ocean.
- Explain why waves on the Pacific shores could be expected, on average, to be more regular in size and period than those on the Atlantic and Gulf shores.
- Describe what occurs when wave trains intermingle and the likely effects.
- List five specific hazards created by set waves.
- Describe why waves arriving at the beach seem to come from the same direction.
- Identify the importance of lifeguards consistently estimating the wave height from lifeguard to lifeguard.
- Describe what is occurring with beaches gaining and losing sand from summer to winter.
- Describe how sandbars help create rip currents.
- List three safety concerns when dealing with inshore holes.
- Identify why it is important to remove or mark large flotsam.
- Identify the main factor that limits longshore current hazards.
- Compare the differences among the four types of rip currents.
- Describe visual clues to identify rip currents.
- Describe how set waves influence rip currents.
- List three strategies that you can use to free yourself from a rip current.
- Compare the differences between rip currents and tidal currents.
- Identify three safety recommendations lifeguards can promote to the public about tsunamis.
- List three safeguards that can be advocated to the public if storm surge is predicted.

CHAPTER
7

Weather

In this chapter you will learn of the many impacts on the open water environment from weather, including storms, lightning, waterspouts, fog, wind, floods, and temperature variations. Impacts from the sun can also be a hazard. You will learn how to anticipate adverse weather conditions and to protect beach users, as well as yourself.

CHAPTER EXCERPT

Lifeguards should be aware of the weather forecast for the coming day and for the next week. This information is not only important for public safety, but also to provide information to inquiring visitors. When will the rain end? How rough will the waves be? What time tonight will a cold front drive thunderstorms to the coast? Will the wind be a problem? What time is fog likely to form? Be ready with answers.

The beach is a unique boundary between land and water, where severe weather can strike suddenly and have devastating consequences. This threat is compounded by the fact that people in a recreational mode sometimes ignore obvious signs of threatening weather until it's too late. At that point panic and injury may occur when people run for cover or are injured by lightning, high winds, or other causes. Prudent lifeguards take steps to anticipate adverse weather conditions so that they can protect beachgoers, and they develop action plans for forecast weather conditions and their associated hazards.

Across the U.S., the National Weather Service (NWS) provides weather, water, and climate forecasts, as well as warnings for the protection of life and property. There are also many private weather forecasting services. Forecasts are disseminated through the news media, over the internet, and through a variety of other means. Lifeguards should be aware of the weather forecast for the coming day and for the next week. This information is not only important for public safety, but also to provide information to inquiring visitors. When

LEARN MORE

The National Weather Service offers a free weather spotter program called SKYWARN® which provides education on spotting and identifying severe storms. This program can help lifeguards better understand how severe weather develops, how to best advise the public of a weather hazard, and actions to take for safety. Lifeguards are an important resource to the NWS because lifeguards can provide real-time reports of hazardous beach conditions, which are then further disseminated by the NWS to the public and media. Find more information at: www.nws.noaa.gov/skywarn

will the rain end? How rough will the waves be? What time tonight will a cold front drive thunderstorms to the coast? Will the wind be a problem? What time is fog likely to form? Be ready with answers.

In addition to forecast information, it's useful to be familiar with the local climate—for your sake as well as for visitors who will ask you questions. How hot does it usually get around here? What's the usual water temperature? Which months are the most threatening for hurricanes or tornadoes or waterspouts? When does the sea breeze usually begin or end? People will ask and you'll want to be prepared to tell them.

Weather predictions are just that—predictions. There's always some degree of uncertainty in any weather forecast, and sometimes these predictions will not prove accurate. Keep alternate scenarios in mind when planning.

A weather monitoring buoy maintained by the National Oceanic and Atmospheric Administration.

The NWS maintains a system of automated and human monitoring capabilities for real-time observations, dissemination, and feedback. Reports from those sources (including lifeguards), in addition to updated weather predictions, are posted on the NWS website (weather.gov) and are also broadcast on the National Oceanic and Atmospheric Administration's *NOAA Weather Radio System.* This system can electronically trigger properly equipped weather radios to sound an alarm when your local NWS office issues weather watches, warnings, or advisories—24-hours a day, seven days a week. Many lifeguard agencies in lightning prone areas have their own lightning detectors or subscribe to services that provide lightning warnings. Phone apps also provide up-to-date predictions and warnings.

The most direct source of information on local weather conditions comes not from the predictions of meteorologists, but from you, the lifeguard, as you are actually on the scene and observing the weather first-hand. By monitoring conditions closely, lifeguards can learn to anticipate likely weather outcomes. Certain cloud formations may signal the potential for a waterspout, for example. Simple weather monitoring can be accomplished with visual observation and use of weather tools, like thermometers and barometers. Keep an eye to the sky. Your observations, quickly communicated to the NWS, and then via the NWS to the general public, can be critical to the safety of thousands—even millions—of people. Contact your local NWS office to schedule training on local weather conditions and severe weather reporting.

LEARN MORE

You can quickly acquire a broad understanding of weather by reading, *The Weather Book,* a richly illustrated text by Jack Williams, published by Vintage.

- Check weather predictions early and often
- Keep abreast of current weather conditions to help anticipate storms and other hazards
- Use a weather radio for updated information
- Subscribe to a lightning warning system or install a lightning detector
- Warn beach visitors of impending storms
- Advise and assist visitors on what safety actions to take in advance of approaching storms

FRONTAL SYSTEMS

As the jet stream changes intensity and position, it affects the motion and strength of warm and cold air masses. Where air masses converge, they form boundaries called "fronts." Fronts are identified by change of temperature, based upon their motion. With a cold front, a colder air mass is replacing a warmer air mass, typically from north to south. A warm front is the opposite in that warm air replaces cold air, typically from south to north.

The motion of air masses also affects where a good portion of precipitation occurs. Hot air rises. The air along cold fronts, a term first used in weather at the time of World War I, is denser than warmer air masses. The cooler dense air undercuts the warmer air mass forcing the warm, moist air to rise up and over the colder air into the atmosphere. As with clashing armies, the most dramatic results often occur near the advancing front where this rising air and moisture can sometimes form lines of thunderstorms. These storms can grow as tall as 50,000 feet and produce severe weather, such as damaging winds and hail.

With warm fronts, there's typically widespread cloudiness and precipitation along and to the north of the advancing front. The air mass transition is usually slower—the "takeover" weather is not typically as dramatic as compared to cold fronts. (Cold fronts usually force air upward more abruptly, so they tend to have more intense weather than warm fronts.)

Another type of frontal boundary, much more localized in nature, is the sea breeze front. It's the result of a sharp boundary that develops near the coast due to a large difference between the air temperature over land versus that over water. The sea breeze is especially common during the late spring, summer, and early fall months at many

Storm front.

coastal locations across the country. Showers and thunderstorms can develop near the boundary as it develops and moves inland. As the sea breeze passes through, air temperature will drop, skies will typically clear, and humidity increase. There can be a significant change in wind direction and speed; often to an onshore direction.

The dangers of storms associated with fronts can include sudden torrential rain and sometimes hail, lightning, and severe winds. Storms along frontal boundaries can develop rapidly, taking beach visitors by surprise. The lifeguard must be aware and ready.

TROPICAL CYCLONES

A tropical cyclone is a low pressure system without any "front" attached, that develops over the tropical or subtropical waters and has an organized circulation (counterclockwise in the northern hemisphere). In the U.S., we commonly refer to them as hurricanes.

There are several favorable environmental conditions that must be in place before a tropical cyclone can form. Some include:

- Warm ocean waters (at least 80°F) throughout a depth of about 150 feet
- An atmosphere that is moist and unstable
- Generally a minimum distance of at least 300 miles from the equator
- Generally light wind speeds high in the atmosphere

If the NWS issues a hurricane watch or warning for the coast, most communities have extensive response plans to mitigate loss of life and property. Beaches are usually closed. Lifeguards are typically a part of the preparedness and response team. Although the storm may be several hundred or thousand miles off the coast, long period swells generated by the storm can arrive on beaches well before any significant weather or rain.

Hurricane Katrina

These longer period swells will cause dangerous rip currents, powerful surf, and high wave run-up on area beaches. This will often surprise beach visitors expecting water conditions to reflect the otherwise tranquil local weather being observed. Surfers and swimmers may be overcome by the unexpected power of the waves. Pedestrians may be swept into the water as waves grow in size and run up on the beach.

WATERSPOUTS

Waterspouts are basically tornadoes over water. Winds in excess of 40 mph are possible. The primary danger is flying debris, so shelter and protection should be sought if it appears that a waterspout may come ashore.

Waterspouts may form during severe thunderstorm events, but waterspouts can also develop on relatively calm, partly cloudy summer days off the beach, over warm water. They can pose a direct threat to beachgoers, fishers, boats, and aircraft. They can sometimes come ashore and threaten beach users. (If a waterspout strikes land, it is by definition a tornado.)

The best way to avoid a waterspout is to move at a 90-degree angle to its apparent direction. Never move closer to investigate a waterspout. Some can be just as dangerous as tornadoes. Lifeguards should report sightings to fellow lifeguards and also to the local NWS office, so that appropriate warnings can be issued.

Credit: Robert Edgerton

Waterspout.

LIGHTNING

Anytime you hear thunder, there's always lightning present, whether you can see it or not. Lightning is a giant, violent electric spark from a thunderstorm that instantly heats the air in its path to about 50,000 degrees Fahrenheit—hotter than the surface of the sun. Thunder, which can be heard at a great distance, is the sound of the exploding superheated air in lightning's path. It's estimated that 15 to 40 million lightning strikes hit the ground each year in the U.S.

Lightning deaths are on the decline in the U.S. During the 30 year period ending in 2015, there were an average 48 deaths per year, but in the more recent 10 year component of that period there were an average of 31.[1] Improved predictions, preparedness, and behavior are no doubt a major part of that decline. Most people killed by lightning are outside in open areas. When combined, fishing and boating are the activities most associated with lightning fatalities, followed by beach recreation.[2]

As is true of drowning, men are disproportionately likely to be killed by lightning, accounting for about 80% of fatalities.[2] The peak months are June, July, and August. While lightning-related fatalities occur in every state, the highest numbers are reported in states bordering the Great Lakes, southern states bordering the Atlantic Ocean and Gulf of Mexico, and the four corners states of Colorado, New Mexico, Utah, and Arizona. As an example, from 2005 to 2014 Florida had the seventh most lightning fatalities when compared to population, while California ranked 44th and Hawaii 48th.[3]

National Weather Service Lightning Specialist John S. Jensenius, Jr. reports of the fatalities: "Many victims were either headed to safety at the time of the fatal strike or were just steps away from safety. Continued

LEARN MORE

Learn more about lightning on the National Weather Service website at: www.lightningsafety.noaa.gov

efforts are needed to convince people to get inside a safe place before the lightning threat becomes significant. For many activities, situational awareness and proper planning are essential to safety."[2] Thus, lifeguards can play a critical role in prevention. Considering that lifeguards have been killed and injured by lightning, that includes preventing injuries to themselves.

Cumulonimbus clouds, commonly known as thunderheads are the tall and sometimes anvil shaped clouds that produce thunder and lightning, as well as heavy rain, strong wind, and sometimes hail and tornadoes. Their formation near the beach should be monitored closely.

The USLA, the National Weather Service, and the National Oceanic and Atmospheric Administration have developed documents to help lifeguards protect themselves and beachgoers from lightning injuries. At www.usla.org/guidelines you can find lightning safety guidelines, a model emergency action plan, and a lightning site preparation checklist. Here are a few selected facts and recommendations, but be sure to refer to the entire documents:

- Lightning most frequently occurs within 10 miles of a thunderstorm (although there are occurrences when cloud-to-ground lightning strikes known as "bolts from the blue" can strike up to 20 miles away from a thunderstorm). It is generally recommended that patrons be notified (or evacuated based on the emergency action plan) and staff take shelter when thunderstorms move within 10 miles.

- Determine the distance of lightning from a location by using the "flash-to-bang rule"
  - Begin counting at the sight of the lightning flash. Stop counting at the sound of related thunder. Divide the count by five (5) to determine the proximity in miles of the lightning strike (5 seconds = 1 mile; 50 seconds = 10 miles, etc.).

- Locations that offer protection from lightning:
  - Fully-enclosed buildings that have grounded wiring and plumbing
  - Lifeguard towers that are fully-enclosed and compliant with NFPA 780 lightning guidelines
  - Fully-enclosed metal vehicles (no soft top convertibles)

- Locations that do not offer protection from lightning:
  - Beaches
  - Water
  - Open-sided pavilions (such as picnic areas)
  - Restrooms, changing facilities, and showers

- Lifeguard stands that are not fully enclosed and compliant with NFPA 780 lightning guidelines
- Tents or umbrellas
- Boats that are not designed or retrofitted to be compliant with NFPA 780 lightning guidelines
- Small personal watercraft (e.g. Jet Skis®)
- Annual training for lifeguards should include lightning awareness and a review of protocols in their hazardous weather safety plan. This includes:
  - Education on facts about the dangers of lightning
  - Locations that provide protection
  - The agency emergency action plan for lightning, along with severe weather watches, warnings and advisories

FOG

Fog is cloudiness that forms near the earth's surface. Fog can result from several situations that cause humid air to cool to its dew point, so that water vapor condenses into tiny droplets. In fog, visibility is restricted, leaving the lifeguard without the most basic tool for identifying people in distress. Swimmers and surfers may become disoriented and panic. Boaters may inadvertently turn shoreward, threatening those aboard and any swimmers in the area.

Like some other weather conditions, fog may not be a major management problem because it tends to keep people away from the beach; but fog may not dissuade surfers and other water enthusiasts. It may also arrive suddenly and unexpectedly, surprising those in the water. How your waterfront will handle fog is a local decision, but plans should be in place.

Fog can arrive suddenly and prevent lifeguards from seeing swimmers.

WIND

Wind plays an important role in the generation of waves at all types of beaches, inland and coastal; but wind also impacts beach operations in other ways. Strong winds may blow beach sand, causing discomfort and injuries to visitors. Wind, particularly sudden gusts of wind, can blow beach umbrellas over, which can result in serious injuries.

Wind can blow balls and other floating objects away from swimmers, causing them to chase these objects into deeper water, from which they are unable to return without assistance. Offshore winds can literally blow people on flotation devices away from the beach. Of course, wind also causes waves, which are discussed in detail in Chapter 6 (*The Surf Beach*).

TEMPERATURE

Air temperature at the beach may place even healthy visitors at risk of heat-related illness, especially when there is little shade. The NWS lists heat as the number one severe weather related killer in the U.S., with over 100 deaths each year.[1] Although heat-related illness is a problem when abnormally high temperature conditions are present, it's also common at resort areas where visitors are not acclimated to otherwise normal local weather.

Cold temperatures and hypothermia are the opposite danger. Cold water removes heat from the body 25 times faster than cold air.[4] Local weather conditions, water depth, and prevailing ocean currents can keep water very cold. Although hypothermia is generally thought to be a problem only at beaches in the northern latitudes, water under 70 degrees Fahrenheit is considered by some medical experts to be cold water. Many lakes, rivers, bays, and surf beaches in warmer climates have water temperatures below this temperature. Several factors will determine the extent of the effects of cold water on swimmers, including immersion time, air temperature, the mass of the swimmer, the health of the swimmer, and wind speed.

The immediate effects of sudden immersion in water below 60°F can be a debilitating, short duration (approximately two to three minute) reflex response called *cold shock*. This response includes life-threatening respiratory and cardiovascular effects. The respiratory effect involves quick onset (<30 seconds) uncontrollable rapid breathing, which impairs breath holding and facilitates aspiration of water (which can lead to drowning death). The cardiovascular response involves an immediate constriction (closure) of the blood vessels near the surface of the body, an increase in heart rate, and a surge in blood pressure. These factors may lead to incapacitation from a cardiovascular accident, such as heart attack or stroke, or death from drowning following aspiration.[4]

LEARN MORE

Learn more about cold water safety at:
www.coldwatersafety.org

After about three minutes, the initial effects of sudden cold-water immersion decline. Thereafter, in those whose airway is clear of the water, progressive whole body cooling occurs, leading to a gradual fall in deep body temperature (hypothermia). Whether a person falls suddenly into cold water or not, and despite whether cold shock is experienced, before a significant level of hypothermia develops there is progressive cooling of the muscles and joints in the exposed limbs. This impairs locomotion and thus swimming performance, which is likely to lead to drowning before a life-threatening level of hypothermia develops, unless the victim is wearing a lifejacket capable of keeping the airway clear of the water.[5] This impairment of locomotion also impedes the victim's ability to assist in the rescue effort.

One very rare complication of contact with cold water is *cold urticaria*. This condition is an allergy-like reaction to contact with cold water, as well as other sources of cold.[6] Within minutes the skin may become itchy, red, and swollen. Fainting, very low blood pressure, and shock-like symptoms can present.

Cold temperatures can also produce ice. While most open water lifeguards are not on duty during periods that ice is present, one of the most challenging types of open water rescue involves the rescue of those who have fallen through the ice. We discuss this in Chapter 15 (*Special Rescues*).

Cold water rescue training.

SUN

Long term exposure to the sun has been demonstrated to cause accelerated aging of the skin and enhance the potential for contracting skin cancer. The most immediate danger from the sun comes from overexposure, which affects both beach visitors and lifeguards. Sunburns can range from minor redness of the skin to serious burns, requiring medical care. Any significant exposure to the sun results in some degree of damage that is cumulative. Problems with overexposure to the sun are not restricted to the more southern latitudes. Anywhere the sun is shining, there's the potential for injury from overexposure.

Prudent lifeguards protect themselves from long-term exposure to the sun.

The problem of overexposure is compounded by the belief of some that sunburn is a normal part of the beach recreation experience and that one or two episodes of overexposure each beach season will not be harmful. Indeed, some visitors accept and even look forward to a sunburn as tangible evidence that they enjoyed themselves at the beach. It has been demonstrated that sunburns, particularly when sustained by young children, can greatly increase the potential for contracting skin cancer.[7] Lifeguards should monitor their beach crowd for people who appear to be overexposed, paying particular attention to people with light skin, along with small children and babies who must rely on their parents to protect them. Lifeguards can recommend use of sunscreen, shade, and protective clothing, for example.

Lifeguards are particularly susceptible to sun related injury. For a full discussion of this issue, please refer to Chapter 16 (*Lifeguard Health and Safety*).

> **LEARN MORE**
>
> You can read about the value of sunscreen on the website of the U.S. Food and Drug Administration at: www.fda.gov

FLOODS

Floods, particularly flash floods, claim the lives of about 80 people in the U.S. each year.[1] While flooding is not typically a threat to beach areas, lifeguards are often called upon to assist in flood rescues due to their aquatic skills and rescue equipment. Some lifeguard swiftwater rescue teams, such as the San Diego Lifeguard River Rescue Team, are primary responders to local and regional flood disasters.

People are most often caught in floodwater when they try to cross apparent low points in vehicles or on foot. They may become stranded or quickly swept downstream.

Credit: San Diego Lifeguard Service

Water rescue team deploys during flooding.

Floodwater is extremely hazardous, perhaps even more so than heavy surf conditions, because like rivers, moving floodwater can be relentless. There's no lull between sets of waves and the water level may rise dramatically in a very short period of time.

Just six inches of fast-moving floodwater can knock over an adult. It takes just 12 inches of rushing water to carry away a small car, while two feet of rushing water can carry away most vehicles. Even standing floodwater poses meaningful problems, including covering debris and sources of injury to rescuers. It also carries pathogens.

Rescuers are also seriously endangered by floodwater. Each year, rescuers are killed in attempts to save the lives of others in swiftwater and flood conditions. Lifeguards who lack special training in swiftwater or flood rescue should make every effort to avoid making a rescue that requires use of a boat or a water entry. Instead, methods which allow rescuers to remain onshore should be utilized. For a further discussion of flood rescue considerations and basic techniques, please refer to Chapter 15 (*Special Rescues*).

CHAPTER SUMMARY

In this chapter we have learned about weather, including storms and how they form. We have learned about the hazard presented by lightning, and how lifeguards can protect themselves and beach users. We have learned about waterspouts, fog, wind, temperature variations, and flooding. We have also learned about the impacts of the sun itself. With a better understanding of weather, we are better prepared for our role as lifeguards.

DISCUSSION POINTS

- Identify the types of frontal storms at beaches that you have visited.
- List three examples of safe shelters from lightning.
- Explain some outcomes that can be expected when fog obscures the water.
- Describe how wind, associated with storms or waterspouts, impacts the safety of beach users.
- Select five methods that lifeguards and beachgoers can protect themselves from the effects of the sun.
- Recognize the factors that make flooding dangerous.

CHAPTER

8

Drowning

I n this chapter you will learn about the drowning process, including the proper definition of drowning. We will provide statistics related to populations at high risk of drowning, as well as activities that are more likely to result in drowning. You will learn about the stages of drowning and the pathophysiology of drowning.

CHAPTER EXCERPT

Studies have demonstrated that the actions of lifeguards in rescue and resuscitation of drowning victims are the most important link in the chain of survival. In fact, the outcome of drowning patients is usually more dependent upon the timeliness and effectiveness of the initial rescue and resuscitation efforts than on the quality of hospital care.

What is drowning? The word drowning can be used to refer to a past event (e.g. she died by drowning) or an action in progress (e.g. he's drowning.) The World Health Organization and the International Life Saving Federation have adopted the following definition: "Drowning is the process of experiencing respiratory impairment from submersion/ immersion in liquid."[1] Drowning is therefore an event that may result in injury or death, or may be interrupted by timely rescue and effective medical care.

Drowning outcomes include death, injury, and non-injury. The terms wet, dry, active, passive, silent, and secondary drowning are unacceptable terms.[1] The drowning process is a continuum beginning with respiratory impairment due to submersion or immersion in liquid. If it is interrupted in time, the affected person may survive with little or no lingering injury. If not, injury or death will occur.

During the period from 2005 to 2009 an average of 3,880 people died annually from unintentional drowning (including boating incidents) in the U.S.[2] Worldwide, drowning is the second leading cause of unintentional injury death after traffic accidents.[1] In the U.S., drowning is the fifth leading cause of unintentional injury death.[3] During the period from 2005 to 2009, an estimated 5,789 people on average were treated annually in U.S. hospital emergency departments for nonfatal drowning and about half of them required hospitalization or transfer for further care.[2]

Those who survive drowning incidents are sometimes left with permanent disabilities including paralysis and irreparable brain damage. In addition to great psychological trauma, both to victims and their families, there are significant costs. The average cost of supporting a person who survives, but is incapacitated by a drowning incident has been conservatively estimated at more than $5 million.[4]

Drowning takes place in a wide variety of environments. Wherever there is liquid, there is the possibility of drowning. Infants have died by drowning in buckets. In a study of people under age 20, in cases where a site was listed, 47% of drowning deaths occurred in freshwater (rivers, lakes, ponds, etc.), 32% in pools, 9% in the home (bathtubs, etc.), and 4% in seawater. According to the study, "Infants were most likely to drown in bathtubs, young children in swimming pools, and older children and adolescents in natural bodies of freshwater."[5] The highest rate of drowning death is in children four and under, with the most common location a swimming pool.[2]

In earlier chapters we have described environmental hazards that contribute to drowning; but not all drowning can be attributed solely to environmental hazards. Human factors such as swimming skill, aquatic safety knowledge, judgment, social pressure, trauma, inexperience, pre-existing illness, and intoxication are substantial contributors. Lifeguards may believe that they have little control over these factors, but they do. You'll learn more about this in Chapter 9 (*Preventive Lifeguarding*).

ACTIVITIES ASSOCIATED WITH DROWNING

About half of all deaths from drowning in the U.S. occur in the open water environment.[2] They may be associated with a variety of activities. This section covers some of the most common.

Swimming

Swimming is the most popular recreational activity in the U.S. for those aged 7–17 and the fourth most popular recreational activity for all age groups.[6] Over 90 million people over the age of 16 swim in oceans, lakes, and rivers each year.[7] Some common environmental

Credit: Kyle Maxwell

contributors are currents, waves, and drop-offs. Many non-environmental factors contribute to drowning while swimming, such as over-estimating one's swimming skills, panic, failing to properly supervise children, swimming in areas without lifeguards, drugs and alcohol, peer pressure (taking a dare, impressing friends), carelessness, trying to rescue others, and underwater blackout from breath-holding (hypoxic blackout).

Recreational Boating

Recreational boating is a very popular pastime in the U.S. In 2012 for example, about 27.3% or 32.3 million of the estimated 118.1 million U.S. households had at least one member who boated.[8] In that year there were over 4,500 reported boating accidents, 3,000 injuries, and 650 fatalities.[9] Of those fatalities, 71% were due to drowning and 82% of those who died were not wearing a life jacket.[10] The two primary accidents involving fatalities are falls overboard and capsizing of the vessel, in that order, not collisions.[10]

Some boaters believe it's not necessary to wear a life jacket when the boat is moored or anchored, but one study found that 46% of boating fatalities associated with falling overboard occurred when the boat was stationary.[11] Alcohol use has been determined to be a significant contributing factor in boating accidents, not only due to the possibility that the boat operator misjudgments will lead to an accident, but also because intoxicated occupants fall overboard. Boating safety courses save lives. Where investigators were able to determine the level of training of the boat operator, in over 70% of the cases involving fatalities, the operators had no training.[10]

LEARN MORE

You can read the latest statistics on recreational boating safety and find a safe boating course at: www.uscgboating.org. The USLA encourages all boaters to take a course in safe boating and encourages the wearing of personal flotation devices by all aboard.

Credit: California State Parks Lifeguards

Survivors rescued from a sinking vessel.

Diving

People who dive and strike the bottom or underwater objects can sustain injuries that incapacitate them, leading to drowning death. Trauma may result directly to the victim's head, causing loss of consciousness, a concussion, fractured skull, brain hemorrhage, or a spinal injury. There were 1,840 spinal injuries reported in 2014 in which the primary cause was diving.[12] Males are more than three times as likely to be injured in diving accidents compared to females. About half of these injuries occur to people in the 16–30 age range.[12] Often, consumption of alcohol is involved, as it inhibits natural fear.

Body surfing injuries are similar to diving injuries when the body surfer surfs down the face of the wave and strikes the bottom. Head and neck trauma may lead to unconsciousness or paralysis rendering victims unable to keep their head above water, or signal for help. A major problem in diving injuries is that the victim may be quickly removed from the water by friends unaware of the spinal injury or lacking training for proper spinal injury management. Information on treating spinal injuries can be found in Chapter 18 (*Medical Care in the Aquatic Environment*).

Alcohol Consumption

According to the Centers for Disease Control and Prevention, "Among adolescents and adults, alcohol use is involved in up to 70% of deaths associated with water recreation, almost a quarter of emergency room visits for drowning, and about one in five reported boating deaths. Alcohol is a central nervous system depressant that influences balance, coordination, and judgment, and its effects are heightened by sun exposure and heat."[3]

Scuba Diving

In the 10 year period ending in 2013 there were an average of 66 recreational scuba diving deaths per year in the U.S. reported to the Divers Alert Network.[13] Most scuba fatalities result from drowning due to panic, entanglement, running out of air, or a heart attack. There are over 1,000 emergency room admissions each year related to scuba diving.[13] Florida and California have the highest diver populations and the highest numbers of associated deaths. For more information, please see Chapter 19 (*Scuba Related Illness and Treatment*).

HIGHER RISK POPULATIONS

People of all races, ethnicities, and ages, both male and female, are susceptible to drowning. No one is immune. However, there is statistical data indicating that some are more likely to drown than others. These are broad-based statistics though, and no average is true of all members of an identified group. The following are based on studies covering the U.S. Experiences in other countries can vary significantly.

Credit: California State Parks Lifeguards

Resuscitation efforts for a scuba diver.

LEARN MORE

Visit the Divers Alert Network at:
www.diversalertnetwork.org/

Youth

Drowning is responsible for more deaths among children aged 1–4 than any other cause except birth defects.[3] About one in five people who die from drowning are children 14 and younger.[3] According to the U.S. Centers for Disease Control and Prevention (CDC), "For every child who dies from drowning, another five receive emergency department care for nonfatal submersion injuries."[3] These emergency department visits are unusual in drowning victims in that more than 50% of all drowning victims treated in emergency departments require hospitalization or transfer for further care (compared with a hospitalization rate of about 6% for all unintentional injuries).[3]

Most of the deaths of children 1–4 occur in backyard (residential) swimming pools. Backyard pool drowning accidents typically result from failure to adequately fence off pools and particularly from inadequate supervision by adult guardians. While open water lifeguards have little opportunity to directly intervene in backyard pool drownings, unless they simply happen to be there when the emergency occurs, lifeguards can help raise public awareness of the problem and thereby help prevent drowning.

Backyard pools should be surrounded by fences at least four feet high which are fully enclosed by locking, self-closing, child-proof gates. If doors from the home enter into the pool area, they should have alarms. Power safety covers are recommended, as well as lifesaving equipment and CPR training for all child guardians. Young children, particularly those unable to swim, should never, ever be left alone anywhere near a pool. A responsible, non-distracted adult at no more than arms-length away should actively supervise all children while in and near the water.

> **LEARN MORE**
>
> The Consumer Product Safety Commission offers pool safety information at: www.poolsafely.gov

Males

Males die by drowning at a significantly higher rate than females. The ratio of male to female drowning fatalities is about 4:1.[3] Adolescent males, in particular, are highly physically active and known to be relatively frequent risk takers. It is often said that teenage males act as though they believe they are immortal. According to the CDC, "Males might be at greater risk because they are more likely to overestimate their swimming ability, choose higher risk activities, or more commonly use alcohol."[2]

Race and Ethnicity

The Centers for Disease Control and Prevention reports that between 2005 and 2009, "The death rate for blacks (1.40 per 100,000 population) was significantly higher than the overall death rate (1.29), and the death rate for Hispanics was significantly lower (1.19). Racial and ethnic disparity in drowning death rates was greatest among children aged 5–14 years (blacks, 1.34; Hispanics, 0.46; and whites, 0.48)."[2] It's important to remember that these are broad averages. Black American swimmers have medaled at the Olympics and set NCAA swimming records. The CDC states, "Factors such as access to swimming pools, the desire or lack of desire to learn how to swim, and choosing water-related recreational activities may contribute to the racial differences in drowning rates."[3]

> The USLA strongly encourages the greatest possible access to public learn to swim programs for purposes of drowning prevention and equal access to aquatic related employment, including lifeguarding. Barriers to public swimming programs can have both lethal and economic consequences that disproportionately affect segments of the U.S. population. Everyone should have the chance to learn to swim. Looking for a learn-to-swim class? Check www.redcross.org or www.ymca.net; or just check with your local chapter of the American Red Cross or YMCA of the USA.

Epilepsy

People with epilepsy are at enhanced risk of drowning. Epileptic seizures usually leave victims without control over their motor functions—a deadly circumstance in the water. While people with epilepsy have differing seizure triggers, those triggers can include photosensitivity to bright lights or flashing lights (as when the light shimmers off the water), extreme temperatures (like cold swimming water or high heat), and physical exertion. The Epilepsy Foundation notes that, "A common cause of accidental death in people with epilepsy is drowning."[14] They advise that those with epilepsy "wear a U.S. Coast Guard approved life jacket while boating, when in or near an open body of water, or when doing water sports."[14]

Credit: East Bay Regional Park District

A lifeguard teaches a free water safety awareness class.

LEARN MORE

You can learn more about epilepsy at: www.epilepsyfoundation.org/

DROWNING STAGES

In the open water environment, the drowning process involves three distinct stages which can be interrupted through timely intervention:

1. Distress
2. Panic
3. Submersion

This process is usually progressive, but not always. Either of the two initial stages may be skipped completely depending upon a variety of factors.

Distress

Drowning can occur for a number of reasons. A non-swimmer who is wading may suddenly step into water that is overhead (a drop-off), or may fall from a boat or dock. A poor swimmer may swim offshore to retrieve a ball or help another person, only to tire and be unable to return to shore. Even a strong swimmer may be overpowered by a rip current or river current. These are just a few examples.

People of different swimming abilities may behave in divergent ways, and this may vary with the environment. For those with swimming skills there is sometimes a gradual period of increasing distress prior to the actual onset of a swimming emergency. In these cases, swimmers are able to support themselves in the water with or without a flotation device, but have difficulty reaching safety. They may be able to call or wave for help, or move toward the support of others. The USLA estimates that more than 80% of rescues at surf beaches are due to rip currents. In such cases, an initial distress phase is typical.

Credit: Doug Leach

A lifeguard swimming to rescue a victim in a rip current.

Some distressed swimmers may not immediately recognize their predicament and may swim against a current without realizing they're making no progress. A distress presentation may last a few seconds or extend for quite some time. As the strength of the swimmer ebbs, the distress presentation will typically digress to panic if the victim is not rescued or cannot make it to safety. Alert lifeguards on a properly staffed beach are usually able to intervene during the distress phase of the drowning process. In fact, it's not unusual for some victims to protest to the responding lifeguard that they need no assistance, because they've yet to realize their peril, though it may be clear to the lifeguard that they are in jeopardy.

Credit: GLC Aquatic Safety Department

In-water distress is serious, but this phase of the drowning process does not always occur. For example, some non-swimmers may be completely unable to keep themselves afloat and simply submerge, or a medical condition may render the person immobile. In any case, rapid intervention can ensure that the victim suffers no ill effects.

Panic

A person who falls off a flotation device or steps off a drop-off into water that is overhead may immediately enter the panic stage, with no initial distress presentation. Alternatively, the panic stage of the drowning process may progress from the distress stage, as a swimmer loses strength and feels a sense of desperation. In the panic stage the victim is unable to adequately maintain buoyancy due to fatigue, complete lack of swimming skills, or a physical problem (e.g. cramps).

Non-swimmers in the panic stage have an ineffective kick. The head and face are low in the water, with the chin usually extended to keep the mouth above the surface. Arms flail at the side in a desperate effort to stay afloat. The victim focuses energy on grabbing breaths of air. Victims in these cases typically press their arms downward toward the surface of the water repeatedly in an ineffective effort to keep themselves afloat. People experiencing this level of distress are unlikely to call for help and nearby swimmers often don't notice them, so alert lifeguards are essential to their safety.

Weak swimmers in the panic stage, particularly in a current, may use an ineffective stroke similar to a dog paddle. Lifeguards refer to the appearance these victims as *climbing out of the hole* or *climbing the ladder*.

The panic stage rarely lasts long because the victim's actions are largely ineffective and consume great amounts of energy. This is the stage where a victim may grab a nearby swimmer in an effort to stay on the surface and breathe, possibly leading to multiple victims. This stage can progress quickly to submersion unless a rescue is performed, so the lifeguard must react very rapidly.

Credit: Leslie Schwene

A lifeguard jumps to the rescue from the stern of a rescue boat.

Submersion

Contrary to common belief, most drowning incidents do not result in a person floating face-down in the water. Even in the enhanced buoyancy provided by salt water, most people without a flotation device who lose their ability to maintain buoyancy, rapidly submerge and sink to the bottom. Aspiration of water, which replaces some of the air in the lungs, contributes to this lack of buoyancy. In the lesser buoyancy of freshwater, submersion can be expected to occur more rapidly. Submersion in and of itself is not fatal if the victim is recovered in time and resuscitation is provided as needed, but this can be a tremendously difficult task.

Unlike the clear water of the pool environment, open water is often murky and water visibility may be as low as zero. Currents and surf action can move the body a significant distance from the point of initial submersion. Once submersion occurs, the chance of a successful rescue declines dramatically. This is what makes intervention at the distress or panic phase crucial.

Based on the experience of professional open water lifeguards, the USLA believes there is a *two minute window* of enhanced opportunity for successful recovery and

LEARN MORE

You can read more about cold water survival on the website of the Minnesota Sea Grant at: www.seagrant.umn.edu.

resuscitation of submerged victims. Thereafter, the possibilities for successful recovery decline very quickly. In colder waters, successful resuscitations have been documented after up to an hour or more of submersion, but these are extremely rare cases and have been related to the rapid onset of hypothermia.

THE PATHOPHYSIOLOGY OF DROWNING

During drowning, breathing typically occurs in fitful gasps on the surface, when possible, and there may be coughing and sputtering as water is inadvertently drawn in with a breath. The inhalation of water into the lungs is known as *water aspiration*, while the swallowing of water into the stomach is *water ingestion*. Both of these usually occur. Victims may attempt to hold their breath to avoid water aspiration. If water gets into their mouth, which is usually unavoidable, they typically try to swallow it. A significant quantity of water is often ingested and may be vomited later, particularly during resuscitation efforts.

Once the victim's airway is underwater, the victim may inhale water, but the larynx will sometimes close reflexively, preventing all but a small amount of water from being aspirated. As is the case on the surface, the victim may swallow significant amounts of water instead. In about 10% of fatal drownings the larynx closes upon initial contact with water and never relaxes, thus preventing water from ever entering the lungs. As the victim loses consciousness due to lack of oxygen in the tissues of the body (*hypoxia*), the larynx may relax, allowing more water to enter the lungs. Vomiting may occur secondary to cerebral (brain) hypoxia or gastric distension.

Unlike sudden cardiac arrest (a heart attack), where the heart stops beating first, death from drowning starts with suffocation. The heart itself is healthy and functioning, but over time there is inadequate oxygen in the blood to support life. Eventually, the healthy heart stops

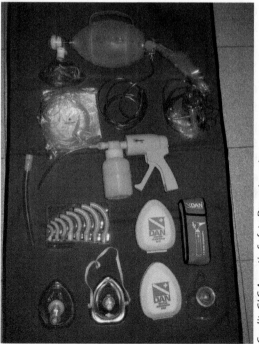

Credit: GLC Aquatic Safety Department

Airway management tools.

Credit: GLC Aquatic Safety Department

Portable oxygen delivery system.

beating. Brain death usually begins in five to six minutes after adequately oxygenated blood stops circulating, although in some very unusual cold water drownings this may be greatly delayed. In these cold water cases, significant hypothermia occurs which decreases the cerebral requirement for oxygen.

Drowning is not simply a case of suffocation. In most cases the lungs are traumatized by aspiration of water. Even if the victim is rescued and revived, this trauma will make it difficult for the lungs to transfer oxygen to the bloodstream and tissues. In addition, the drowning process produces a frothy liquid (pulmonary edema) in the airways. When a submerged drowning victim is recovered, the person is typically experiencing severe hypoxia. Immediate resuscitation efforts, beginning with ventilations, are therefore needed, ideally with administration of oxygen and, if possible, positive pressure ventilation.[15] For more information on resuscitation, please refer to Chapter 18 (*Medical Care in the Aquatic Environment*).

The effects of freshwater and seawater drowning differ somewhat. In freshwater drowning, water quickly enters the bloodstream through the lungs. In seawater drowning, the aspirated seawater can actually draw fluid from the bloodstream into the lungs. On the part of the lifeguard, treatment is the same for both cases.

Studies have demonstrated that the actions of lifeguards in rescue and resuscitation of drowning victims are the most important link in the chain of survival. In fact, the outcome of drowning patients is usually more dependent upon the timeliness and effectiveness of the initial rescue and resuscitation efforts than on the quality of hospital care.[16]

Lifeguard speeding to a victim.

Credit: GLC Aquatic Safety Department

Automatic external defibrillators (AED) have become a common tool of lifeguards. They are primarily intended to correct problems associated with sudden cardiac arrest. Automatic external defibrillators can sometimes stop *ventricular fibrillation*, an uncoordinated beating of the heart. Ventricular fibrillation is rare in submersion victims.[15, 17] Most drowning victims have healthy hearts that simply cease to function due to hypoxia. The best approach in treating drowning victims is to prioritize immediate CPR measures, ideally with high flow oxygen. If available, an AED should be used, in accordance with the manufacturer's instructions, in the relatively unlikely case the victim is experiencing an arrhythmia that can respond to defibrillation.

Automatic External Defibrillator (AED).

Credit: GLC Aquatic Safety Department

Regardless of the drowning process, treatment of a recovered drowning victim by the lifeguard is the same, whether water has been aspirated or not. Successful rescue ventilation occurs even with aspirated water in the lungs. Abdominal thrusts (such as the Heimlich maneuver) should not be used in resuscitation of drowning victims, except in cases that repeated repositioning of the airway suggests a foreign body obstruction (other than water). This maneuver will not remove significant amounts of water from the lungs. It may cause regurgitation and aspiration of stomach contents and other serious complications to resuscitation and recovery of the victim.[15]

Sudden Submersion Syndrome

In some cases, people in water are rendered unconscious, disabled, or dead due to situations that may include heart attacks, cardiovascular accidents (strokes), epileptic seizures, head or neck injury, severe trauma, alcohol or drug overdose, cold shock, and other conditions. A victim on the surface suddenly submerges, usually without a struggle. We define this as *sudden submersion syndrome*. Sudden submersion syndrome is particularly difficult to prevent. The victim may have shown no prior indication of problems and be in a water area with no obvious hazards. The tremendous challenge involved in spotting a victim of sudden submersion syndrome, particularly with a large beach crowd under observation, makes the importance of effective surveillance critical. Even with the most effective surveillance by trained and experienced lifeguards, sudden submersion syndrome may still occur.

Hypoxic Blackout

When people submerge and hold their breath, they can proceed to unconsciousness. This is often preceded by the individual hyperventilating prior to submersion. The loss of consciousness can have several causes. It's usually related to hypoxia with low levels of carbon dioxide (CO_2). When an individual breath-holds, oxygen level decreases (hypoxia) and CO_2 level increases. The rising CO_2 level is what triggers the urge to breathe and this usually occurs long before the hypoxia is so advanced that the individual becomes unconscious; however, after hyperventilation, CO_2 is abnormally low and one can lose consciousness before ever getting the cue to breathe. The person could either be moving in a vertical plane in the water column (swimming forward underwater) or they could be static with very little movement.

Credit: none public domain

The depth of the water has no significance to the outcome of unconsciousness. Lifeguards who observe individuals who are practicing hyperventilation and extended breath-holding should discourage it and educate people about the dangers involved. The term *shallow water blackout* has been misapplied to this malady. It is a term related to a specific diving problem, not breath-holding.

Delayed Effects

Part of the drowning process involves water aspiration. People who are rescued from drowning (or who rescue themselves) may initially appear to be healthy, but if they have aspirated water or vomitus, they may later suffer serious complications. This is typically due to damage to the lungs and their oxygen exchange capabilities. One possibility is acute respiratory distress syndrome (ARDS), which can have a rapid onset and cause death hours or days after the drowning event.[18]

Victims who have been rescued from drowning are often in a state of denial or embarrassed and simply want to walk away. It's very important to carefully evaluate those who appear to have aspirated water for signs and symptoms of water aspiration. Specific guidelines for treatment of drowning victims and for determining whether they should be sent to the hospital for further care can be found in Chapter 18 (*Medical Care in the Aquatic Environment*).

CHAPTER SUMMARY

In this chapter we have learned about some of the most common activities associated with drowning, including swimming, boating, scuba diving, diving from heights, and consumption of alcohol. We have learned about populations at higher risk of drowning, which include young people in general, males, some members of racial/ethnic groups, and epileptics. We have learned about the classic stages of drowning: distress, panic, and submersion. We have also learned about the pathophysiology of drowning.

DISCUSSION POINTS

- Compare activities that are associated with drowning.
- Identify factors that cause young males to have a significantly higher drowning rate than young females.
- Contemplate how affluence might play a factor in drownings.
- Examine the stages of the drowning process.
- Examine how the physiology of drowning has an impact on medical aid procedures.
- Identify the value of providing ventilations and oxygen to a drowning victim.
- Name a cause of sudden submersion syndrome.

CHAPTER
9

Preventive Lifeguarding

I n this chapter you will learn about the importance of the lifeguard's primary role—prevention of injury and death. You will learn that there are a wide variety of tools that can be employed to prevent drowning and other accidents. These include public education, rules and regulations, signs and flags, identification of pre-events, taking on-site preventive actions, special operation modes, appropriate operational hours, after hours and post-season response plans, maintenance, and even facility design.

CHAPTER EXCERPT

Lifeguards, more than any other providers of public safety, have an ongoing responsibility for accident prevention.

The primary role of many providers of public safety is one of responding to emergencies after they have developed. For example, firefighters typically respond to reports of fires to suppress them and minimize damage. Responding to emergencies is also an important role of lifeguards, but lifeguards, more than any other providers of public safety, have an ongoing responsibility for accident *prevention*. In fact, prevention is the primary role of lifeguards. This is critical because the worst outcome of water emergencies is death by drowning and the drowning process can be very rapid. There are also many other types of injuries (and loss of property) that can occur at the beach, which can be prevented by timely and appropriate action by lifeguards.

PUBLIC EDUCATION

If lifeguards wait until people arrive at their beach to provide information about its hazards and about ways to safely enjoy the beach, important opportunities are lost. Most days, lifeguards cannot possibly individually meet each arriving visitor to personally educate them. Even if this were possible, it would be very inefficient and distract the lifeguard from more immediate duties, like water surveillance. Beach users arriving when lifeguards are off-duty or at beaches with no lifeguards receive no benefit from this approach. For these reasons, a comprehensive and effective drowning prevention program involves multiple layers of protection that starts with efforts to reach beach users well before they arrive at the beach.

Effective programs include activities and materials developed to teach people about the hazards that exist in the aquatic environment and how they may avoid or escape some of these hazards. Lifeguard agencies can encourage people to learn to swim, conduct junior lifeguard programs, and regularly remind the public about the importance of swimming near lifeguards. Public education programs also promote better understanding of lifeguard services and procedures, generating support for and patronage of areas protected by lifeguards.

Educational Materials

The USLA produces public educational material through various print and electronic means that can be used by lifeguard agencies and the general public. Individual lifeguard agencies also produce their own. Educational information can be disseminated through posters, bumper stickers, handouts, brochures, coloring books, and similar methods. All of this material can be provided to local schools, hotels, clubs, restaurants, or any other place where potential beach users may be. Many lifeguard agencies will also post these materials at beach bulletin boards or in window displays, and will provide visitors with handout materials on request.

Websites are a particularly useful method to offer public education materials. Safety information can be placed on agency websites with links to organizations like the USLA. As people research and plan activities for their beach visit, they can also find information on how to make their visit safer and more enjoyable. By posting brochures on websites and making them printable, lifeguard providers facilitate a wide dissemination of materials at low cost. A wise strategy is to include how-to information integrated with safety information. For example, including a map of nearby parking lots with the nearest lifeguard posts and the USLA slogan *swim near a lifeguard* may encourage people to park near and swim in guarded areas.

Some agencies and communities have developed safety videos to address local conditions and circumstances. These can be disseminated on websites, online video sharing platforms, on incoming public transit, or through distribution of recorded video material.

Sun & Heat Safety

- Use a high SPF sunscreen (15 or above).
- Wear loose fitting, light colored clothing, a hat & sunglasses with a full UVA/UVB protection.
- Drink plenty water or non-alcoholic and caffeine-free liquids.

Stings, Bites, & Cuts

- For all types of jelly-fish and man-o-war stings, remove tentacles using a glove or towel, rinse area using seawater and apply ice. Do not rub the area with sand! For any serious reaction, **call 9-1-1** and get the person to advanced medical care.
- Stingrays and many types of fish frequent shallow ocean waters and can thrust a sharp shaft into a foot or ankle.
- One good preventative action is to shuffle your feet while wading.
- Remember there is a high concentration of bacteria on objects in the water and near the beach. Clean even minor wounds well and monitor for signs of infection.

SWIM NEAR A LIFEGUARD

U.S.L.A.
UNITED STATES LIFESAVING ASSOCIATION
www.usla.org

U.S.L.A.
UNITED STATES LIFESAVING ASSOCIATION

Our Purpose

We are America's nonprofit, professional association of beach lifeguards and open water rescuers. USLA works to reduce the incidence of death and injury in the aquatic environment through public education, national lifeguard standards, training programs, promotion of high levels of lifeguard readiness, and other means. The USLA accomplishes these goals through a variety of activities and in partnership with many other organizations with related goals.

Member Benefits

- Affiliation with America's water rescue professionals and drowning prevention advocates
- Subscription to American Lifeguard Magazine
- Lifeguard educational conferences
- Local, regional and national Board of Directors meetings
- Public education materials
- USLA decal and other items
- The latest information on open water rescue
- Networking among other open water rescuers

Membership is open to anyone. You don't have to be a lifeguard!

Additional Resources

Activities and resources offered to the public by USLA and affiliated agencies:
- Junior lifeguards
- Surf camps
- Public relation endeavors
- Teacher educational materials
- Promotional materials
- Collaboration with schools, museums, & health agencies
- Guest speaking engagements
- Beach and water safety materials and activities
- Lifeguard competitions
- Legislation related to aquatic safety

For more information go to: www.usla.org

The USLA offers a variety of public education materials and resources in the Public Education section of: www.usla.org.

Social Media

Social media provides an opportunity to disseminate information in real time. Many lifeguard agencies use social media platforms to provide information on current conditions (tides, surf, rip currents, etc.), unusual rescues or rescue numbers, parking problems, and a variety of other issues that may be of interest to beachgoers. Because people increasingly seem to use social media to share photos and videos of stunts, or other dangerous activities, lifeguards can also use them to discourage this activity or point out the negative outcomes when they occur. Using the same communication method as other can help ensure the message is received by all.

On social media, people traveling to the beach can learn of any unusual circumstances before they arrive. The news media follow social media and is therefore notified of information of interest to the public, which they may then rebroadcast, increasing the reach exponentially. Use of social media comes with challenges related to misuse or mistakes, so great care is needed. It is usually best to restrict access to an agency's social media account to a limited few who are trained and authorized, such as designated public information officers.

Recorded Information Lines

Special telephone lines with regularly updated, recorded information on local beach conditions are a popular and inexpensive way to provide water safety information. Using this approach, lifeguards update the recorded information throughout the day, with the latest water and weather conditions. These recordings can include surf conditions, tides, safety tips, lifeguard hours of protection and locations, and any unusual circumstances, like closures due to water contamination or severe weather. An important audience for recorded beach information lines is employees in the tourism industry, who may wish to provide their guests with the latest information. Boaters, scuba divers, and surfers may also find the service valuable. As with brochures, interweaving information that interests these users with safety messages helps get the message out. An added benefit of recorded information lines is that they reduce the number of individual phone calls that must be fielded for routine questions.

Credit: East Bay Regional Park District

A lifeguard makes a classroom visit to present water safety awareness.

Public Appearances

One of the most effective ways to provide public information is to have lifeguards attend special events and deliver lectures to school and civic groups. In these cases, the investment of a few hours of time may provide concentrated delivery of the safety message to large numbers of people. These events also result in "pass-along" education, as the attendees tell friends and family about what they've learned.

Providing local employees who are likely to come in contact with tourists with basic aquatic safety information is also of great value. Front desk personnel at hotels are good examples, but so are police, cab drivers, and bellhops. These employees, though rarely experts in aquatic safety, may often be asked for water safety information, such as, "Where's the safest place to swim?" They need to be prepared to provide good advice or know how to refer those inquiring to more authoritative sources of information, like a lifeguard agency's recorded information line or website.

It's a good practice to produce a computer-based presentation with photos or video in preparation for these events. The next step is to contact school principals, the leaders of local civic organizations, hotel owners, and others to offer presentations. In seasonal areas, it's best to schedule presentations just before the season begins, so that information is timely and more likely to be remembered. Public appearances can continue throughout the beach season, either at the beach or in parks, campgrounds, or other recreation areas.

News Media

Television, newspapers, radio, and other news media are an excellent way to inexpensively disseminate public safety messages to a broad audience. There are a variety of ways this can be accomplished. When lifeguard agencies establish a rapport with newspapers and television stations, for example, lifeguards may be interviewed about current topics. The news media can be invited to cover interesting events, like a lifeguard training program, special holiday preparations, or the deployment of new lifesaving equipment. In the case of a special event that might be considered newsworthy, some lifeguard agencies issue a news release with pertinent details and deliver the release in person, by fax, email, or via the agency's website. Multiple methods of distribution and follow-up phone calls are most successful. A particularly effective strategy is developing public service announcements, both for radio and television, which some media outlets will air free of charge. Working with a local college's production lab may allow this to be created at low cost.

Special Events

Lifeguard agencies sometimes work with local schools to sponsor water safety related poster contests, essay contests, or beach field trips, for example. In some areas, lifeguard agencies tie in sponsorship of other special events, including concerts, fundraising events, fairs, and sporting events, like triathlons. These special events can include opportunities for spreading information on water safety and for generating support of lifeguard services.

Each year, just prior to the beginning of the summer beach season, the USLA sponsors *National Beach Safety Week* in an effort to remind beachgoers to use caution in the aquatic environment. The USLA Public Education Committee is responsible for coordinating National Beach Safety Week through direct efforts and through the nine USLA regions.

United States Lifesaving Association regions, local chapters, and lifeguard agencies can assist in promoting National Beach Safety week by requesting that their local and state political leaders issue

Credit: East Bay Regional Park District

A lifeguard providing water safety awareness education at a local community event.

LEARN MORE

Information on *National Beach Safety Week*, including a sample resolution for local political bodies, is available in the Public Education section of: www.usla.org.

proclamations declaring National Beach Safety Week and by sponsoring press conferences to inform the public. These activities can help draw media attention at a time when water safety education is of particular interest to the beach-going public. To encourage political leaders to declare National Beach Safety Week, it's best to send a letter to the political leader, along with a sample proclamation. A sample letter and proclamation are available in the Public Education section of www.usla.org.

Lifeguard competitions are conducted at many beaches throughout the U.S. These events combine motivation for physical fitness among lifeguards, a fostering of interagency relationships, a demonstration of the physical demands placed on open water lifeguards, and an appreciation for the challenges inherent in the beach environment. United States Lifesaving Association-sanctioned lifeguard competitions take place across the country, culminating each year at the USLA National Lifeguard Championships. In addition to the events themselves, which draw attention to lifeguard readiness and fitness, public information materials and advice can be disseminated at these events through posters, brochures, signs, or even simple reminders on a public address system to *swim near a lifeguard,* for example.

Credit: Rich Schlatter

Credit: Kyle Maxwell

Information on pending lifeguard events of national interest may be posted, with permission of the webmaster, at: www.usla.org.

Credit: Eric Nurse

Lifeguard presents a water safety talk to children.

Special Programs

In addition to special events, many lifeguard agencies sponsor or assist in ongoing programs to develop water skills and water safety awareness. Although open water lifeguards are not swimming instructors during work hours, many lifeguard agencies contribute to learn-to-swim programs or promote them. Basic information on lifesaving may be provided to local police and firefighters. One of the most effective programs of this nature is the junior lifeguard program. For more information on these programs, see Chapter 26 (*Junior Lifeguard Programs*).

RULES AND REGULATIONS

Most jurisdictions overseeing a beach area establish rules and regulations to help prevent accidents and injuries, as well as to ensure that all beach visitors can enjoy the beach experience without being unduly bothered by others. These regulations can address a number of issues. Common examples include banning littering, regulating pets, and requiring that lifeguard directions be followed. In addition to local beach rules and local ordinances, many beach areas are protected by national, state, or regional laws which regulate boat or aircraft traffic, or which are intended to protect the environment.

Separating Incompatible Activities

There are a wide variety of activities practiced at aquatic areas. These activities are sometimes incompatible. Conflicts can arise which cause disputes and can threaten public safety. An effective practice in promoting beach and water safety is taking steps to separate incompatible activities. An obvious example of incompatible activities is motorboating and swimming. A swimmer can easily be injured or killed by a motorboat, so it's important to separate motorboats from swimmers. Another example is surfing and swimming. On the beach, keeping ballgames away from sunbathers could be expected to reduce conflict and injury. Rules and regulations may also establish special procedures for participating in particular water or beach activities. Permits may be required for surfing or scuba diving, or those activities may be restricted to established time periods. Evaluating these issues in advance and taking proactive steps to separate incompatible use can reduce the potential for injury, while enhancing the enjoyment of everyone.

Credit: Adam Abajian

Separating boat and swim areas reduces the chance of conflict and injury.

Enforcement

Lifeguards are usually provided with some degree of authority to enforce regulations. Without lawful authority to enforce rules and regulations, it can be very difficult to manage a beach area, since violators who learn that lifeguard warnings will not be enforced may ignore them. Lifeguard enforcement authority may be limited to issuing warnings which, if disobeyed, will ultimately be enforced by police officers summoned to the scene. Even if police are readily available, this can become very time consuming and police are sometimes reluctant to become involved in disputes over beach regulations they may consider of minor importance. For this reason, in some areas lifeguards are appointed as law enforcement officers and authorized to enforce local and state laws to the point of citation or arrest. In cases where lifeguards lack ultimate enforcement authority, it's important that they establish a good rapport with the primary enforcing authority in order to help assure support when requested. In either case, good public contact skills are invaluable in gaining voluntary compliance whenever possible.

Lifeguards should be experts on regulations that pertain to the beach area under their supervision. Enforcement often involves lengthy discussions with people who want a detailed explanation of the rules. Lifeguards need to be in a position to fully explain what is and what is not permissible.

Enforcement of beach regulations requires tact and patience. People visiting the beach are in a recreational mode. Often they have driven long distances and had a difficult time finding parking. Perhaps they have had a very stressful work week. They want to play. They may therefore be angered if told that the form of recreation they want to practice must be modified or terminated.

Before intervening in any conflict or enforcing rules, a lifeguard should evaluate the safest approach for the lifeguard and other lifeguards. This may sometimes mean avoiding intervention until law enforcement has been summoned and has arrived on-scene. Knowing when to avoid contact is as important as knowing when to intervene. Personal safety is paramount.

In enforcement of minor beach regulations, lifeguards should normally approach in a friendly manner, perhaps first engaging in conversation over unrelated issues. Whenever possible, this should be done by a lifeguard whose primary assignment is to patrol the beach or provide backup to lifeguards assigned to surveillance. This way, surveillance of the area is not compromised during the contact.

It is often helpful for the lifeguard to remove sunglasses, and if the person is sitting or lying, to squat or kneel down, so as to be at eye level of the person to whom you are speaking. A polite and courteous lifeguard is less likely to evoke a negative reaction. The lifeguard should explain the regulation and, if known, the basic reason for it. It's important that the person understand why the lifeguard is taking the time to enforce the regulation. At the same time, it's not the lifeguard's responsibility to justify regulations.

As an example, many beach areas prohibit glass containers because of the possibility of breakage and resultant injury to barefoot beachgoers. Unfortunately, beachgoers sometimes arrive unknowingly with all of their drinks in bottles. If the lifeguard approaches and simply states that bottles are not permitted, the beach patron may immediately consider the regulation unreasonable and react negatively. On the other hand, if the lifeguard explains that the intent is to prevent injury (to their party and others) from broken glass, most people will respond in an understanding manner.

In any enforcement contact, it is important to clearly explain the action the person must take to come into compliance. For example, in the case of the bottle, after explaining the regulation, the lifeguard might direct the person to immediately remove the bottle from the beach to a nearby car. The person now knows what the regulation is, the reason for it, and what must be done to achieve compliance.

Another excellent technique in enforcement of regulations is to *provide alternatives*. The beachgoer told that football is impermissible on the beach may be very upset. Perhaps this was the primary reason to visit the beach. Is there a nearby park where football is permitted that this person could visit instead? Is there an unused portion of the beach where football could be tolerated? Providing options shows concern for the person's needs and a desire to help.

> An excellent technique in enforcement of regulations is to *provide alternatives*.

The professional lifeguard maintains a calm disposition throughout an enforcement contact. It may be very frustrating to observe a person acting in an inappropriate manner, but the lifeguard should avoid making judgments about the person's motivations. The lifeguard should be positive, polite, and avoid becoming confrontational, while listening attentively to the beach patron's feedback. A cool temperament, even in face of abusive language, is usually the best approach. Avoid complicated discussions and reasoning. The lifeguard's approach can simply be "These regulations exist for your safety and the safety of others." If resistance to compliance persists, attempt to reduce tension by expressing empathy over the individual's frustration and offer information about where they can pursue their concern further. If compliance is completely resisted, the next step depends upon agency policy and the level of authority provided to the lifeguard.

Credit: Desi Stoyanova

Rescue boat crew advises a swimmer of the importance to swim inside the designated area.

Beach disputes sometimes arise between two beach users or groups of users. In these cases, the lifeguard may have to assume the role of referee. A valuable tool in helping defuse confrontations between people is to separate them. This is done by asking to speak with each party individually, but out of earshot of the other, to get their side of the story. If both parties are assured that they will be heard in full, this technique prevents one from interrupting the other or becoming more hostile based on what is said to the lifeguard. As well, many people want to tell someone in a position of authority why they feel that they have been wronged. The lifeguard can often perform this role quite effectively. After considerately hearing both sides, listening thoroughly without interrupting, and carefully considering the issue, the lifeguard may be able to propose a resolution with which both parties can agree. This is the ideal outcome. If not, informing each party of the decision quietly and individually may reduce resistance.

SIGNS, KIOSKS, AND FLAGS

Regardless of how effective a lifeguard agency may be in providing local public education about the beach, many beach visitors are tourists, some from areas of the country or world with no beach. Others are simply unaware of local regulations or hazards, or oblivious to adverse conditions. Signs, kiosks, and flags can help.

Information kiosks at beach entrance points are an alternative to brochures and more detailed than signs. They avoid the need to print brochures and the litter that sometimes results. They can be detailed, offering in-depth explanations of various rules and local phenomena, including natural hazards. They are particularly effective where there are concentrated entry points to a beach that most people must walk by. They are less effective at beaches with diffuse entry points. Not everyone will take the time to visit a kiosk but those who do may inform other members of their party.

Signs can help gain voluntary compliance to regulations. When aware of the local regulations, most people will follow them. Signs detailing regulations, posted at beach access points, will typically greatly improve compliance. Positive phrasing may help reduce resistance to regulations. For example, a sign banning glass containers at the beach could state, "No Glass Containers," or it could state, "For Your Safety, Glass Containers Prohibited." The first is a purely regulatory message. The second indicates that the regulation exists for the benefit of the beachgoer. Informational signs should include pictograms as well as language, so that those who do not read English can understand the message. In addition to rules and regulations, signs can be used to convey safety information. Some lifeguard agencies also fly flags for this purpose.

Signs and flags, though a valuable component of a comprehensive prevention strategy, are limited in their effectiveness. Studies have demonstrated that a surprisingly small percentage of people pay attention to signs and warning flags. Others may not understand them or worse, may misinterpret their meaning. Of course, signs and flags cannot rescue people in distress. They are therefore no substitute for the staffing of properly trained and equipped lifeguards. Rather, they are one element of a comprehensive prevention strategy.

Credit: Kekai Brown

Credit: Desi Stoyanova

Warning Flag Guidelines

For decades, lifeguard agencies in the U.S. and around the world have employed flags to notify swimmers of conditions, to warn of hazards, to identify safer areas for swimming, and to notify beach users about regulated areas. Unfortunately, inconsistent use of flags limited their effectiveness. For this reason, in 2004 the International Life Saving Federation developed international guidelines for warning flags. These guidelines have been adopted, in part, by the International Standards Organization and endorsed by the United States Lifesaving Association. By consistently following these warning flag guidelines, lifeguard agencies can help ensure a universal understanding of their meaning and thus improve their effectiveness.

One of the greatest challenges to the effectiveness of warning flags is the general nature of the message they convey. For example, a flag may be flown intending to encourage caution by all beachgoers, due to rougher than normal conditions, but the enhanced hazard level will impact water users with varying skill levels differently. The novice may indeed need this caution, while the experienced swimmer may view the same conditions as nothing particularly challenging.

To be fully effective, the use of warning flags to notify the public of current hazard levels should be used consistently, based on objective, measurable criteria that can be logged and tracked, and then changed as conditions change. They should be accompanied by good public education efforts to explain the meaning of the flags flown. Flying flags that indicate a heightened level of hazard when conditions are relatively calm is similar to crying wolf and likely to cause people to ignore the flags on days when they carry a pertinent message.

Ocean conditions vary throughout the U.S. Conditions that may be considered relatively mild in some places may be seen as a significant safety threat in others. Therefore, in each area where warning flags are employed, the USLA recommends that specific local criteria be developed and that the public be clearly notified of those criteria. The first three flags (see table) are intended to provide general notification of overall conditions for a beach area. That is, if it is decided that water conditions present a "medium hazard" on a given beach, it should cover the entire beach, not a portion or area of beach. This does not prevent use of additional flags of the same warning level to accentuate the notification, but a single beach should not fly a yellow flag in one area and a red flag in another.

Some or all of the flags listed may be employed. It may be decided, for example, to adopt the first two, but none of the others. This is a local decision. However, the USLA strongly discourages use of flags that conflict with the meaning of those listed. This would negate the value of national consistency about the meaning of beach flags and confuse the public. In any case, with the exception of the double red, which indicates a closed beach, the first two should never be flown simultaneously. Where warning flags are flown, the public should be notified of their meaning via signs placed at multiple, conveniently located places. Examples might include beach access-ways, ramps, lifeguard towers, parking lots, and the flagpoles themselves.

Credit: Lindsey Gerkins

Lifeguard tower displaying red warning flag.

In some areas of the U.S. green flags are flown to indicate calm or mild conditions. The International Life Saving Federation (ILS) considered this carefully and decided not to adopt the green flag. The primary reason is the fact that there is always a potential hazard present and the view that it is best to notify people when conditions are unusually challenging, rather than suggesting that they are ever completely safe.

According to the ILS standard, "Flags may help reduce the incidence of injury and drowning, but cannot assist those in distress. Therefore, these flags are only to be used on beaches where lifesavers qualified to ILS standards are on duty. Flags are not an acceptable substitute for properly trained and equipped rescuers, but rather a tool for their use." The full ILS standard is available on the ILS website at: www.ilsf.org.

The following are specific definitions for each of the flags. Please refer to the accompanying graphic.

- Yellow—Medium hazard. Moderate surf and/or currents are present. Weak swimmers are discouraged from entering the water. For others, enhanced care and caution should be exercised.

- Red—High hazard. Rough conditions such as strong surf and/or currents are present. All swimmers are discouraged from entering the water. Those entering the water should take great care.

- Double red—Water is closed to public use.

- Purple—Marine pests, such as jellyfish, stingrays, or other marine life which can cause minor injuries are present in the water. This flag is not intended to indicate the presence of sharks.

- Red/yellow (halved red over yellow)—The area is protected by lifeguards. These flags may be used in pairs spaced apart to indicate a designated area or zone along a beach or waterfront that is most closely supervised or patrolled by qualified lifeguards, and where swimming and/or body surfing is permitted. These flags may be used singly to indicate that swimming is permitted in front of the area where the flag is flown and that the area is under the supervision of a qualified lifeguard.

- Black/White (quartered)—These flags may be used in pairs spaced apart to indicate a designated area or zone along a beach or waterfront that is used by those with surfboards and other non-powered watercraft.

- Yellow flag with central black ball—Surfboards and other non-powered watercraft are prohibited.

- Orange windsock—This cone shaped device is used to indicate the direction of offshore winds and to show that it is unsafe for inflatable objects to be used in the water.

- Red/White (quartered)—Emergency evacuation. Swimmers should leave the water because of an emergency. Emergencies may include, but are not limited to, dangerous marine creatures are present, such as a shark, the water is contaminated, or lifeguards need to perform a search of the water area, for example search for a lost child. (The double red flag may alternatively be appropriate.)

USLA Approved Beach Warning Flags.				
Beach Safety Flag	**Color**	**Meaning**	**Pantone (PMS)**	**Shape**
	Yellow	Medium hazard	PMS–124	Rectangle
	Red	High hazard	PMS–186	Rectangle
	Red over Red (Two flags)	Water closed to public use	PMS–186	Rectangles
	Purple	Marine pests present	PMS–266	Rectangle
	Red over Yellow	Recommended swimming area with lifeguard supervision	PMS–186 PMS–124	Rectangle with equal, parallel halves.
	Black and White (quartered)	Watercraft area	PMS–6 (black)	Rectangular flag with four equal rectangular quarters. Black upper left and lower right. White upper right and lower left.
	Yellow flag with Black ball	Watercraft use prohibited (e.g. no surfboards)	PMS–124 (yellow) PMS–6 (black)	Rectangular yellow flag with central black ball shape, 500mm diameter.
	Orange windsock	Offshore winds present, inflatable's should not be used	PMS–166	Cone shape 500mm at the hoist-tapering to 300mm x 1500mm long
	Red and White (quartered)	Emergency Evacuation	PMS–186 (Red)	Rectangular flag with four equal rectangular quarters. Red upper left and lower right. White upper right and lower left.

IDENTIFYING PRE-EVENTS

Before an accident occurs, any accident, there is a pre-event. For example, a person driving a car may spill hot coffee, causing them to swerve and collide with another car. Driving with hot coffee is the pre-event that ultimately resulted in the accident. The same is true of the beach environment. If lifeguards can identify pre-events, and effectively intervene, they may be able to prevent the accident from occurring. Identifying common pre-events also helps lifeguards key in on activity that is more likely to lead to injury or death, and provides greater lead time in preparing to respond to an emergency.

Every beach area has unique hazards, but also shares similar hazards with other beach areas. A pre-event to an accident at just about any beach might be a game of football in close proximity to other beachgoers. A lifeguard can easily imagine the possible outcome of a player going for a pass and colliding with another beachgoer, resulting in injury. At a surf beach, the pre-event might involve a person walking into a rip current. At a flatwater beach, the pre-event might be a ball being blown offshore, which the owner may then try to retrieve.

By identifying pre-events likely to result in accidents at a beach, lifeguards can prepare to intervene before the event takes place or, if unable to do so, to respond to the event early on. One way to identify pre-events is through a review of past accidents. What were the pre-events? Once that's known, lifeguards can be instructed to watch for them occurring in the future. Another way is to simply survey the environment. Is there an area that is always slippery at low tide? Are there rocks with shellfish attached that people swim near? By identifying these circumstances, lifeguards may be able to better focus their attention and to more effectively prevent accidents.

ON-SITE PREVENTIVE ACTIONS

For every rescue effected, responsible lifeguards log tens, if not hundreds of preventive actions. Timely preventive actions can reduce the number of rescues and injuries at a

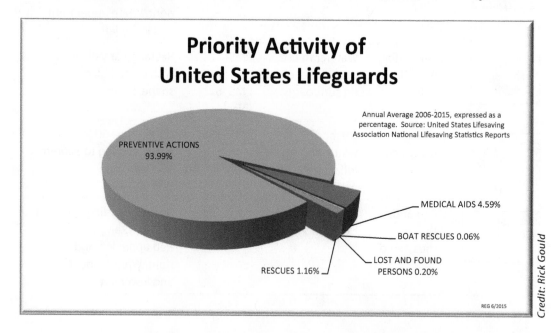

Priority Activity of United States Lifeguards

Annual Average 2006-2015, expressed as a percentage. Source: United States Lifesaving Association National Lifesaving Statistics Reports

PREVENTIVE ACTIONS 93.99%

MEDICAL AIDS 4.59%

BOAT RESCUES 0.06%

LOST AND FOUND PERSONS 0.20%

RESCUES 1.16%

REG 6/2015

Credit: Rick Gould

beach to manageable levels. They can be critical in the avoidance of injury, death, and property loss.

Preventive work starts when the lifeguard comes on duty. In includes a visual survey of the beach for anything unusual, identifying hazards and taking steps to mitigate them, posting daily information signs, and informing other lifeguards of notable observations. As the day progresses, preventive actions may include directing visitors away from a rip current area, counseling poor swimmers to move to shallow water, or discouraging people with flotation devices from entering deep water. All preventive actions should be noted in the lifeguard tower log. Each preventive action logged indicates that a lifeguard identified a safety concern and addressed it, or that a potentially hazardous situation was developing and mitigating action was taken. Logging activities, just as police officers and firefighters do, is one key way lifeguards can demonstrate the value of their work.

The use of recreational equipment often fosters a need for preventive actions. Boats and other water vehicles can pose a threat to swimmer safety. Inexperienced boaters and sailors can intrude on a swimming area, where they may strike people in the water. Other types of watercraft that can pose a danger are surfboards, bodyboards, flotation devices, and a wide variety of beach and water toys. Keeping them separated from those they might injure, where possible, is an important element of accident prevention.

Credit: San Clemente Lifeguards

Lifeguard offers alternate options during a preventive contact.

Although preventive actions are important in averting possible accidents and injuries, lifeguards must use good judgment in determining when an activity becomes too dangerous to permit. It's sometimes difficult to determine what activities should be considered unusually dangerous, since occasional injuries are an inherent part of physical recreation. For example, throwing a flying disc may be viewed as an innocent act of recreation on a little used area of beach or may be seen as a potentially dangerous activity on a crowded beach, which could lead to the injury of someone in the immediate vicinity. One good rule to follow is that whenever the recreational activity of one person significantly threatens the safety of another, it should be stopped or modified. A high speed boat in the vicinity of swimmers is an example of an unusually dangerous activity.

> Whenever the recreational activity of one person significantly threatens the safety of another, it should be stopped or modified.

Lifeguards who overuse preventive actions can create problems for themselves and their agencies. Not all accidents can be avoided by preventive actions and repeated warnings can become tiresome to both lifeguards and beach patrons. They may unreasonably restrict recreational opportunities, some of which inevitably involve a degree of risk. Constant warning and overly intensive supervision can also lead to unnecessary confrontations, repeated complaints, or active non-compliance with requests. Each agency, according to its own philosophy of preventive lifeguarding, should establish guidelines for the use of preventive actions by lifeguards. Once an agency's preventive action guidelines are established, lifeguards should receive ongoing in-service training on their practice to ensure consistency.

Lifeguards are experts on recognizing hazardous situations that beachgoers often overlook. Beachgoers view lifeguards as safety monitors of the area and expect lifeguards to take preventive actions to protect them. Fulfilling this role not only improves safety by reducing injury, but often has the added benefit of increasing lifeguard attentiveness by broadening the sense of responsibility. Nevertheless, the primary goal must always be toward preventing the most serious outcomes—death and injury. Therefore, an effort to terminate a beach game that poses a minor hazard, for example, may have to be delayed for a time if it would compromise drowning prevention needs.

SPECIAL OPERATION MODES

Natural hazards can be intensified during periods of high surf, wind, fog, and other weather conditions. Unusually high attendance can also make safety more difficult to maintain. During these periods, many agencies initiate special operation modes. These may involve modified operations, actual beach closings, or beach advisories.

Modified Operations

Certain water, weather, or crowd conditions may lead lifeguard supervisors to modify operations. This may include suspension of certain activities. For example, high offshore winds may lead to restrictions on the use of flotation devices to prevent users from being blown far from the beach. Beach activities that take up a large amount of space may be curtailed or restricted during periods of heavy beach congestion. At most agencies, the authority of lifeguards to suspend or restrict activities is detailed in the agency's policies.

Modified operations may also take the form of special lifeguard procedures. When rescue volume increases dramatically or weather draws unusually high crowds, lifeguard management must be prepared with plans to handle increased beach activity or hazards. Regular staffing levels may otherwise be completely overwhelmed in case of a heat wave, for example.

Could you pick out a person in distress in this crowd? Open water events require special preparation and staffing to ensure safety.

Open water swim competitions, triathlons and other water events also call for modified lifeguard operations. Lifeguard management must integrate preventive measures into event logistics when planning with the organizers. Clear criteria should be established for environmental conditions that would cause the event to be modified or cancelled. A maximum number of competitors and heat size may need to be determined. Adequate lifeguard surveillance is critical and is usually best done with some combination of powered and non-powered rescue craft. Specific action plans should be established in the event of rescue, medical, or search emergencies. The USLA has developed *Open Water Swimming Event Safety Guidelines*, which may be found at: www.usla.org/guidelines.

> **LEARN MORE**
>
> The United States Lifesaving Association has developed *Open Water Swimming Event Safety Guidelines*, which may be found at: www.usla.org/guidelines.

Beach Closings

Some conditions necessitate closing a beach area to swimming and other water activities. Examples include water contamination and lightning. Decisions to close beaches call for careful judgment, and are usually made only by supervisors following specific, predetermined criteria. Once these criteria have been met, patrol lifeguards are advised and warning signs or flags may be erected to inform beach visitors. Public address system announcements may also be broadcast regularly during such periods. In case of urgent, pending threats, care must be taken to avoid causing panic. Convey the message calmly, while emphasizing the need to evacuate in an orderly manner. Police presence may be helpful in cases that reluctance to leave is anticipated.

Advisories

Lifeguard agencies lacking the authority to close beaches may instead initiate special advisories. Advisories are also utilized by agencies with closure authority when it is believed that outright closure is unjustified, but strong caution should be urged. When criteria for advisories are met, lifeguards are notified and warning flags or notices may be erected to inform the public. Regular lifeguard operations continue, but lifeguards may be required to approach visitors to verbally warn them against participation in certain activities. When conditions stabilize, lifeguards are notified of the suspension of the advisory and warnings are removed.

Shark Sightings

The fear of sharks creates great concern on the part of beachgoers, but as explained in Chapter 17 (*Aquatic Life and Related Hazards*), the statistical chance of being injured (or even seeing) a shark is miniscule. Nevertheless, in some areas, shark encounters are more likely than in others. The USLA has developed *Shark Bite Prevention and Response Guidelines* to assist lifeguard agencies in dealing with shark sightings and shark bite incidents. This section is based on those guidelines. The most recent version of these guidelines can be found at: www.usla.org/guidelines.

Lifeguards should be trained to recognize sharks common to their area of responsibility and shark behavior that may be considered threatening. When behavior of a shark or sharks appears to present an unusual hazard to swimmers, an evaluation should be made as to whether it is appropriate to warn those involved in aquatic activity or to advise them to leave the water.

In areas where shark bites are known to occur with greater frequency than normal, posted signs may be appropriate to warn of the elevated hazard. If a shark bite occurs, people in the water in the area should be advised and encouraged to leave the water until such time as the immediate threat appears to have abated. Lifeguards in adjacent areas should be notified and advised to maintain heightened vigilance. Local ordinances may require that the water be closed. Since shark behavior is unpredictable, a closure may involve a fixed period of time or observed criteria, such as the absence of schooling fish that may have attracted shark activity. In the case of a shark attack where the shark repeatedly bites or pursues a human, the water in the immediate area should be cleared of all swimmers and kept clear until it can be determined that the immediate threat is over.

In beach areas where shark bites have historically occurred with a frequency that is significantly higher than normal, specific policies appropriate to local conditions are recommended. These policies should be based, in part, on consultation with shark experts and local emergency medical authorities.

APPROPRIATE OPERATIONAL HOURS

In some areas of the U.S., daily lifeguard hours of operation have traditionally been from morning (for example 8:00 a.m. or 9:00 a.m.) until dusk, while in other areas they have traditionally terminated at some time before dusk. These patterns developed in response to the time periods that beaches were most heavily used. Changing demographics and lifestyles in recent years however, have resulted in increased beach use in early morning and evening hours.

One way that lifeguard agencies have found to extend coverage into early morning and late evening hours is by use of staggered shifts. Under this approach, part of the staff arrives early and part arrives later in the day, with an overlap mid-day. In this manner, while morning and evening staff may be lower, mid-day staff remains at peak levels. Since beach attendance levels in morning and evening are lower than at mid-day in most areas of the U.S., this approach generally ensures that lifeguard staffing levels mirror daily variations in attendance levels, while broadening safety protection.

Another method lifeguard agencies have employed is to move from traditional eight hour shifts to 10 hour shifts. In this way, a 9:00 a.m. to 5:00 p.m. shift is extended to 7:00 p.m., for example. This normally means that the lifeguards so assigned will work four days a week, rather than five, but that the time of beachgoer protection is enhanced. A combination of 10 hours shifts and staggered scheduling can extend protection even more.

AFTER HOURS AND POST SEASON PREVENTION

Aquatic emergencies don't just happen during daylight hours or in summer. They also happen at night and during periods of the year when lifeguards are not on duty. Perhaps someone decides to go for an evening swim and becomes distressed, or a pedestrian slips and falls into the water, or a boater encounters problems. In any of these cases, lifeguards can provide essential lifesaving assistance if they can quickly respond to the scene.

In much of California, Florida, and Hawaii year-round open water lifeguard coverage is typical, with staffing levels varying in accordance with anticipated beach use. Other areas of the country may have coverage in place for seasons as short as eight weeks. Gaps in lifeguard coverage arise when lifeguards go off-duty, both at the end of the day and the season. Those gaps can be filled in several ways.

One strategy to ensure expeditious response of lifeguards to aquatic emergencies that occur after regular lifeguard staffing hours, as well as in off-season months, has been the organization of special response teams. Two California communities, Los Angeles County and San Diego, have found after hours call volume so high that they keep response teams of lifeguards on full duty 24-hours a day, 365 days a year. In San Diego, this includes a fully staffed 9-1-1 lifeguard dispatch center.

Other communities, unable to justify this level of staffing, have organized community resources, including lifeguards, emergency medical services, dive teams, fire departments, police departments, and allied services to respond in concert when the emergencies arise. Under these systems, an automatic response occurs, with roles of members of the team predesignated and designed to work under the *incident command system,* which is described in detail in Chapter 15 (*Emergency Planning and Management*). Some members may be off-duty, but prepared to respond via a call-back system when summoned, while others may be on regular duty.

These special response teams require the preparation of emergency operation plans that detail response protocols to ensure cooperation among responders who may not normally work together. In some instances interagency agreements, as well as amendments to local ordinances and state statutes, must be enacted to provide authority for response and to assure that liability and insurance protection is provided for responders.

One example of a year-round special response team in an area with seasonal lifeguard protection can be found in central New Jersey. Agreements enacted by adjacent communities (Avon-By-The-Sea, Bradley Beach, Neptune, Neptune City, Ocean Grove) created the Area Network of Shore Water Emergency Responders (ANSWER). This includes lifeguards as rescue swimmers; a dive team; rescue craft; and EMS, fire and police personnel. Unique dispatching protocols, including the cooperation of the United States Coast Guard's Shark River Lifeboat Station, provide the capability of year-round rescue swimmer response within a few minutes. Drills are conducted by the cooperating emergency management offices involving application of incident command system principles and rehearsals of various emergency operation plans.

Some communities address after hours and post-season aquatic emergencies through less structured callback systems, whereby off-duty rescuers are contacted and dispatched to emergency scenes. A common approach involves issuing pagers or two-way radios, or using text messaging to contact those willing and able to respond as needed. Other agencies maintain telephone numbers of lifeguards residing near the beach. These lifeguards must typically respond in private vehicles and may have little equipment available. This is, of course, a less certain method of summoning off-duty lifeguards.

For seasonal lifeguard agencies, a response plan can be particularly challenging during off-season months when lifeguards may not reside in the immediate area. Even in cases that lifeguards reside in close proximity, designated personnel may be away from the area and unable to respond when called. Nevertheless, for communities unable to justify the staffing of lifeguards throughout evening hours or year-round, a callback system provides some possibility of response of qualified rescuers. The chances of success are greatly improved when lifeguards in a callback mode are provided emergency response vehicles.

A fourth type of special response team involves communities without available trained lifeguards. In this case, personnel from other public safety services, such as police or firefighters, are trained in aquatic rescue. The USLA offers the *Aquatic Rescue Response Team* (ARRT) certification program to help ensure these teams are trained to adequate levels. Agencies which follow the minimum training requirements of this program can help ensure that anyone assigned to effect aquatic rescues has a minimum standard of training and preparedness required of this arduous work. This is especially important in the case of off-hours or post season rescue, which can involve darkness, colder water, and particularly challenging conditions.

LEARN MORE

For more information on the Aquatic Rescue Response Team certification program, visit the Certification section of: www.usla.org/certification.

The ARRT Certification Program is aimed at members of the agency selected to effect water rescue. For obvious reasons of safety, these are the only members of the agency who should be expected to attempt a rescue of a person or persons in distress in the aquatic environment. This does not however, prevent teams from including support personnel who do not meet the minimum standards, so long as they are not the people assigned to effect aquatic rescue.

In areas where USLA certified open water lifeguard agencies exist, the USLA strongly recommends that any aquatic rescue response team work in concert and under the general direction of that lifeguard agency. Likewise, aquatic rescue response teams are strongly encouraged to tap the resources of a USLA certified lifeguard agency in conducting training, setting policy, and recruiting prospective team members. Since the ARRT program is generally confined to response and rescue, it represents a level of certification more limited in scope than that of the minimum standard for lifeguard agencies.

> The United States Lifesaving Association recommends that all open water lifeguard agencies develop plans to address the need for lifeguard response during all hours of the day and all days of the year to ensure that rescuers qualified to USLA recommended levels can be summoned as needed during these periods

MAINTENANCE

Beach maintenance is an aspect of preventive lifeguarding. With the exception of routine maintenance of lifeguard facilities and equipment, lifeguards should not be assigned to general maintenance duties, but every lifeguard has a responsibility for monitoring the beach and water for potential hazards. For example, hazardous flotsam must either be removed by the lifeguard or reported immediately to beach maintenance crews for removal. At lake facilities, underwater plant growth should be monitored closely and removed as needed before becoming a hazard.

One purpose of routine beach patrols is to look for beach hazards, including broken glass, abandoned fire pits, and other sharp or hazardous materials. Lifeguard agencies must follow special procedures for protecting the public and themselves when any type of potentially hazardous material is found along a beach area, including medical waste and drums, or containers that may contain toxic waste.

If hazards cannot be immediately removed from the beach area, lifeguards should keep people away from the area until the hazard can be removed. As a standard practice, beach patrons should be kept at least 500 feet back from any potentially explosive device. The local bomb squad or fire department should be summoned for consultation and disposal.

At seasonally protected locations, beach and underwater areas should be

Credit: California State Parks Lifeguards

Lifeguards remove beach hazard.

closely inspected for hazards prior to each season. Winter storms often cause hazardous submerged objects or other shoreline damage to occur. Dry land environmental hazards include rock outcroppings, cliff areas, and similar topographical features which may cause injuries. Human made structures and improvements can also inflict injury. These may include bathhouses, piers, floats and docks, parking lots, playgrounds, boardwalks, cycle paths, and so forth. Lifeguards should make it their business to be aware of all the potential hazards in areas under their responsibility, attempting to mitigate them as appropriate.

FACILITY DESIGN

From conception to construction, beach facilities should be designed carefully with public safety in mind. This is particularly true for any improvements such as roadways, parking areas, walkways, and bathhouses. Facility designers and engineers should consider ways to overcome natural hazards, which may include the installation of railings, the removal of water hazards, and even redevelopment of the sandy beach and swimming area.

While most lifeguard agencies are not directly involved in design of public improvements at the beach—except those directly related to lifeguard activities—many lifeguard agencies have a role in designing safety into the beach environment. At flat-water beaches, swim lines may be installed to delineate the swimming areas, drop-offs, and other hazards. At surf areas, it is more difficult to install safety equipment in the water due to the dynamic conditions of tides and surf. Still, some beaches install swim lines, buoy markers, or flags to delineate swim areas or protected zones. To regulate boat traffic, appropriately marked buoys may be placed at the perimeters of swim areas to warn boaters to stay out. Facility design may also include special safety considerations regarding docks, floats, and any play equipment installed on or near the water, including slides, diving boards, or rope swings.

For a detailed discussion of lifeguard towers and related facilities, please refer to Chapter 24 (*Lifeguard Facilities and Equipment*).

CHAPTER SUMMARY

In this chapter we have learned that preventive lifeguarding is a primary responsibility of any lifeguard and should be considered in the broadest terms. Public education is one preventive strategy. We have learned about using educational materials, websites, recorded information lines, public appearances, social media, mass media, special events, and special programs to reach people before they arrive at the beach. We have learned about the use and enforcement of rules and regulations, including separating incompatible activities. The value of signs and flags has been discussed, including international warning flag standards. We have learned about pre-events to accidents and on-site preventive actions that can be taken. Additionally, we have learned about special operation modes, appropriate operational hours, after-hours and post season responses strategies. Finally, we have learned about the importance of beach maintenance and facility design to further minimize the possibility of injury.

DISCUSSION POINTS

- Identify the importance of educating the public about beach hazards before they arrive at the beach.
- Describe how a recorded information line is a benefit to public safety.
- Describe how a website can be used to promote water safety.
- Discuss one benefit of how the mass media can be used to disseminate information on beach safety.
- Explain why rules and regulations are necessary at beaches.
- List five incompatible activities commonly seen at the beach.
- Discuss the value of providing alternatives when enforcing beach rules.
- List five benefits of signs and flags.
- Discuss an example of a pre-event to a drowning.
- List five preventive measures lifeguards can perform to mitigate incidents on their beach.
- Identify one need for a lifeguard to implement a special operation mode.
- Describe the value of staggered shifts when extending lifeguard coverage.
- List three ways after hours and post season aquatic emergencies can be handled.
- Identify three examples of maintenance and facility design that can reduce the potential for injuries.

CHAPTER
10

Water Surveillance

In this chapter you will learn about techniques for effective water surveillance. This includes learning to evaluate beach users to help anticipate who might later need your help and learning to identify signs of distress. We provide techniques for effective water observation, which is critical if lifeguards are to rescue those in need in a timely manner. You will learn about establishing areas of responsibility and zones of coverage. You will learn how to maintain vigilance while assigned to surveillance duties; and you will learn about coverage systems.

CHAPTER EXCERPT

In emergency medicine there is often reference to a golden hour—the period of time after a traumatic injury during which effective medical intervention is essential to the saving of life. In open water lifesaving, that time frame is an unknown luxury. Lifeguards measure the opportunity for successful intervention not in minutes, but in moments.

To prevent injuries or successfully intervene before a fatal drowning occurs, the primary skill a lifeguard must employ is effective observation. This is not simply a question of vigilance. The ability to accurately assess and recognize the need for assistance is a skill which requires training, experience, tremendous concentration, and good judgment. Long before an emergency occurs, experienced lifeguards can sometimes predict when people at their beach will need assistance. Many of the visual cues lifeguards use to do this will be discussed in this chapter.

Unlike depictions commonly seen on television and in movies, it's not always obvious when a person is in distress or even experiencing panic in the water. This varies depending upon swimming skills, environmental conditions, and the individual. As detailed in Chapter 8 (*Drowning*) a non-swimmer who steps off a drop-off into water that is overhead will typically press their arms downward toward the surface of the water repeatedly in an ineffective effort to keep themselves afloat. A person with strong swimming skills caught in a rip current may swim against the current and make some progress, though the swimmer will tire much more quickly than would be the case were there no current. Some people submerge with no prior sign of a struggle. Lifeguards must be alert and adept at anticipating problems in order to recognize these sometimes subtle presentations of distress or panic, often without ever hearing a cry for help.

In emergency medicine there is often reference to a golden hour—the period of time after a traumatic injury during which effective medical intervention is essential to the saving of life. In open water lifesaving, that time frame is an unknown luxury. Lifeguards measure the opportunity for successful intervention not in minutes, but in moments.

RECOGNITION AND ASSESSMENT

In order to provide successful rescue of people in the drowning process, it's important to be able to identify signs that may help to indicate various drowning presentations. Once these signs are recognized and the situation is assessed, the lifeguard can respond appropriately.

Credit: Leslie Schwene

A lifeguard elevates to scan the water from the door of a lifeguard vehicle.

Dry Land Observation

Observation of beach visitors ideally begins before water entry. Lifeguards can use a number of clues and statistical facts to key in on people most likely to experience problems. While these clues can suggest those who may merit particular attention, lifeguards should not exclude any water user from their surveillance.

- **Age**—As explained in Chapter 8 (*Drowning*), those under 14 are particularly susceptible to drowning. Infants and toddlers can drown in water no deeper than their arm length due to their inability to easily get to their feet after falling over. Older children may lack the judgment or willingness to recognize their own limitations. Older adults may lack the physical strength necessary to fight an unexpected current or to quickly move away from a breaking wave. Any unattended child should be watched to ensure that there is adequate adult supervision.

Young children are particularly vulnerable to drowning.

- **Body Weight**—People who are overweight may become easily exhausted and are likely to be less able to move quickly to avoid a hazardous condition.
- **Skin Complexion**—If a light skinned person arrives at a sunny beach with no tan whatsoever or badly sunburned, it's an indication the person may not be a regular beachgoer and therefore may be inexperienced or unfamiliar with the open water environment. This is a particularly useful clue in an area frequented by tourists, since they may lack familiarity with local water conditions.

Credit: Eric Nurse

Lifeguards fitting U.S. Coast Guard approved lifejackets.

- **Intoxication**—Those demonstrating behavior suggesting a impairment of normal coordination due to alcohol or drugs should be viewed as potential rescue candidates. These behavioral cues include, but are not limited to: slurred speech, an unstable gait and erratic behavior. One study found that alcohol was detected in the blood in 30% to 70% of fatal drowning victims.[1] Individuals who are under the influence of alcohol (or drugs) should be discouraged or excluded from participating in aquatic activities.[2]

- **Flotation Devices**—Properly fitted and worn U.S. Coast Guard approved lifejackets are the only truly safe flotation devices. Even so, only Type I and Type II lifejackets have a design that can, in some cases (though not reliably), turn an unconscious victim face up. Reliance on flotation devices such as inflatable rafts, balls, and swim noodles can be very hazardous. While flotation devices are sometimes used by accomplished swimmers for purely recreational purposes, they are also used by weak and non-swimmers. Non-swimmers often use flotation devices to access deep water so that they can stay with friends who can swim; but if the non-swimming user of a flotation device becomes separated from the flotation device, submersion and death can occur very rapidly with little or no observable struggle. One of the most chilling sights to a lifeguard is a flotation device offshore with no one around it.

Parents of small children often give them flotation devices, believing they can pay less attention to their children as a result. It's not unusual to see very small children with inflated rings around their upper arms to assist in swimming, but if such devices deflate unexpectedly or fall off, death by drowning may be the

Credit: San Clemente Lifeguards.

No one should use a flotation device without immediate supervision unless the person has the skill to easily swim to shore from the area where the device is being used.

result. Some swimming areas ban use of flotation devices due to the danger they present. Since flotation devices can completely prevent a lifeguard from determining whether a person can swim at all, it should be assumed by the lifeguard that a person using a flotation device is a non-swimmer, until the lifeguard is certain that the person is competent without the device.

- **Improper Equipment or Attire**—In most climates, under normal, summerlike conditions, those planning to swim wear a swimsuit. Bodysurfers will usually equip themselves with swim fins. In cold water, experienced swimmers can be expected to wear a wetsuit to prevent loss of body heat and exhaustion. Any person who enters the water wearing street clothes should be watched carefully. Clothes offer a negative buoyancy factor and restrict swimming ability. While some people with strong swimming skills may simply lack the funds to purchase swimsuits, the wearing of street clothes while swimming is a possible sign of a lack of water knowledge. On the other hand, it's easy to dismiss from consideration those who arrive at the beach with an impressive array of equipment under the assumption that they must have extensive water skills, though this is no guarantee. Particular attention should be paid to those who have unusual difficulty donning their equipment or whose equipment fits poorly. The poorly fitting wetsuit, for example, may be borrowed by a non-swimmer from a friend who is a swimmer. Generally, variations from local norms may indicate lack of familiarity with the area or with water conditions.

- **Disability**—People with special needs who have physical limitations are increasingly using open water areas for recreation. Some areas furnish ramps for wheelchairs to help wheelchair users move across the beach. Other areas furnish beach wheelchairs specifically designed to move through the sand. Most physically challenged people know their limitations and make prudent decisions, just like other beachgoers; but just like other beachgoers, people with disabilities may overestimate their abilities. Given the same hazard (e.g. a rip current) and all other things being equal, a disabled person is likely to have more difficulty than a fully able-bodied person. It's important though, not to presume that a disabled person is an incompetent swimmer. Lifeguards will find that just like able-bodied swimmers, there are disabled swimmers who are very strong and some who are very weak. Lifeguards should make their evaluations on a case by case basis.

Distressed Swimmer Indications

Once beach visitors are in the water, a number of signs can signal problems. The following are several of these signs.

- **Double Arm Grasping**—Usually the head is tilted back, with the chin up, and victims press their arms downward toward the surface of the water repeatedly in an ineffective effort to keep themselves afloat. This is most typical in flatwater, but can happen anywhere when the non-swimmer is suddenly in water that is overhead.

- **Climbing the Ladder**—As the term implies, the action duplicates an upward crawling motion. It is also known as climbing out of the hole. Again, the chin is high with attention focused upwards. Neither action provides any forward mobility. This is typical of people with limited swimming skills.

- **Facing Shore**—The first indication of trouble from people beginning to feel anxious or experiencing distress is that they typically face shore or continually glance in

that direction. This is a very important clue for a lifeguard, particularly at a surf beach where most swimmers will be facing away from shore, watching for incoming waves. Even at a non-surf beach, groups of swimmers may be playing and facing each other, but one may be anxiously looking toward shore. In some cases an offshore platform may substitute for the safety of shore and the swimmer may instead look toward this platform.

- **Low Head**—Competent swimmers remaining in a stationary location hold their heads high. They tread water, breaststroke, or float on their backs. The chin is usually clearly above the water level. Swimmers whose heads hang low in the water demand a focus of attention to determine competency.

- **Low Stroke**—This normally accompanies a low head and can be visualized as a stroke that is very low to the water with the elbows dragging.

- **Ineffective Kick**—Under normal circumstances, a weak swimmer displays little or no kick. The lack of a break in the surface of the water should cue the lifeguard to a possible problem. In these cases, the body plane changes to a more vertical position and little forward progress is made. In some cases, an overly aggressive kick is also ineffective.

- **Lack of Forward Progress**—Any swimmer attempting to swim and making no forward progress is a distress indicator.

- **Waves Breaking Overhead**—Most people who are competent at swimming in the surf, dive under waves. When waves wash over a swimmer's head with no apparent attempt by the swimmer to duck under them, it's a strong indicator that this is a rescue candidate.

- **Catching Large Waves without Bodysurfing**—The primary goal of a swimmer in distress is to make it to shore. These people may be willing to pay the price of going over the falls of a large wave to accomplish this goal. Those who allow themselves to be carried by a breaking wave without making an attempt to bodysurf or duck under the wave should be eyed very carefully. Often, weak swimmers who go over the falls on a breaking wave find themselves disoriented and in worse shape than before. They can also be injured by striking bottom.

- **Hair in the Face**—The natural instinct of people in control of themselves in the water is to brush the hair out of their eyes. People who make no attempt to do so are usually under stress and concerned about other things—like keeping their heads above water.

- **Glassy, Empty, Wide, or Anxious Eyes**—Eyes can be a window to emotion. Experienced lifeguards can read the fatigue and fear in the eyes of a distressed or panicked person. Depending on distance, this may only be detectable with binoculars or not detectable at all.

- **Heads Together**—When other swimmers suddenly converge on a particular swimmer or simply cluster together, it may be an indication that one or more needs assistance. Often people in distress are unable to signal to a lifeguard or don't think to do so. Instead, they call to the people nearest to them for buoyancy or moral support. This request for aid may not be perceptible to the lifeguard, but the actions of other swimmers can suggest that a rescue is needed. When swimmers congregate for any significant length of time, the situation should be investigated with binoculars or in person.

- **Hand Waving**—Waving an arm, particularly in the water, is a natural sign of distress, perhaps because in water it is usually the only way to attract attention other than by yelling. The wave is a particularly important signal in the case of scuba divers who are generally taught in training that they should never wave unless they are in distress. This distress signal is regularly abused by people waving to friends ashore or nearby in the water. Although waving by swimmers in distress is a relatively uncommon occurrence, any person facing shore and waving should be assumed to be signaling for help until it can be ascertained that the person is fine. If it's determined there is no distress, lifeguards should make an effort to counsel those responsible about the appearance of an emergency that is created by a wave from the water, particularly in the case of scuba divers.

- **Fighting or Being Swept Along by a Current**—Currents are a major source of distress. Lifeguards should know the locations and characteristics of currents that regularly present themselves in the same place. At beaches susceptible to unexpected currents, lifeguards should be constantly on the alert for the appearance of currents and watch current areas with particular scrutiny. The first sign of potential distress in a current is the simple fact that a swimmer is moved by the current; however, it is impossible to know whether the swimmer will be able to resolve the problem until the swimmer comes to recognize the pull of the current and tries to get out of it. Even water-wise swimmers may initially attempt to fight the current and strong swimmers may succeed in doing so; but once a swimmer begins to fight a current stronger than the swimmer's skills, the drowning process has begun and will only be resolved in one of four ways:

  1. The current relaxes.
  2. The swimmer swims out of the current.
  3. The current circulates the swimmer back toward shore.
  4. The swimmer is rescued.

When a swimmer concludes that fighting the current will be futile and if the swimmer does not know to swim out of the current or feel comfortable treading water, panic will quickly set in. Therefore, as soon as a swimmer nears a dangerous current or becomes caught in it, experienced lifeguards begin preparing for a water rescue.

- **Swimming Away from Shore**—People swimming away from shore or staying offshore in large surf may be an indication of fear to return to shore. Regardless of surf size, this may also indicate suicidal intentions.

- **Erratic Activity**—Any activity out of the ordinary should always be given close scrutiny. It may be someone who is showing off or horsing around, or perhaps disoriented and out of touch with the reality of the environment. Show-offs intentionally take risks to attract attention and often find themselves in over their heads.

- **Clinging to Fixed Objects**—Swimmers who are fearful or in distress sometimes try to cling to piers, rocks, pilings, buoys, or other apparent objects of security. This is a sign that the person may either too frightened or too exhausted to continue swimming and demands close scrutiny. In addition, aquatic life such as barnacles and mussels attached to these objects can cause significant injuries that will need treatment.

EFFECTIVE WATER OBSERVATION

Firefighters, police, and lifeguards are all expected to respond expeditiously and efficiently once an emergency arises. Firefighters and police most often respond to emergencies based on reports from others who have observed a problem. While lifeguards also respond to such reports, people in trouble in the water usually can't telephone for help, so a basic responsibility of lifeguards is to watch over water areas to locate people in distress. In this sense, lifeguards report the emergencies *and* respond to them. In fact, the vast majority of lifeguard emergency responses are self-initiated and therefore effective water observation is a critical skill for lifeguards. Since drowning victims can't call 9-1-1, lifeguards must be able to observe, evaluate, identify, and respond to emergency situations quickly and effectively, without anyone telling them they're needed.

Observation Techniques

Because of the suddenness of aquatic emergencies, swimming areas should be scanned completely at least every 30 seconds. If this effort is impeded by attendance levels or unusual activity, additional assistance (backup) should be requested. Good observation techniques include the following basic points.

Visual Scanning

Observation of a swimming area is accomplished through visual scanning. The lifeguard visually sweeps the area, checking quickly on each swimmer or group of swimmers. At beaches where specific hazard areas regularly cause problems (e.g. rip currents, jetties, drop-offs) those areas demand particular attention. If a sign of distress is noted, further assessment of the person in apparent distress should take place. When a distress clue is noted that is less than conclusive, the lifeguard should further evaluate, but should not forget to keep scanning the remainder of the swimming crowd. The distraction posed by a person in possible distress should not exclude the possibility that others may need attention just as much or more. If two or more lifeguards are working together at a station, one lifeguard can alert another to a distress sign and study that person or group, while the other guard continues scanning. Using two-way communications (e.g. radio or telephone), lifeguards at different locations can contact each other for a second opinion on what is taking place or for a cross-check from another angle.

Scanning should continue, within reason, at all times that a lifeguard is on duty. Even when a lifeguard is talking to other lifeguards or a member of the public, lifeguards should keep their eyes on the water. Professional open water lifeguards take great

Credit: Diana Schwene

Continual scanning is an essential part of effective, preventive lifeguarding.

pains to avoid ever turning their back to the water, even when they are not specifically assigned to water observation. This is a core element of lifeguard professionalism. The more lifeguards facing the water and watching activity there, the less the chance of an unnoticed emergency. In some areas it is mandated by agency protocol.

In 2011, the Lifeguard Standards Coalition, a rigorous review co-sponsored by the USLA, the American Red Cross, and the YMCA of the USA, researched scanning techniques and many other lifeguard functions. They found that there was insufficient evidence to make a recommendation for or against specific lifeguard scanning techniques.[2] Similarly, in 2012 the Royal National Lifeboat Institution of the United Kingdom studied the question. They found that, "Lifeguards are equally efficient at detecting swimmers in trouble in the water regardless of the type of scanning pattern adopted." They recommended that, "Training programs for surveillance should not be specifically focused on training lifeguards to use prescribed scan techniques."[3]

The Lifeguard Standards Coalition did find that the evidence supports scanning all fields within a scanning zone using maximal head movements (versus only eye movements), and that lifeguards need to be aware that when individuals within a population are similar in appearance, it takes longer to identify potential drowning incidents. Distractions of all types have been shown to greatly affect the scanning process, so they should be minimized. Not surprisingly, the evidence also shows that the probability of identifying a target, in this case a victim needing assistance, decreases as the number of patrons increases, which is why prudent lifeguard agencies adjust staffing levels in accordance with crowd conditions.[2]

The Lifeguard Standards Coalition also identified some advice for lifeguard management. New lifeguards should be assigned to practice scanning with supervision and feedback. Generally, supervision and frequent encouragement improve the quality of scanning for all who are assigned to this task. A plan should be in place to provide backup support when rule enforcement duties or incidents affect the ability of a lifeguard to effectively scan. Finally, people assigned to scanning tend to observe what is in front of the total viewing area and spend less time searching areas to the right and left of the visual field. For this reason, lifeguard management should endeavor to assign lifeguards to observe the narrowest field of view possible.[2]

Use of Observation Tools

Binoculars are critical tools for assessing possible distress signs over distance and should be available to all lifeguards assigned to water surveillance. When a potential problem is observed through visual scanning, lifeguards can use binoculars to study the situation more closely. The use of binoculars can also let other lifeguards know that a lifeguard has noticed something and has momentarily ceased scanning to focus on a situation. However, since binoculars limit the field of vision in favor of focusing on a small area, they should not be used for continual scanning. Instead, lifeguards should scan with their eyes and use binoculars only when a distress clue warrants further investigation.

Spotting scopes and high power binoculars mounted on tripods are also used effectively by some agencies, particularly when large beach and water areas must be observed. These scopes sometimes have compass points on them so that coordinates for a boat in distress or the last seen point of a missing swimmer can be fixed.

Sunglasses are also critical observation tools. Polarized sunglasses are essential because they help eliminate glare, which can obscure large portions of swimming crowds. Sunglasses used by lifeguards should have frames that do not block peripheral vision. In addition to aiding in surveillance, sunglasses protect lifeguards, as we explain in detail in Chapter 16 (*Lifeguard Health and Safety*).

Overlap

Beaches with multiple lifeguard stations or locations generally divide the entire water area into sections or zones, but it is critical to provide for some type of overlap area between stations to avoid uncovered areas. A standard principle of overlap for a contiguous beach area with several towers is that each lifeguard is made responsible for the water area to the next staffed lifeguard station on either side. In this way, the lifeguards in each tower are equally responsible for the water area between them. One important reason for this overlap is that it is very difficult to clearly define boundaries in the water. It also creates a sense of shared responsibility and doubles the level of protection of swimmers in the area.

Lifeguards should never worry that they might be watching people in another lifeguard's assigned area or ignore distress signs there. Lifeguard administrators should take care to ensure that all lifeguards feel a sense of responsibility for the entire beach area so that egos do not result in a delayed response or lack of response due to fear of embarrassing a fellow lifeguard who may not see a person in distress. A strong sense of group responsibility is essential to effective open water lifeguarding.

Cross-Checking

Glare caused by the sun can obscure large swimming crowds and effectively blind lifeguards to a particular water area. Lifeguards must utilize a system of cross-checking to counteract this problem. Whenever a lifeguard assigned to water observation is unable

Glare can be a serious problem.

to see an assigned water area for any reason, lifeguards in adjacent locations, should be advised to cross-check. On a beach with several staffed lifeguard towers, this is easily accomplished. In other cases, an alternate method is to post a lifeguard in a vehicle or on foot to cross-check areas with serious glare. At beaches where glare is experienced, standard operating procedures should be developed to address the problem. Glare aside, cross-checking is also used for purposes of getting a second opinion from another lifeguard as to the need for rescue.

AREA OF RESPONSIBILITY

All lifeguard services should define an *area of responsibility* as clearly as possible. The area of responsibility is defined as that area of the water, beach, and related facilities where lifeguards are expected to be primary responders. The defined area of responsibility generally includes:

- **Water Areas**—Lifeguards are typically expected to be responsible for all water areas offshore of defined protected beaches, including those above and below the water surface.
- **Offshore Limit**—Some agencies define an offshore limit for lifeguard services, particularly for situations that may involve boating accidents a good distance from shore. If such a limit is defined, lifeguards should be instructed on what other agency or agencies should be summoned if an emergency beyond the offshore limit is observed.
- **Beach Area**—Most lifeguard agencies are responsible for observing beach areas and responding to emergency situations there.
- **Adjacent Facilities**—Many lifeguard agencies, while not actually responsible for observing activities in adjacent facilities, such as parking areas and bathhouses, are subject to calls to emergencies that may occur in those areas.
- **Off-Site Areas**—Off-site areas may include facilities, roadways, business districts, hotels, and residences that are not actually connected to the defined beach facility or park. Some lifeguard agencies are responders to emergencies in these areas due to their relative proximity and ability to provide immediate response.

Regardless of the defined area of responsibility, lifeguards must avoid tunnel vision. While lifeguards should concentrate on the assigned area of responsibility, they can provide essential reporting in cases of emergencies or other problems in adjacent areas.

Zones of Coverage

Once the overall area of responsibility has been defined, priority zones should also be defined. This provides lifeguards with a sense of the most important areas upon which they should concentrate. The three major priority zones, in order of importance, are usually as follows:

- **Primary Zone**—The water is a lifeguard's top priority. The primary zone for each lifeguard station is the water area for which the lifeguard is personally responsible. On beaches with several towers, the primary water zone generally extends to the next staffed lifeguard station on either side. This zone automatically extends when lifeguards in adjacent stations are on a response or the adjacent station is closed.

- **Secondary Zone**—This usually includes adjacent water areas (including primary zones of other lifeguards), the beach, immediately adjacent park areas, the sky, and the water to the horizon. Less frequent scanning of this zone is required, but the lifeguard checks this zone regularly. If the adjacent tower lifeguard is occupied, that part of the secondary zone becomes primary.

- **Tertiary Zone**—Generally the tertiary zone includes all other areas within sight of lifeguards. It could include adjacent streets and parking lots, for example. This zone is scanned least frequently.

MAINTAINING VIGILANCE

Lifeguards are, by their very nature, athletes. They must be physically capable of responding quickly and effectively in arduous conditions to save the lives of others. Water surveillance however, is a tedious and sedentary job, with which many athletes struggle. It's both monotonous and stressful. A lifeguard may scan for hours, days, or weeks without observing anything requiring a critical response. Then, a subtle visual clue may indicate a serious, life-threatening emergency. If the lifeguard is not alert, it may be missed and a life lost. Maintaining vigilance is therefore a vital issue for lifeguards. The Lifeguard Standards Coalition reviewed all available research on vigilance. The information in this section relies primarily on the coalition's findings.[2]

- **Sleep Deprivation**—Sleep deprivation decreases vigilance even after a recovery night of sleep, so it is important for lifeguards to have a full night's sleep before assuming lifeguard duties—otherwise the ability to spot victims in distress may be compromised.

- **Recreational Drug Use**—The use of recreational drugs affects vigilance, even when the user is not under the influence. It has been scientifically determined that there is a residual, negative impact on vigilance. So the use of recreational drugs by lifeguards negatively impacts lifeguarding.

- **Caffeine**—The consumption of caffeinated, *non-sugared* drinks has been demonstrated to benefit vigilance, but there is no evidence that sugared drinks are beneficial.

- **Sleep Apnea**—For reasons similar to sleep deprivation, people with untreated sleep apnea have been shown to have a decreased ability to maintain vigilance.

- **Heat**—Heat has been shown to negatively impact vigilance, so reasonable steps should be taken to protect lifeguards from high temperatures. These can include providing sun protection for outdoor activities (e.g. sun shades, protective clothing), air conditioning towers, adjusting indoor temperatures, and decreasing the length of shifts when temperatures are unusually high.

- **Hydration**—Ensuring that lifeguards stay well hydrated can be expected to reduce drops in vigilance associated with heat.[4]

- **Screening**—Because sleep apnea and drug use negatively impact vigilance, screening for them and taking other steps to reduce or eliminate the impacts can be expected to improve overall vigilance of a lifeguard agency.

- **Time on Task**—Vigilance has been repeatedly shown to decline over time. The USLA encourages limiting continuous assignment of lifeguards to surveillance duties to one hour, followed by a break of at least 15 minutes. Even so, the Lifeguard Standards Coalition's research revealed that supervision and regular encouragement during each 30 minutes of watch improve vigilance; so supervision of lifeguards that includes regular contact and encouragement can be expected to beneficially impact vigilance.[2]

* **Exercise**—*Aerobic* exercise can positively impact a subsequent vigilance task, so lifeguard management should encourage it and lifeguards should avail themselves of the opportunity when possible. Ideally, this involves training in lifeguard skills such as running, swimming, and use of rescue boards, for example.

* **Background Noise**—Noise has been demonstrated to negatively impact vigilance. The impact of listening to music or a radio broadcast while involved in water surveillance should be carefully considered. During times of very low beach and water activity, this may have a beneficial effect of relieving boredom. (If lifeguards are permitted to listen to music or radio broadcasts, volume should be kept low and earphones should never be used.) Research suggests however, that as sensory information increases, there may be deterioration in the lifeguard's concentration span and scanning ability.[2, 4] Therefore, particularly during busy periods, music and radios may negatively impact vigilance. This can also interfere with the ability to hear two-way radio transmissions or calls for assistance from the public.

* **Distractions**—The use of computers, mobile phones (talking, texting, viewing), reading materials, and the like are inappropriate *at any time* for lifeguards assigned to water surveillance. Use of electronic voice communication tools, such as wired telephones, mobile phones, and two-way radios should be restricted to conversations necessary for lifesaving duties. Carrying on personal conversations through these means while assigned to water surveillance poses an unacceptable distraction.

Lifeguard remains vigilant during surveillance duties.

When a lifeguard assigned to water observation must interrupt that task to provide medical attention, preventive services, or for other essential reasons, lifeguards in neighboring towers should be advised, so that they can help maintain continuous surveillance. In some cases, it may be appropriate to send backup lifeguards.

Even when lifeguards are given frequent breaks, boredom can negatively impact vigilance. One approach that seasoned lifeguards employ is running imaginary scenarios through their minds. If the man jogging had a cardiac arrest, what would I do? What if that boat turned suddenly toward the surfline? What if one of those three people on the inflatable raft fell off and immediately disappeared? Running these imaginary scenarios has a dual value. It helps the lifeguard remember key skills and helps relieve boredom. The lifeguard must be careful though, not to allow this process to devolve into daydreaming, which would negatively impact vigilance. Running scenarios is an active and intentional mental process.

Staying vigilant is clearly essential to effective surveillance. No matter how effective a lifeguard's scanning techniques may be, if the lifeguard is daydreaming or allowing distractions to interfere the best scanning techniques will be rendered useless. Lifeguards should use the information in this section to develop their own approach to ensuring they remain ever vigilant in watching over those who are counting on their protection. Remember, an emergency can arise at any moment.

COVERAGE SYSTEMS

Coverage systems are plans for providing protection to an area of responsibility. The development of a coverage system is a complex task for any emergency service. A fire chief, for example, must consider the size of the community served, the types of fires expected, the size and configuration of buildings and structures that must be protected, concentrations of commercial and residential areas, and other related factors. With that information, fire department managers can determine the staffing level and deployment needed to provide an adequate level of preparedness and response. This is a coverage system.

Like other emergency services, lifeguard agencies must develop coverage systems. Considerations in this process include beach and water attendance, the size of the facility, the area of responsibility, the beach season, water and marine life hazards, the scope of the service, past rescue experience, and so forth. These factors help determine the number of lifeguards, their deployment, and daily scheduling.

Basic Coverage Principles

Basic coverage principles include the following:

- **Area of Responsibility Defined**—The first step to creating a coverage system is a clear understanding of the area of responsibility.
- **Operation Period Defined**—This includes the days of the year lifeguards will be on duty and the times of day coverage will be provided.
- **Protection Provided with No Break in Service**—As with other emergency services, once lifeguard protection begins, using established hours, protection must continue uninterrupted. While some lifeguard services may reduce coverage due to lower than expected crowd conditions, coverage should not be completely eliminated for routine breaks or meal periods. Instead, backup coverage should be provided for this purpose. It is an unacceptable practice for all lifeguards on duty at a beach to leave the beach unprotected for a lunch break. If supervisory personnel determine that coverage should be terminated early due to weather conditions or extraordinarily low attendance, beach patrons should be notified.
- **Working Conditions Are Reasonable and Clearly Understood**—In many areas, working conditions are established through adherence to labor laws and employee contracts. Nonetheless, the paramount concern is that an atmosphere is maintained that ensures safety for both the employee and those being protected.

Example Coverage Systems

As examples of how basic coverage principles are followed, the following are four different fictional lifeguard operations.

Single Site Operation

Whispering Willows State Park is a small day area located on a pond. The area is open from 9:00 a.m. to 8:00 p.m. daily and gates control access to the 60-car parking lot. The beach is approximately 100 yards long and is protected from two lifeguard stands.

Six lifeguards are assigned to work at Whispering Willows, each working a 40-hour week during the summer season, composed of five eight hour days. Two lifeguards have Monday and Tuesday off, two have Wednesday and Thursday off, and two have Friday and Saturday off. With this schedule, there are four lifeguards working Monday through Thursday, five on Friday and Saturday, when attendance increases, and all six on Sunday, the busiest day.

Credit: Adam Abajian

The lifeguards cover the beach from 9:00 a.m. to 8:00 p.m. on a rotating schedule. Each day, at least two lifeguards report to work at 9:00 a.m. and work to 5:00 p.m. Then, at least two report at noon and work to 8:00 p.m. On Friday, Saturday, and Sunday the additional lifeguards arrive during shifts in between, such as 10:00 a.m. to 6:00 p.m. Coverage is thereby maintained from 9:00 a.m. to 8:00 p.m., seven days each week, without a break in service. Backup is available at all times. The lowest level of coverage exists during the early morning and late evening hours when attendance is lowest. The greatest coverage is provided midday, when attendance is highest.

Multi-Tower, Independent Operation

Lengthy Beach is a moderate-sized coastal town with a one-mile protected beach. The Lengthy Beach Patrol has established five lifeguard towers along the beach, providing continuous coverage over the one mile beach for the summer season. Fifteen lifeguards work 40-hour weeks in addition to supervisory staff, with three lifeguards assigned to each tower on a schedule very similar to that of Whispering Willows. On any given day, two lifeguards will work each tower and provide breaks for each other during the course of the operation day.

Multi-Tower Operation With Backup

Wide Island County provides lifeguard services over three miles of sandy beach from 12 towers during the summer. Twenty-one seasonal lifeguards are hired for forty hours each week, covering the beach from 9:00 a.m. to 6:00 p.m. Each tower operates with a single lifeguard. Two lifeguard supervisors work daily from vehicles to provide backup and oversight.

Tower Zero Operation

Surf City, a major population area in a warm climate, operates a lifeguard service year round covering ten miles of beaches. There are several large, three story towers, with an enclosed observation deck. These towers have a wide area of view, while numerous smaller, numbered towers are spread along the beaches. During the busier season, the operation at Surf City is very similar to Wide Island County. The smaller towers are staffed by seasonally employed lifeguard personnel. The main observation towers are not numbered (thereby the reference to "Tower Zero"). They are used primarily for overall observation and supervision of the area and are staffed by more senior personnel who coordinate responses and backup. The seasonal lifeguard personnel are relieved and backed up by mobile lifeguard units dispatched by lifeguards at the main tower.

In high season, lifeguards are staffed from dawn to dusk on staggered schedules. The first lifeguards on duty staff only the main observation towers. Those not assigned to water observation prepare equipment and patrol the beach in vehicles. As midday approaches and more lifeguards arrive for their shifts, the smaller, numbered towers are opened, with preference given to those known to have high rescue activity and those furthest from the main tower. During midday all towers are staffed. As evening approaches, the smaller towers and those with the lightest crowds are closed one by one until all are closed. A lifeguard remains on duty in Tower Zero until the end of scheduled lifeguard protection.

During months of lower attendance, the small towers are not staffed and all observation is provided from the larger, fixed towers. From these towers, a smaller staff of lifeguards can observe the entire beach area using powerful binoculars and communicate with beach visitors over a public address system. They patrol the beach regularly in mobile lifeguard units and when trouble is noticed, mobile lifeguard units are dispatched to the scene.

Credit: San Clemente Lifeguards

The Tower Zero system requires a main station with a commanding view.

CHAPTER SUMMARY

In this chapter we have learned how to recognize and assess signs that may help indicate drowning presentations. That includes observations before people even enter the water, as well as signs of people in distress in the water. We have learned methods of effective water observation. We have learned that all lifeguard agencies should define the area of responsibility and zones of coverage. We have learned about the challenge of maintaining high levels of vigilance and ways to do so. We have learned about coverage systems and have seen some examples of these systems.

DISCUSSION POINTS

- List five examples of how to identify a person in distress.
- Outline some of the indications of beachgoers on land that may suggest the need for future assistance in the water.

- Explain what the double arm grasping or climbing the ladder indicate.
- Explain why it is important to scan the entire water area every 30 seconds.
- List three common observation tools used by lifeguards.
- List the values of overlap and cross-checking.
- Explain why areas of responsibility must be defined.
- Explain the concept of zones of coverage and how it used for water observation.
- List five techniques that have been demonstrated to help maintain vigilance.
- Identify three basic coverage principles.

CHAPTER

11

Communication Methods

I n this chapter you will learn about methods lifeguards use to communicate among themselves, with allied public safety agencies, and with the public. You will learn about electronic communication methods, including two-way radios, wired telephones, mobile phones, public address systems, and the internet. You will learn about visual and audible communication methods. And you will learn about the 9-1-1 system.

CHAPTER EXCERPT

The USLA strongly recommends that open water rescuers use two-way radios to communicate in the beach environment. Alternative methods, such as whistles, are not recommended as a primary method of rescuer to rescuer communication.

A fundamental measure of any emergency service is its ability to communicate quickly, broadly, effectively, and efficiently in a wide variety of conditions. It is the nature of lifeguard services that personnel are spread over large areas as they monitor and respond to problems in the beach environment. This creates a challenge for communication which must be met.

COMMUNICATION NEEDS

All lifeguard services should have the capability of communicating effectively in the following three areas:

- **Internal Communication**—Communication among lifeguards is an integral aspect of effecting a rescue. An initial alert to others requires immediate, effective communication. During a rescue, communication among lifeguards onshore is needed to determine what backup is needed for the lifeguard on the rescue, if any. Lifeguards in emergency vehicles, rescue boats, and on foot need to be updated and directed. Effective communication is essential during periods of emergency response, for maintaining effective coverage of supervised areas during normal operations, and for routine business in a work environment where lifeguards are necessarily widely dispersed. When lifeguards need backup, whether in emergency or non-emergency incidents, they need to be able to quickly and effectively request it.

- **External Communication**—Lifeguards must be able to communicate effectively with other emergency services, including neighboring lifeguard agencies, police, fire, rescue, and emergency medical services. In some areas, other services may also be of importance, such as the U.S. Coast Guard and any other source of rescue helicopters. For routine communication, lifeguards may need to contact animal control providers, tow trucks, child welfare workers, and so on.
- **Public Communication**—Lifeguards need to pass information efficiently and understandably to beach visitors in order to provide directions during emergencies or approaching weather, to move people out of dangerous areas (preventive lifeguarding), to help locate missing persons, and to provide important information about general beach conditions.

COMMUNICATION METHODS

There are two general types of communication systems used by lifeguard agencies across the U.S.—electronic and non-electronic.

Electronic Communication Methods

The most effective form of routine and emergency communication is electronic communication. Electronic communication systems include two-way radio systems, mobile telephones, wired telephones, data sharing systems, and public address systems. Effective electronic communication systems allow for the transmission of a message over long distances with full clarity.

Two-Way Radios

The USLA strongly recommends that open water rescuers use two-way radios to communicate in the beach environment. Alternative methods, such as whistles, are not recommended as a primary method of rescuer to rescuer communication. There are several reasons that two-way radios are a highly desirable tool for lifeguard communications. Like the telephone, the two-way radio allows for two-way conversation over long distances. While whistles, for example, may allow some limited information to be transmitted within audible range, the two-way radio can normally transmit well beyond this range and lifeguards using a two-way radio system can be very specific about their circumstances and their needs.

Unlike a wired telephone, when a lifeguard must leave the stand for a medical aid or warning to a beach visitor, the two-way radio allows a lifeguard to stay in communication at all times, able to request specific forms of backup if a problem develops.

Credit: Lindsey Gerkins

Two-way radio for lifeguard communication.

This is also helpful for supervisory personnel who can direct operations from a distance based on information provided.

Unlike a mobile phone, a radio frequency serves as a constant conference call in which all members of the organization are immediately made aware of a message and can respond at will. For example, if a lifeguard sends a rescue alert, all adjacent lifeguards with radios are immediately made aware of this, as are backup resources. Attention is immediately directed to the area of need.

At agencies where radio traffic is high, multiple channels are useful to segment radio traffic in geographic areas of the operation and to separate emergency radio traffic from routine business traffic. If possible, additional tactical radio channels can allow moving major incidents to a separate channel during the incident, avoiding conflicts with other operations. For example, in cases of a search and rescue operation for a missing swimmer, it can sometimes be helpful to move the responders to a separate channel, thus allowing other lifeguards who are continuing to address routine public safety needs to continue to communicate without distraction or radio interference.

The most effective radio systems include the ability to converse with other local emergency service providers. This can be of tremendous benefit in emergencies, allowing direct communication with responding resources and continual updates. It is particularly useful when the incident command system is invoked. Very inexpensive radios which allow direct communication with U.S. Coast Guard resources and private vessels are available from marine supply outlets.

Hard hull rescue boats may have communication gear similar to lifeguard emergency vehicles.

Credit: San Diego Lifeguard Service

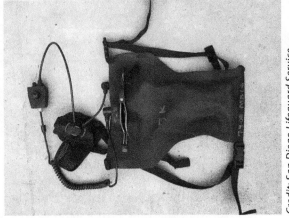

One approach for PWC communication is a waterproof bag for the two-way radio, with a push to talk headset.

Credit: San Diego Lifeguard Service

The effective use of lifeguard rescue boats requires direct communication with lifeguards ashore. For small boats, like personal watercraft (PWC), waterproof radios or watertight pouches are needed. Waterproof headsets can allow operators to communicate hands-free. Larger boats are normally outfitted with mobile radios designed for vehicles.

Some lifeguard agencies use *codes* while speaking on the radio. Many people are aware of the radio code "10-4", which generally means an acknowledgment of a message received.

This is one of the 10-codes, so-called because they start with the number 10. There are many others, which vary from agency to agency and from state to state. The rationale for codes is two-fold. First, they can replace commonly used phrases; thereby reducing the amount of time spent transmitting a message. This is particularly valuable in an emergency when seconds count and radio traffic needs to be limited. For example, the term *Code 4* is used in some areas to mean, "no further assistance needed." In this case, a two syllable code replaces an eight syllable phrase. The second major value of codes is that they can help mask the meaning of transmissions to prying ears. For example, if an offshore rescue boat recovers the body of a missing swimmer, it is of immediate interest to all lifeguards, but by using codes, most beach patrons who might overhear the radio traffic would not know what the radio transmission means.

While these are valuable reasons to use radio codes, a downside is that they can be difficult to learn and remember. In addition, for lifeguard agencies that often communicate on the radio with other agencies, codes can be confusing. The U.S. Coast Guard, for example, does not use codes. Lifeguards used to using codes may have a difficult time transitioning between a conversation with an agency which uses codes and one which does not. The alternative to codes is known as *clear text*, i.e., simple language. Effective clear text requires that lifeguards carefully consider their words before transmitting and use the fewest words possible to get the message across as clearly as possible. For example, rather than stating, "I would like to ask for some additional lifeguard assistance here at Tower 4," the lifeguard could state, "Request backup, Tower 4."

The U.S. Coast Guard typically uses *clear text* to communicate over the radio, since they communicate via radio with many different agencies and with civilians.

Two-way radios can send and receive messages, but can only do one or the other at once. When one person is speaking, others normally cannot do so. Therefore, it's important that before a lifeguard transmits, the lifeguard confirms that another conversation is not already taking place. As well, the lifeguard should take great care to make transmissions brief and to the point, so that if a more urgent message must be broadcast by someone else, that person can use the radio frequency for the higher priority message.

Telephones

The first electronic communication method acquired by most lifeguard agencies was the wired telephone. All lifeguard agencies should have access to telephones for communication with outside resources, and to allow the public to call for assistance or with questions. Many lifeguard agencies also use telephones for communication among towers or stands.

Mobile telephones allow for telephonic communication without the need for wiring. They can be a very useful tool for lifeguards and lifeguard supervisors, particularly in major emergencies and in areas where a wired telephone is prohibitively costly. In most beach communication among lifeguards however, the two-way radio is a better alternative because of the open broadcast of messages it provides that allows for simultaneous notification of all users.

Another use of mobile phones involves communication with off-duty lifeguards. This is obviously valuable for routine communication, but some lifeguard agencies use bulk texting of staff to notify off-duty lifeguards of urgent, unexpected needs for lifeguard staff.

We have noted in Chapter 10 (*Water Surveillance*), but repeat here for emphasis, that the use of electronic communication tools, such as wired telephones, mobile phones, and two-way radios, should be restricted to conversations necessary for lifesaving duties. Carrying on personal conversations (whether by voice or texting) through these means, while assigned to water surveillance, poses an unacceptable distraction.

Members of the public will sometimes observe emergencies or other incidents requiring lifeguard response. If they cannot immediately speak with a lifeguard face-to-face they will most likely call 9-1-1. It is therefore essential that lifeguard agencies have excellent relationships with the 9-1-1 operations center that services their area to ensure that emergency calls requiring lifeguards are handled appropriately. This can be challenging for a variety of reasons. Many calls about beach and water emergencies come from mobile phones and ascertaining the location of the caller can sometimes be very challenging. Beachgoers reporting emergencies are often tourists unfamiliar with the area who have difficulty explaining the location. Operators at 9-1-1 centers commonly rely on street addresses, but there may be none available near a beach incident. And 9-1-1 operators may be unfamiliar with the area themselves.

Once the 9-1-1 operator receives a call describing the need for response, relaying the information to the proper emergency provider can generally take one of three forms depending on protocols and agency capabilities: call transfer, call referral, or direct dispatch. The simplest system is direct dispatch. This is primarily utilized by smaller communities with a central dispatch center for all emergency services. Under this system, the central dispatch center receives the 9-1-1 call, gathers pertinent information, and directly dispatches the emergency service provider, typically by two-way radio.

Credit: Pamela Schwene

Call referral and call transfer are used in areas where emergency services maintain separate dispatching centers. Under call referral, the initial 9-1-1 operator elicits necessary information from the caller about the emergency, then calls the appropriate emergency provider by telephone and advises of the details. This system requires expertise on the part of the 9-1-1 operator about what details to elicit from the caller, so that the emergency service will have what they need. Call transfer is a system under which the 9-1-1 operator makes a quick initial assessment, decides which is the most appropriate emergency provider, and immediately transfers the caller to that agency for further call screening. A dispatcher for the agency that will ultimately respond to the emergency thereby has the opportunity to speak directly to the caller about details of the emergency.

Credit: San Diego Lifeguard Service

A lifeguard dispatch center with full 9-1-1 capabilities.

In some areas, lifeguard agencies are designated and equipped as secondary public safety answering points, with dedicated phone lines and technology that allows identifying caller location. In these cases, 9-1-1 operators use a dedicated call transfer system. For most lifeguard agencies though, another method will be used. All lifeguard agencies should have clear protocols worked out well in advance of how emergency calls requiring lifeguard assistance will be handled. This should include determining how emergency calls will be handled that come in during hours of the day lifeguards are not on duty. Will there be a call-back system? Will lifeguards be called on mobile phones? Whatever the system, 9-1-1 operators need to know.

For routine calls from the general public and from other public safety agencies, lifeguard agencies should have a published phone number. This helps lessen the likelihood of overuse of 9-1-1 for nonemergency inquiries and it allows for routine business to be conducted by phone.

Data Sharing Systems

Data sharing systems allow lifeguards to communicate key information among themselves and with allied agencies. For example, incoming paramedics can receive key information on patients. This avoids duplication of efforts in recording key information, avoids the need for voice communication, and assists with documentation. This is especially true in electronic patient care reporting (ePCR).

Public Address Systems

Public address (PA) systems are electronic voice amplification devices used primarily to provide information or direction to beach visitors. Public address systems can be installed along beaches, on towers, on vehicles or vessels, or can be carried as portable megaphones. Public address systems can be of great value in preventive lifeguarding. People in a rip current, even far from shore, can be advised how to extricate themselves. Lifeguards offshore involved in rescue activity, swimming or on rescue boards for example, can be updated and directed. Beachgoers can be advised of approaching bad weather.

In missing persons searches the PA can be invaluable. A single broadcast of the description of a small child can immediately turn the entire beach crowd into a search team. If an area must be suddenly closed to conduct an emergency search or evacuated, the public address system conveys the message broadly and immediately. Public address systems are also used in some areas to remind beach users of general regulations in an effort to gain compliance without personal contact. At the end of the day, the PA system can be utilized to advise beach users, even those swimming offshore, of the departure of lifeguards.

One pitfall to avoid with the PA is overuse. People visiting the beach are trying to relax. They want to avoid some of the stresses of everyday life. Constant use of a PA system can be annoying and can ultimately cause beach users to "tune out" the broadcasts, so that when a truly important message is broadcast it is ignored. Lifeguard services with PA systems are wise to develop guidelines aimed at moderating use.

Credit: Devyn Bisson

Lifeguard vehicle equipped with a PA system.

The Internet

The internet allows lifeguard agencies to provide a wide range of information to beachgoers and those considering beach visits. Some will even view an agency's website while they are at the beach on their mobile phone or tablet. Please refer to Chapter 9 (*Preventive Lifeguarding*) for details on effective use of the internet.

Non-Electronic Communication Methods

Arm Signals

The use of arm signals among lifeguards provides an essential form of communication when electronic communication is impractical. For example, a lifeguard swimming offshore usually lacks access to a two-way radio and certainly to a telephone. Basic arm signals are an essential component of a lifeguard communication system. The USLA has adopted four basic signals which all lifeguard agencies should utilize. These simple signals allow for national consistency and effective communication among lifeguards working for different agencies. Each signal, when given by a lifeguard in the water, should be repeated by lifeguards on shore. This lets the lifeguard in the water know that the signal was seen and understood. These signals can also be used by lifeguards ashore to communicate with lifeguards in the water, and they can be used by lifeguards on land communicating to other lifeguards on land.

- **Under Control**—Also referred to as "no further assistance needed." The lifeguard touches the fingers together over the head, forming a large circle with the arms. An alternative is to touch the middle of the head with the fingertips of one hand, but this signal is not as visible. Either of these signals simulate the commonly used "OK" hand signal made by creating a circle with the thumb and forefinger. They are used primarily when the lifeguard has determined that a rescue can be accomplished without the help of others and the victim is stable. It's important to note that this does not mean lifeguards ashore can ignore the rescue in progress. The situation can deteriorate and the lifeguard in the water will need to be able to signal the change to someone watching from shore.

Credit: Pete DeQuincy

Under control.

- **Assistance Needed**—The lifeguard raises, *but does not wave* one arm. The lifeguard in the water needs further assistance. This could be due to a badly panicked victim, multiple victims, an injury the lifeguard sustained in the response, etc. Backup should be sent immediately.

Credit: Eric Nurse

Assistance needed.

- **Resuscitation Case**—The lifeguard raises *and waves* one arm. In situations involving non-breathing victims, or those with seriously lowered respirations, backup staff must be advised that some degree of resuscitation will most likely be required once the victim is brought back to the beach. This allows backup staff to prepare resuscitation equipment for use once the victim has been retrieved. It also signals the need for in-water assistance. Managing a non-breathing victim in the water is best addressed by two or more lifeguards and additional equipment, such as a rescue board or a rescue boat. Lifeguards ashore, seeing the lifeguard wave an arm, may be able to determine that an ambulance will likely be needed and either request an ambulance in advance or place an ambulance on standby. This can greatly lessen ambulance response time and thus the time to transport the victim to the hospital.

Credit: Eric Nurse

Resuscitation case.

- **Code X**—The lifeguard raises both arms and forms an X overhead. This is the most serious signal of all. The lifeguard could not reach the victim in time. A swimmer is missing and presumed submerged. The lifeguard in the water believes that search and recovery procedures need to be initiated. This signal allows a lifeguard in the water to advise lifeguards ashore of the need for immediate, substantial backup without interrupting an initial search for the submerged victim by having to swim to shore. Lifeguards on shore receiving this signal should immedi-

Credit: Eric Nurse

Code X.

ately take bearings to fix the point of the lifeguard, as well as prepare an appropriate response. For more details, please see Chapter 20 (*Underwater Search and Recovery*).

Whistles

For years, whistles have been identified as communication equipment used by lifeguards. In many areas, whistles are used as attention-getting devices, followed by hand signals or other types of communication to impart messages or directions. Some agencies have developed complex whistle codes used for communication among lifeguards. The use of whistles should be seen as an ancillary form of communication which has limited application in the beach environment due to the restricted ability of whistle systems to convey complete messages with certainty.

CHAPTER SUMMARY

In this chapter we have learned the value of two-way radios in lifeguard work, which is the preferred method of beach communication among lifeguards. We have also learned about use of telephones, including mobile telephones, and public address systems. We have learned about how lifeguards can maximize the value of the 9-1-1 system in receiving reports of aquatic emergencies. We have also learned about non-electronic communication methods including arm signals and whistles.

DISCUSSION POINTS

- Identify the reasons that two-way radios are considered the preferred method of beach communications among lifeguards.
- List the steps a lifeguard agency should take to ensure that it is notified of reports of emergencies received via the 9-1-1 system.
- List three benefits of public address systems.
- Explain the benefits of using the internet to enhance beach safety.
- Demonstrate the four USLA approved arm signals that a lifeguard should use to inform first responders on shore.
- List the uses and limitations of whistles.

CHAPTER

12

Standard Rescue Equipment

I n this chapter you will learn about the standard equipment used by lifeguards throughout the world. You will gain a basic understanding of how this equipment is used effectively. Skills for effective use of rescue equipment require extensive practice and experience. This chapter provides an overview. To effectively utilize the information in this chapter, you will also need to participate in practical training exercises.

CHAPTER EXCERPT

The rescue flotation device (RFD) is the principal piece of rescue equipment used by professional lifeguards in the U.S. and in most advanced lifesaving organizations around the world.

The rescue equipment described in this chapter is the mainstay of professional open water lifeguard agencies—core equipment which should be available to all open water lifeguards. To comply with USLA national certification guidelines, there should be at least one rescue flotation device (RFD) available for each lifeguard on duty, swim fins readily accessible to lifeguards (as appropriate according to local conditions), and spinal stabilization equipment—including spineboard, head and neck immobilization devices, and fastening devices, readily accessible at each staffed beach area. Additional equipment required under ULSA guidelines is discussed in Chapter 18 (*Medical Care in the Aquatic Environment*) and Chapter 20 (*Search and Recovery*).

Standard rescue equipment is essential for the following reasons:

- **Support of the Victim**—To reverse the drowning process, buoyant support must be provided for the victim. This support must be sufficient to maintain the victim's airway above the surface of the water.
- **Lifeguard Safety**—A panicked victim desperate for buoyant support is a very real threat to an approaching rescuer. The victim may attempt to grab the lifeguard, forcing both underwater and into a mutually life-threatening situation. When buoyant rescue devices are provided to victims they usually have an immediate calming effect, as the primary source of fear (submersion) is eliminated, which enhances lifeguard safety.

- **Increased Speed and Efficiency**—Some rescue devices can reduce lifeguard response time, which is a critical factor in drowning prevention. Many rescue devices provide increased efficiency for the lifeguard by augmenting the lifeguard's swimming skills or by providing support for the victim so that the lifeguard can devote more energy to swimming. For example, rescue flotation devices (RFDs) increase the speed with which victims can be removed from the water and allow for the rescue of multiple victims by a single lifeguard.

In the open water setting, most rescue equipment used by lifeguards consists of devices used for in-water rescues. Some open water facilities may also find uses for equipment like reaching poles or ring buoys near docks, piers, jetties, or in rescue boats. Open water lifeguards assigned to flood and swiftwater also use throw bags and similar devices very effectively. At open water areas however, it is a very rare situation that allows for an effective throwing or reaching rescue. Therefore this text will not cover such rescues in detail. Suffice it to say that if a victim can be easily and reliably rescued by throwing a line or extending a pole, this method should be considered. Nevertheless, lifeguards must always be prepared to enter the water to effect a rescue.

RESCUE FLOTATION DEVICES

The RFD is the principal piece of rescue equipment used by professional lifeguards in the U.S. and in most advanced lifesaving organizations around the world. The two types of rescue flotation devices are the *rescue buoy* and the *rescue tube*.

Credit: Joel Gitelson

Rescue buoy.

Rescue buoys are also known as rescue cans, torpedo buoys ("torps"), and Burnside buoys. The latter name stems from the primary designer of the modern rescue buoy. These devices are oblong and molded from lightweight, hard plastic. They have handles molded into the sides and rear, which allow the victim to maintain a firm, comfortable grip during rescue. Rescue buoys are available in different sizes for different conditions. Most are very durable and highly visible.

The rescue tube used by open water lifeguards, also known as the Peterson tube, after the lifeguard who designed it, is a flexible foam buoy with an embedded strap and a vinyl skin. The embedded strap is connected to the lanyard leading to the lifeguard. In a rescue situation, the tube can be wrapped around the victim and secured. The ends of the tube are typically fastened together with a ring (on one end) and snap-hook (on the other), or by a plastic fastening device. This is particularly useful when taking a victim through breaking surf, wherein the

Credit: Aaron Roth

Rescue tube.

rescuer and victim might otherwise be separated. Rescue tubes are available in several sizes. (Rescue tubes adapted for pool lifeguards are designed differently.)

The three major components of an RFD are:

- Float
- Lanyard
- Harness

The two primary types of RFDs each have distinctive characteristics and many lifeguard agencies select one over another for specific reasons. For example, agencies where multiple victim rescue situations are common may employ large size rescue buoys because of the extra buoyancy they provide. Another approach is to employ both types of RFDs, thus allowing equipment selection appropriate to the rescue. Rescue buoys have handles that several victims can hold at once, while rescue tubes are primarily designed to encircle a single victim, but they can also be used for multiple victims, holding the tube.

RFDs should always be available in a number adequate to allow all lifeguards at a beach to use one if a major rescue takes place. At some agencies, RFDs are assigned to lifeguards as pieces of personal equipment, for which they are responsible during all duty hours. At other agencies, RFDs are assigned to locations rather than lifeguards. When lifeguards leave these locations, they are always expected to take an RFD along. Many agencies require the use of an RFD on all rescues in addition to other equipment that may be selected.

There are good reasons for such policies:

- **Constant Readiness**—While on duty, lifeguards should be ready at all times to respond appropriately and expeditiously to a person in distress. If a lifeguard is away from the station for some reason, a fundamental piece of rescue equipment should always be at hand for an immediate response.

- **Identification to the Public**—RFDs are very distinctive and recognizable, even more so than uniforms, thus allowing people in need of assistance to quickly locate lifeguards. The RFD also helps to symbolize the authority of the lifeguard when approaching a beach patron. In a rescue situation, the RFD helps identify a lifeguard during water entry, which may help to clear the way on a crowded beach or help avoid confrontations. When a lifeguard responds to a rescue with an RFD (even a shallow water assist), people will often focus their attention to the water area, which can be helpful in bringing family members to the scene to assist with information or ensure better future supervision (e.g. in case of an unsupervised child needing assistance). In the water, a victim seeing a lifeguard approach would have no way of visually identifying the approaching swimmer as a lifeguard without the presence of the RFD.

- **Identification to Fellow Lifeguards**—Like other people at the beach, lifeguards are easily lost in the crowd; but the characteristic shape and color of the RFD allows lifeguards to spot each other much more easily. In the water as well, an RFD helps other lifeguards quickly locate the lifeguard using it and its presence signals that a rescue is likely in progress. As a signaling device, the RFD helps lifeguards in the water identify lifeguards on the beach and any signals they are giving. RFDs of different colors can be used to differentiate specially trained or assigned lifeguards, lifeguard supervisors, or junior lifeguards.

- **Multiple Uses**—RFDs can be used in conjunction with other equipment and can be taken along without interfering with other devices. RFDs can be adapted to almost any rescue situation. For example, with a boat tow, described in Chapter 14 (*Specialized Rescue Equipment*) attached to the rear handle of a rescue buoy, it can be used to swim a boat away from the surf. Some are modified in their design to carry and store special rescue equipment, such as one-way breathing masks. They can be used for a wide variety of signals on the beach and in the water; and rescue buoys are even useful as self-defense tools in particularly dangerous public confrontations.

RFD Advantages and Limitations

Each type of RFD has distinct advantages and limitations.

Rescue Buoy Advantages

- **Multiple Victims**—Rescue buoys have particularly high buoyancy, allowing the simultaneous support and rescue of several victims.
- **Victim Avoidance**—A conscious victim can be instructed to use the rescue buoy without any need for lifeguard contact with the victim.
- **Durability**—Rescue buoys are generally very durable.

Rescue Buoy Limitations

- **Lack of Victim Security**—Victims can't be strapped to a rescue buoy.
- **Hard Exterior**—Although softer than the original metal design, modern rescue buoys are still hard plastic and can cause minor injuries.

Rescue Tube Advantages

- **Hydrodynamic**—The rescue tube is particularly streamlined, creating very little drag against the lifeguard towing it.
- **Victim Security**—The victim can be encircled in the tube, which is particularly useful for an unconscious victim or surf extrication.
- **Rescue Boat Use**—The soft design keeps rescue tubes from bouncing around in a rescue boat.

Rescue Tube Limitations

- **Single Victim Use**—The rescue tube can be used for more than one victim, but is primarily designed for a single victim.
- **Lower Buoyancy**—Rescue tubes have lower buoyancy than rescue buoys.
- **Requires Physical Contact with Victim**—Wrapping a rescue tube around the victim requires physical contact with a possibly panicked victim.
- **Requires Extra Maneuver**—Unlike the rescue buoy, which is simply pushed to the victim, the rescue tube requires that the lifeguard take an extra step of wrapping and fastening.
- **Fending Off**—Rescue tubes cannot be effectively used to fend off a panicked victim.

The snap-hook of a rescue tube can cause lacerations or other injury. This is very unusual, but it is best to secure the tube around the victim to avoid this problem. Rescue tubes are more susceptible to environmental degradation than rescue buoys. They should be stored in an elongated position out of the sun.

Rescues with Rescue Flotation Devices

The rescue process will be described in the following chapter. The following are some basic principles.

- **Water Entry**—RFDs are equipped with a harness, which secures it to the lifeguard, and a lanyard, which connects the harness to the RFD. The lanyard and harness can trip the lifeguard during the entry run. Care should be taken to unwrap the lanyard and don the harness while holding the lanyard off the ground. This can be done by holding the lanyard in the same hand being used to hold the RFD. At surf areas, lifeguards should expect to feel extra drag after waves pass by, which is caused by the force of the wave against the RFD.

Credit: Lindsey Gerkins

Entry with rescue buoy. Note that the lifeguard has one swim fin in each hand.

- **Removal from Water**—In many situations, lifeguards can simply drop RFDs as they move to assist or carry victims from the water. In some surf conditions however, an unsecured rescue buoy could be washed with force against the lifeguard or victim, potentially causing injury. If heavy surf conditions are present, lifeguards may want to carry the RFD completely out of the water or have the victim do so.

- **Fouling**—If the lanyard becomes wrapped around an object, the lifeguard can be placed in serious jeopardy. For example, the lanyard could become wrapped in the propeller of a rescue vessel. For this reason, it is essential that the attachment between the lifeguard and lanyard allow for quick release.

- **Lanyard Length**—The length of the lanyard may reflect individual preference of each lifeguard. In general however, the lanyard should be long enough to allow the buoy to clear the kicking feet of the lifeguard while swimming, plus a foot or two. The longer the lanyard, the more likely it is to trip the lifeguard or become fouled, but in large surf conditions, a longer lanyard may allow lifeguards to more easily submerge under waves. If buoys are shared at an agency, lanyard length should take into account the lifeguard with the longest legs.

Rescues with Rescue Buoys

Most conscious victims will quickly grab and hold tightly to the rescue buoy handles. The lifeguard can then swim toward shore. A weak or unresponsive victim will require assistance. In these situations, the lifeguard should move to the rear of the victim facing the victim's back while keeping the RFD in front of the victim. Then the lifeguard reaches under the victim's arms, alongside the victim's upper back, to grasp a side handle of the rescue buoy. The rescue buoy is pulled close to sandwich the victim between the RFD and the lifeguard. The rescue can now proceed, with forward propulsion achieved by kicking the feet. Swim fins are extremely valuable in these cases. Even with swim fins, it can be difficult to bring a victim ashore in this manner, so additional lifeguard assistance should be considered. This same technique should be used in heavy surf, even when the victim is conscious and alert, to prevent having the victim become separated from the rescue buoy. This maneuver allows for in-water mouth-to-mouth resuscitation, if needed.

Rescues with Rescue Tubes

Perhaps the most valuable feature of the rescue tube is its ability to be wrapped around the victim and secured. For a single victim, it should always be used in this way, not as a device to be held by the victim. In most presentations, the lifeguard should first be concerned with establishing control by providing the support of the tube to the victim and letting the victim calm down and stabilize. Then, if possible, the lifeguard can direct the victim to move on the tube to a position where the victim is facing the tube with both arms over it and the tube is nestled under the armpits. The lifeguard can then move to the rear of the victim and bring the ends of the tube together for connection. Note that this requires the lifeguard to come into close contact with the victim, which should not be done until the lifeguard is certain that the victim will not panic and grab the lifeguard.

If the victim is unconscious or unresponsive, the process of securing the victim in the tube is more difficult. While facing the victim, the lifeguard can pull one arm of the victim over the extended tube to armpit level, then carefully work the other arm over the tube to the same position and connect the tube from the rear of the victim. Another technique is to swim to the rear of the victim and provide support with one hand under an armpit while placing the tube in front of the victim's face. From that point, the lifeguard can lift one, then the other arm of the victim over the tube to the armpit level and finally connect the tube at the victim's back.

If a victim must be moved through heavy surf, the lifeguard moves to the rear of the victim and holds on to the tube and victim with the lifeguard's face to the victim's back. The lifeguard should check behind frequently, while kicking toward shore, and advise the victim when to expect the force of a wave.

SWIM FINS

The USLA recommends that swim fins be issued and used as part of the lifeguard's basic rescue equipment. The obvious advantage to the use of swim fins is the added speed and power they give to the responding lifeguard. When lifeguards are unable to use arm strokes, due to the need to hold on to victims, swim fins can be essential to making rapid progress. In rocky areas or on reefs, swim fins provide protection for the feet. They can also be useful during search and recovery procedures requiring diving.

Fins protect lifeguards from rocks during training.

Use and Selection of Swim Fins

The use of swim fins is indicated in most rescue situations especially those involving, multiple victims, deep water rescues, or surf. They are also useful when lifeguards need to provide additional support to victims in deep water, such as situations involving resuscitation. Swim fins are not as useful in shallow water rescues or in rescue situations a short distance from shallow water. In these situations, the time necessary to don swim fins can delay response unnecessarily.

Swim fins which float or have neutral buoyancy are preferred because a lifeguard can remove them if necessary, without fear of loss. Lifeguards should use fins with a fixed heel strap that is appropriate to the size of their feet. Shoe-type fins are unacceptable because they are difficult to don and easily come off. Adjustable heel-strap styles are undependable because the straps can release or break under stress.

Typical swim fins used by lifeguards.

Rescues with Swim Fins

When swim fins are used on rescues, the lifeguard dons the RFD harness, then grabs the RFD and lanyard in one hand, and both fins in the other, running with them into the water. Upon entering the water, the lifeguard drops the RFD and takes one fin in each hand. At this point the fins can be used as paddles (one in each hand) until the lifeguard is in water approximately chest deep. The lifeguard can also porpoise, a technique described in detail in the next chapter, holding the heel strap of each fin in each hand. Once swimming becomes the most expeditious manner of making forward progress, the lifeguard stops and dons the fins. This can rarely be done with the head above water, therefore lifeguards who use fins must be adept at donning their fins blind.

Experienced lifeguards always keep their fins in the same orientation to each other onshore, so that when they enter the water, they know which side of the fin is up without looking. When the fins have been donned, the lifeguard swims to the victim. Although it takes a few moments to don fins, the increased speed of the lifeguard in swimming to the victim usually offsets this short delay.

Swim fins are not normally worn while running on shore or in shallow water. An exception to this guideline is a water entry in a rocky area. Swim fins can be put on immediately in this situation, as the fins provide protection for the feet. High strides will cut down the resistance caused by the swim fins.

Upon return to shore, swim fins are usually removed upon reaching shallow water, before the lifeguard begins walking again. Another alternative, if the lifeguard must support the victim, is to walk backwards. In rare instances, the lifeguard may need to discard swim fins upon reaching shore in order to support the victim better or to provide resuscitation. This is why swim fins that float are desirable.

RESCUE BOARDS

Rescue boards (known also as paddleboards and rescue surfboards) are a valuable piece of rescue equipment which evolved from the surfboard. While surfboards and rescue boards have a common ancestry, lifeguard rescue boards are not primarily intended (or designed) for surfing.

Lifeguard rescue boards are lightweight, typically 10' to 12' long, and shaped to move quickly through the water. The rescue board includes a skeg (fin) attached to the bottom of the board at the rear to help maintain stability. Skegs are sometimes quite sharp and can cause serious injuries if they strike a person. A design that helps avoid such injuries is a skeg with a leading and trailing edge made of soft, flexible material.

Credit: Nicholas Enns

Rescue boards are often equipped with inlaid handles for use by lifeguards and victims. The primary use of a rescue board is water rescue of swimmers. They can also be used in boat rescue, for patrolling, for swim/surf crowd control, and, in a pinch, as a spineboard to remove an injured victim from the water or as a platform for CPR, although these latter uses should only be employed as a last resort.

Rescue Board Advantages

- **Speed**—When properly used in low to moderate surf, rescue boards can allow lifeguards to cover considerable distances much faster than swimming with fins. In flat water, rescue boards are almost always the fastest method of accessing victims, other than power boats.

- **Buoyancy**—Rescue boards are very buoyant and can support many more victims than RFDs. In rescues involving multiple victims, the rescue board can be used as a raft for several victims to hold while waiting to be ferried to the beach by lifeguards using RFDs, for example. In calm water, rescue boards can even be used to support the victim while administering rescue breathing. When rescuing a single victim using a rescue board, the victim is almost completely removed from the water, significantly increasing the victim's sense of security.

- **Weight**—When compared to a rescue boat, the low weight of the rescue board allows it to be carried, launched, and operated by one lifeguard, and easily transported atop a lifeguard vehicle. (But it's heavier than an RFD—see disadvantages below.)

- **Viewing Platform**—The deck of the rescue board provides an excellent platform from which a sitting or kneeling lifeguard can observe the swim area. This makes the rescue board a rudimentary patrol device and a useful tool in surface searches of swim areas.

Credit: Eric Nurse

Lifeguard using a rescue board as an observation platform.

Rescue Board Limitations

- **Surf Conflicts**—A rescue board is difficult to move through heavy surf. A swimming lifeguard can usually more easily penetrate heavy surf than a lifeguard on a rescue board. Trying to return to shore with a victim in these conditions is quite challenging, particularly with an incapacitated victim. Loss of the rescue board is a real risk. If the board is lost, the lifeguard may be left without rescue equipment and lose contact with the victim. Other swimmers may be endangered by an uncontrolled rescue board in surf. Rescue boards with ethylene-vinyl acetate (EVA) foam skins and inflatable rescue boards reduce the potential for injuries, as do skegs with rubberized edges. Regardless of the type of rescue board though, it is advisable to carefully consider use of a rescue board through large, breaking surf. Due to the chance of being separated from the rescue board, it is a good practice to take an RFD and fins while effecting a rescue with a rescue board, particularly in large surf conditions. In this way, if the rescue board is lost, the lifeguard will retain an ability to effectively complete the rescue. If necessary, the lifeguard can also abandon the board in extreme circumstances.

- **Weight**—Foam core boards may be as heavy as 30 pounds, which can make them difficult to remove from racks or carry to the water, particularly for smaller lifeguards. Some newer rescue board designs reduce this weight to 25 pounds or less, and inflatable boards are lighter still. Even so, compared to an RFD the rescue board is a heavier and more challenging piece of rescue equipment.

- **Lack of Maneuverability**—Rescue boards operate best when paddled in a straight line with small corrections in direction made occasionally. A congested swimming area may present the lifeguard with too many obstacles to move around en route to the victim. Similarly, congested swimming areas may provide the lifeguard with difficult obstacles during retrieval.
- **Maintenance**—Rescue boards with a hard skin can be easily damaged (dinged), which can contribute to periods when the equipment is unusable because of maintenance requirements. Rescue boards in a poor state of repair can cause injury to both lifeguards and victims.
- **Skill Requirements**—Lifeguards must regularly practice rescue board skills to maintain proficiency. Without proper skills and practice, the rescue board can be an awkward piece of equipment that can actually pose a hazard to beach visitors.

Rescues with rescue boards

Entry

Running with an RFD is generally faster than swimming. This is not necessarily the case when using a rescue board, due to its weight and cumbersome nature. Instead, it may be preferable to carry the rescue board directly to the water. Since an experienced lifeguard paddling a rescue board is much faster than a swimming lifeguard, the loss of speed onshore can be offset by a gain in speed in the water.

On most days, a lifeguard can move a rescue board to the water by lifting the board up at the middle and carrying it nose first toward the water at the lifeguard's side. Some rescue boards are equipped with handles or carrying slots to facilitate this. On windy days, the wind may cause the board to sail during this carry and the board may become very difficult to manage. Should this situation present itself, the lifeguard can grasp the forward end of the rescue board and drag the tailing end of the board in the sand. Dragging the board is not recommended under normal conditions, since the practice will eventually wear away the board's protective covering. During the launching process, an RFD (if also carried, as we have recommended) can be dragged behind the lifeguard or carried with the board. Running to the water with a rescue board requires caution to avoid striking beachgoers.

At a flatwater beach, boards should be launched and mounted at about knee depth. This is important, since attempts to launch a board in shallower water may result in the skeg catching on the bottom, which will stop the board and throw the lifeguard off. On sand beaches the lifeguard can gain good speed by running with the board, with the nose pointed toward the water. When the appropriate depth is reached, the lifeguard grabs the board by each rail (side) at about the center, deck inward, and without letting go, pushes the board forward. When this motion is followed by the momentum of the lifeguard's weight, the board is propelled at considerable speed for a short distance. When the board hits the water, the lifeguard simultaneously mounts the board, assuming a prone or kneeling position. This is a single, fluid motion, which requires practice. Effective use of the rescue board requires a considerable amount of balance and awareness of the orientation of the board. If the lifeguard is too far forward, the nose dives beneath the surface of the water, slowing or stopping it abruptly. If the lifeguard's center of gravity is too far toward the tail, the board will become unstable and slower.

Credit: Eric Nurse

Launching a rescue board in calm water.

In surf conditions, one object of launching a rescue board is to initially carry the board over incoming waves. Once the water becomes too deep to run more efficiently, the board can be placed on the water and pushed along the water's surface at the side of the lifeguard. When oncoming waves are going to lift the board above waist high, the lifeguard can lift the front of the board over the wave and as the wave passes under, put the weight of their upper body onto the board while their legs leave the ground and swing free; thereby allowing the wave to lift the lifeguard and the board with the wave passing under both. When the wave passes, the lifeguard can regain footing and proceed.

Once deep water is reached, the lifeguard must commit to paddling. The board is mounted and a paddling position is assumed. Like surface diving through waves, the aim with a rescue board is to present the smallest possible forward surface to the incoming wave. Generally, this means taking a perpendicular angle to the wave.

The initial goal of using a rescue board in the surf is to get out beyond the breakers. A lifeguard who is swimming can easily duck under breaking waves, but breaking waves landing on a lifeguard on a rescue board will sandwich the lifeguard between the force of the breaking wave and the board. In this case, the lifeguard may lose the board or may be thrust into the board by the incoming wave, causing injury. The lifeguard may also be pushed a significant distance shoreward or become separated from the board.

When approaching the incoming foam line of a wave that has already broken, the lifeguard should adjust body weight somewhat toward the tail so that the nose rides up over the foam line. When a wave approaches that will break over the lifeguard, the

Credit: Joel Gitelson

A lifeguard competitor crests a wave on a rescue board.

lifeguard can try to force the nose of the board down by leaning forward in a push-up position. This helps keep the board from being lifted and carried shoreward by the breaking wave.

The simplest and most common method to move a rescue board through heavy surf is to *turtle* the board. Perpendicular attitude is critical. To employ this maneuver, the lifeguard inhales deeply just before the impact of the oncoming wave and rolls the board over so that the bottom of the board faces toward the sky and the lifeguard holds on tightly underneath. Once the wave has passed, the lifeguard turns the board over and continues paddling.

Credit: Eric Nurse

Approach

The rescue board can be propelled using coordinated arm-strokes from a prone or kneeling position. It's important to maintain a good trim—a position on the board where the board remains flat, or slightly nose high, on the water. In practicing paddling, each lifeguard will find a position on the board that results in the board staying in trim.

The prone position (lying face down on the board) is the easiest to master, since a low center of gravity is maintained for a stable ride. Arms are used in a crawl or a butterfly stroke, with the hands and arms dug into the water deeply for efficient movement. In the prone position however, the lifeguard's stroke length is limited and only the arms contribute to forward momentum. This will result in a tired lifeguard over a relatively short distance. Many lifeguards prefer the kneeling position, particularly for distance paddling. It's normally faster and more efficient, since more of the muscles of the body contribute to the stroke and the stroke is longer, but it requires more skill to paddle in this manner because the lifeguard's weight is concentrated in a single area of the rescue board, the center of gravity is higher, and balance is more difficult to maintain.

The kneeling position is usually assumed from the prone position. After a few strokes to develop momentum and stability, the lifeguard moves from the prone position to kneeling by holding onto the rails and pulling the knees up to the center of the board, spread somewhat to maintain stability and trim. The head is kept down to maintain a low center of gravity and the arms dig in deeply to grab water and pull backward. Arms are recovered with hands low and elbows high.

To make small changes in the direction of the board, several techniques can be used. These include dragging a foot, shifting weight, or reaching out and pulling water from the direction of the turn. If the lifeguard wants to turn the board completely around, the lifeguard stops the board by sitting on the deck with legs hung over both sides. The lifeguard then slides back on the board, which picks the nose up. Then, by using an eggbeater kick and/or by paddling with the hands, the board can be twirled to the desired direction.

Approaching a victim with a rescue board should be done in a manner that will place the nose of the board just slightly to one side of the victim. When the lifeguard

has drawn nearly beside the victim, the lifeguard slips off the far side of the board so that the board is between the lifeguard and the victim. Then, if necessary, the lifeguard moves the board to the victim using a swimming kick and the lifeguard reaches over the board to pull the victim to the support offered by the board. This keeps the lifeguard separated from the victim in much the same manner as pushing an RFD to the victim.

Retrieval

Once the victim has been stabilized, the retrieval process can begin. There is no requirement that victims be loaded onto rescue boards for retrieval. In many situations, lifeguards can simply begin swimming kicks that will move the board and the victim toward shallow water while holding the victim's arms on the board. In other situations, victims may stay in the water and hold onto rescue board handles or the trailing RFD while the lifeguard mounts the board and paddles in.

More skilled lifeguards will usually choose to bring a strong, conscious victim aboard. One way to do this is to begin by treading water at the nose of the board and stabilizing the board for the victim by holding both sides. The victim is then instructed to mount the board facing the nose. Once the head and shoulders are supported by the board, the lifeguard can assist by pulling the legs onto the deck, if necessary.

If the victim is unconscious or unable to mount the board using the foregoing method, an alternative method of bringing the victim aboard the rescue board involves rolling the board. The lifeguard dismounts the rescue board and turns it over, bottom side up. The middle of the overturned board is positioned between the lifeguard and the victim.

Credit: Kekai Brown

Lifeguard assists a conscious victim onto the board and paddles to safety.

The victim's hands are pulled across the board so that the victim's armpits are against the rail opposite the lifeguard. The rescue board is then turned back over, flipping it toward the lifeguard. The victim will now be lying across the middle of the rescue board. The final step is to carefully move the victim's body on the board to a lengthwise position.

Once the victim is aboard the rescue board, the lifeguard can assume a position at the tail and push the board to shore by kicking. Alternatively, the lifeguard can carefully mount the board from the tail to assume a position over the victim's hind quarters with the victim's legs on either side. The lifeguard adjusts the board's trim and begins to paddle to shore.

Credit: Adam Abajian

Bringing an unconscious victim aboard a rescue board and retrieving the victim to shore.

Surf conditions complicate retrievals of victims on rescue boards. At many agencies, lifeguards are instructed not to bring victims through breaking surf on rescue boards. Instead, victims are transferred to rescue boats or to lifeguards with RFDs for retrieval. If a victim must be brought through breaking surf on a rescue board, no attempt should be made to catch or ride waves with victims aboard. Lifeguards should keep the board perpendicular to waves and shift weight heavily toward the tail of the rescue board when overtaken by a wave. This may include moving the victim to the rear of the board and sandwiching the victim between the board and lifeguard while holding both rails. The victim should be held tightly, sandwiched between the body of the lifeguard and the rescue board, and advised of what to expect.

Removal from the Water

In most situations, lifeguards must either tend to the removal of the rescue board or removal of the victim. Rescue boards should not be left unattended, especially in moving or turbulent water. Another lifeguard may help with removal of the rescue board while the responding lifeguard deals with the victim.

Maintenance

Care is a must for a rescue board. Rescue boards should be inspected daily and any holes or cracks repaired. Any opening in the skin of the board can allow water to seep in and may eventually ruin it. Rescue boards should never be leaned upright against other objects as the wind can sail them into people. They should be stored horizontally or be fully secured if stored vertically.

SPINAL STABILIZATION DEVICES

Several sources of spinal injury are present at all open water beaches. These include shallow water diving, body surfing, striking a sandbar or other underwater object, wave action, dry land falls, and others. Therefore every lifeguard agency should have spinal stabilization devices available for immediate use. All lifeguards should be fully trained in the necessary techniques. For a discussion of the recognition and treatment of spinal injuries in the aquatic environment, please refer to Chapter 18: (*Medical Care in the Aquatic Environment*).

Spinal Stabilization Device Components

Spinal stabilization devices consist of three parts: spineboard, head and neck immobilization device, and fastening devices to hold the person to the spineboard. Use of spinal stabilization devices may be regulated by local emergency medical service authorities. They should be used in a manner consistent with agency protocol and training.

- **Spineboard**—The spineboard is also known as a backboard. A spineboard is a rigid, flat surface to which a person, lying face up (supine) can be attached. The most basic version of a spineboard is a flat, rectangular piece of wood of dimensions slightly greater than that of an average male lying supine. Better versions have handles in the sides to improve the grip of rescuers. The most advanced models for aquatic use have positive buoyancy and are slightly contoured. They have handles and specially designed areas for securing straps.
- **Head and Neck Immobilization Devices**—Neck immobilization devices were initially known as cervical collars (C-collars).

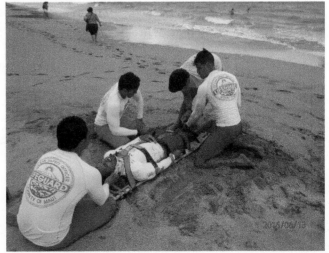

Credit: Kekai Brown

Spinal stabilization training.

Modern versions are quite rigid and significantly limit neck movement. These can be known as hard collars, Philadelphia collars, or by the brand name. Further stabilization to prevent head movement is provided by head immobilizers. These are placed on either side of the head as the body lies on a spineboard. They may be commercially manufactured or may be improvised material, such as sandbags, rolled towels, etc.

- **Fastening Devices**—Fastening devices are used to secure the trunk, head, and legs to the spineboard. These may be pre-designed harnesses, heavy tape, or Velcro straps.

CHAPTER SUMMARY

In this chapter we have learned about the standard rescue equipment used by lifeguards. We have learned about rescue flotation devices, including rescue buoys and rescue tubes, their advantages, disadvantages, and how to use them effectively. We have learned about the advantages of swim fins and how they are donned during a rescue response. We have learned about rescue boards, including their advantages and limitations, as well as how they are used effectively. And we have learned about spinal stabilization devices.

DISCUSSION POINTS

- Explain why each lifeguard on duty should have an RFD.
- List three values of standard rescue equipment.
- List five reasons that lifeguards keep RFD's with them at all times.
- Describe the benefits of the rescue tube and rescue buoy.
- Identify the advantage of using a rescue buoy in a multiple victim rescue.
- Identify the advantage of a rescue tube in large surf.
- Explain the advantages of using a rescue board.
- Cite the steps needed to launch a rescue board on a surf beach.
- Identify potential problems related to using a rescue board in heavy crowds and large surf.
- Identify the needs for the use of spinal stabilization devices in the open water environment.

CHAPTER

13

Basic Rescue

I n this chapter you will learn the fundamental steps involved in the successful accomplishment of an open water rescue. We will break down an open water rescue into the three major components and the steps involved in each component. You will learn what is involved in each component and each step.

CHAPTER EXCERPT

Before a lifeguard enters the water on a rescue, it is important that someone else knows that a rescue is being performed, since the lifeguard will be exposed to a potentially dangerous situation and further assistance may be needed for the rescue.

LEARN MORE

The USLA offers an educational video on the components of a rescue which you can purchase at: www.usla.org/store.

To the beach visitor, rescues performed by lifeguards may seem like dramatic, spontaneous events. Suddenly, a lifeguard springs from the station, runs to the water's edge and plunges in. The lifeguard quickly swims out to a person in distress (a drowning victim) and contact is made. Returning to the beach, the lifeguard assists the victim to dry land and returns to the station, prepared for the next rescue to develop. Those who had riveted their attention on the sudden action go back to their recreational activities. It's all over, for now.

To the experienced lifeguard, most rescues are routine; but while many rescues may seem quite simple, they actually represent a carefully planned response to a specific set of circumstances. The lifeguard first recognizes distress, panic, or drowning signs, which are carefully and quickly assessed. The decision to respond is made. An entire backup system is activated. Rescue equipment is selected based on the requirements of the rescue. The lifeguard plans an approach to the victim and carries it out. Throughout the approach, the lifeguard endeavors to maintain constant visual contact with the victim. Upon arrival, the lifeguard calms the victim, signals to shore, and completes the save by bringing the victim to shore. Following these events, the lifeguard evaluates the victim for any complications, completes reports necessary to document the event, and prepares for another response.

COMPONENTS OF A RESCUE

The United States Lifesaving Association recognizes three basic components of every open water rescue. Each component includes specific steps. The three components of every rescue are as follows:

1. Recognize and Respond.
2. Contact and Control.
3. Signal and Save.

   Specific rescue procedures may differ somewhat from agency to agency; but these three rescue components are valid for all rescue situations, from wading assists to rescues with multiple victims. Each rescue includes all three components. What follows is a detailed description of each component and the subordinate steps involved.

Recognize & Respond

The first component of a rescue—*recognize and respond*—includes four steps:

   a. Recognition.
   b. Alert.
   c. Equipment selection.
   d. Entry.

Recognition

Before a rescue can take place, there must be *recognition* of distress. Typically a lifeguard determines through observation that a person needs assistance in the water. Perhaps a swimmer has fallen off a floating support in deep water or is being swept into deep water by a current. In some cases, lifeguards are summoned to respond by beach visitors who have noticed something wrong in the water. Although unusual, the lifeguard may actually hear cries for help from the victim. The 9-1-1 telephone system and the marine radio system are also sources of reports of emergencies, particularly for areas outside the direct observation of lifeguards. Regardless of the source of information, the process begins when a lifeguard recognizes the need for a rescue.

Alert

Before a lifeguard enters the water on a rescue, it is important that someone else knows that a rescue is being performed, since the lifeguard will be exposed to a potentially dangerous situation and further assistance may be needed for the rescue. An *alert* to others triggers procedures that will provide backup assistance for the lifeguard. This may be part of the agency's emergency action plan. It will also ensure that other lifeguards begin to cover the water area of the lifeguard leaving on the rescue.

   The best alert systems are two-way radios, which allow for the lifeguard initiating the rescue to confirm that the alert has been received by others, to briefly detail circumstances of the response, and to request any special assistance which may appear necessary. The alert for a routine rescue may be very brief, such as, "Tower #1, rescue, single victim." The lifeguard in Tower #1 thereby states that a rescue of one person is being initiated. For further information on lifeguard communication, please refer to Chapter 11 (*Communication Methods*).

The importance of the alert cannot be over-emphasized. Alerts are standard practice in all emergency services, including fire departments, police agencies, and emergency medical services. Without an alert, lifeguards expose themselves to potentially life-threatening situations without anyone else being aware. A significant component of drowning statistics is attributable to untrained people who die while trying to assist others. Although lifeguard training significantly reduces this potential, lifeguards are at risk on every rescue.

Equipment Selection

Once the alert is made, or simultaneous to this notification, the responding lifeguard must make an *equipment selection*. Proper equipment selection requires a thorough familiarity with all assigned rescue equipment, a proper evaluation of the incident, and the foresight to consider ways that apparent circumstances of the incident may change during the response.

This lifeguard can select a rescue tube, rescue buoy, rescue board, or some combination of the three, depending on the circumstances of the rescue.

Sometimes the lifeguard who has observed distress develop may actually determine that other personnel should respond based on proximity or the availability of special rescue equipment. For example, a rescue boat may be very near the victim and advised to effect the rescue. In our hypothetical rescue, the lifeguard selects a rescue buoy, which we have described in Chapter 12 (*Standard Rescue Equipment*).

Entry

Once proper rescue equipment has been selected, the lifeguard determines the most efficient path to the victim and effects a water *entry*. It's very important to attempt to maintain visual contact with the victim throughout the rescue. Victims may move with a current or submerge prior to the lifeguard's arrival. (In the latter case, lifeguards must be able to fix a *last seen point* which is explained Chapter 20 (*Underwater Search and Recovery*).

Once in the water, the lifeguard may be too low to keep a constant eye on the victim, particularly in waves. Moreover, there are usually no stationary objects offshore that the lifeguard can use to help maintain a steady course toward the victim. For this reason, it is sometimes valuable to take a *bearing* from fixed points on land. Buildings, trees, and other stationary objects ashore can be used for this purpose. One of the best methods is to line up two stationary objects ashore that are one in front of the other, such as two trees. By staying a course that keeps the two objects consistently lined up, the lifeguard can maintain a straight line while swimming.

The drowning process can progress rapidly through the distress and panic stages to submersion, so speed is important. To increase the speed and efficiency of entries, several points should be considered for swimming rescues:

- **Get There Safely**—As important as speed may be in a water rescue, if the lifeguard is injured en route to the victim, the victim may not survive. Lifeguards must protect themselves at all times, while trying to get to the victim as soon as possible.

Lifeguard runs on shore before entering the water for a rescue.

- **Running Is Faster than Swimming**—Running to the closest point on shore to the victim is usually much faster than swimming a diagonal route to the victim. In planning the entry, lifeguards should usually run down the shoreline to the point closest to the victim before entering the water.

- **Use the Current**—If the victim is caught in a current, the best point for water entry will vary. For example, if the victim is caught on the edge of strong, out-flowing current from a tidal bay, the lifeguard could run to a point adjacent to the victim, jump into the center of the current and be swept past the victim. In this case, as in a river, the lifeguard may need to intentionally enter upstream and swim diagonally toward the victim. At a surf beach, if a victim is caught in a rip current moving perpendicular to the beach, the best entry point will usually be at the rip current feeder. The current then helps carry the lifeguard to the victim. At lower tides, rip current channels are sometimes bordered by sandbars that are waist deep or even shallower. The lifeguard may be able to run out on the sandbar to a point very near the victim before jumping into the rip current channel and swimming to the victim.

- **Run in Shallow Water**—Running in shallow water is faster than swimming. Upon entering the water, the best technique is to kick high out of the water (high-step) while running to minimize the resistance of the water. Another technique is to keep the knees low, but whip the lower legs to the side. At the same time, lifeguards should always be conscious of the potential for uneven bottom conditions that can cause serious joint injuries.

- **Use Surface Dives to Get to Swimming Depth**—On a gradually sloping beach, upon reaching deeper water the lifeguard will eventually be unable to continue the running entry. At this point, however, swimming may not yet be the fastest method of moving forward. Wading to swimming depth is a possibility, but it takes considerable energy and may be quite slow. At surf beaches, incoming waves will further impede forward progress. The lifeguard's goal is to present as little of the body as possible to the oncoming wave. In such cases, when running is no longer effective, but swimming is not yet the fastest method of forward propulsion, a surface dive or surface dives should be used. At a surf beach, the lifeguard dives under incoming waves that are too large to jump over or through. As the lifeguard dives forward, the head and neck must be protected. This can be accomplished by fully extending the hands and

Lifeguard practices entries with rescue tube.

arms forward as the dive is initiated, but if the water depth is unknown, a very shallow dive is appropriate.

- **Porpoise**—A more advanced technique involves *porpoising* (also known as dolphin diving) through shallow water to swimming depth. Porpoising is accomplished by springing forward in a shallow dive with the arms fully extended. If swim fins are used, they are held in each hand. As the forward glide slows, the lifeguard grabs the sand and pulls the feet under the body in a crouching position, then springs forward using the legs in another forward dive. This arcing,

Lifeguard springs forward while porpoising.

dive-glide-recover pattern is repeated until swimming depth is reached. Porpoising can be used in both surf and flat water, but is particularly effective in surf.

At beaches with a steep slope, the period spent running or porpoising through the water will be very brief. On the other hand, beaches with long, gradual slopes necessitate extensive running and porpoising through the water. Under either circumstance, the lifeguard begins swimming when running, wading, or porpoising are no longer faster than swimming.

Contact and Control

The second component of a water rescue—*contact and control*—includes the following three steps:

a. Approach.

b. Contact.

c. Stabilize.

Approach

Once swimming depth is reached, the lifeguard approaches the victim as quickly as possible, using swimming strokes that will allow frequent checking on the position of the victim. The crawl stroke is best because it is fastest. Using the heads-up form of water polo players, the approaching lifeguard can usually maintain visual contact with the victim. In some situations, the lifeguard will be unable to see the victim no matter what stroke is used. This may occur when water conditions are rough or when a drowning presentation has progressed to a submersion. In these cases, the bearings that were taken on water entry become critical for fixing the last seen point of the victim.

Credit: Eric Nurse

Lifeguard using a head high crawl to maintain a visual on the victim's situation.

To further assist, lifeguards ashore must be prepared to provide easily understandable signals to the lifeguard in the water. Upon losing sight of the victim, the responding lifeguard can turn to shore for this assistance. Audible devices, such as public address systems and whistle systems may be useful, but should not be solely relied upon because the lifeguard in the water may not be able to hear them. Simple shore based arm signals are as follows:

- **Move to Right or Left**—A rescue flotation device (RFD) is extended to the right or left at the end of a fully extended arm by the lifeguard ashore.
- **Go Further Out**—An RFD is held vertically between two upraised arms.
- **Stay There**—Arms are extended horizontally to the sides without holding a rescue buoy.
- **Move Offshore and Wait**—An RFD is held horizontally in both hands overhead. This is generally used when a boat or helicopter is being sent to retrieve the lifeguard and victim.

In addition to these shore-based signals, other arm signals intended primarily for use by a lifeguard in the water can also be used by lifeguards ashore. These are covered later in the *Signal and Save* section of this chapter and in Appendix A.

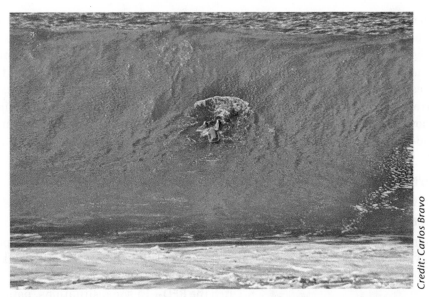

Credit: Carlos Bravo

When rescuing in surf conditions you may lose sight of the victim. A shore-based lifeguard can assist with arm signals.

Contact

Upon nearing the victim, the lifeguard should maintain a safe distance to avoid being grabbed by the victim, while providing reassurance and instructions. The lifeguard should watch the victim's eyes and facial expression for signs of fright or panic, while verbally reassuring the victim that they are going to rescued. It's well worth taking the time needed to calm the victim, because a panicked victim can be very dangerous. The final few feet of the approach are covered with the rescue buoy extended toward the victim and the lifeguard using swimming kicks for thrust. The lifeguard assumes a defensive position by pushing the buoy toward the victim, who will typically grab for it immediately.

During contact, lifeguards must be constantly aware of the dangers presented by people experiencing panic in deep water. Distressed swimmers sometimes move toward responding lifeguards and may desperately try to grab the lifeguard for support. Usually the mere presence of another person in the water who seems calm and knowledgeable will have a very positive effect and by maintaining an appropriate distance, the lifeguard is not grabbed by the victim. In unusual situations though, some victims may even choose the support of the lifeguard over the support of an extended RFD and make a quick grab for the lifeguard. Preventing these situations is the best strategy.

Credit: Pete DeQuincy

Lifeguard keeps defensive position and extends rescue buoy.

The behavior of panicked victims is quite uniform. The victim sees that the lifeguard is buoyant and tries to climb to safety. The victim will grab at any exposed part of the lifeguard and quickly pull into a hugging position at the highest point of support; usually the head. The lifeguard is submerged, either due to the victim trying to climb to safety or simply the added weight of the panicked victim. People in panic can demonstrate extraordinary strength. Children can incapacitate adults. Anticipation of victim movement and quick, decisive actions can often prevent the establishment of a firm head-hold. The following are techniques to avoid being grabbed and to escape if grabbed.

- **Don't Turn Your Back**—Unsupported or unstable victims may grab you.
- **Don't Move Through a Group**—People who seemed stable may grab you.
- **Don't Get Too Close**—A panicked person can jump onto you.
- **Defend Yourself**—Block an attack by placing a foot on the victim's chest, pushing away and swimming in the other direction. Continue to face the attack while swimming to safety.

Credit: Pete DeQuincy

By placing feet on the victim's chest, the lifeguard can push off.

- **Ditch the RFD**—In some situations, panicking swimmers may use the RFD lanyard to pull themselves toward the lifeguard instead of toward the floating buoy. Disengage from the RFD and swim away.
- **Go Limp and Submerge**—If grabbed, this is the best and most effective escape strategy. Use this one method before the others. Since the victim grabs the lifeguard in an attempt to climb up for air, if the lifeguard no longer provides buoyancy, the victim will almost always immediately release. Swim away from the victim underwater and reconsider the best approach.

- **Wrist Grip Escape**—If the victim grabs the lifeguard's wrist with one or both hands, the lifeguard should use the free hand to grab their other hand and pry upward in one quick motion.

Credit: Pete DeQuincy

Lifeguard goes limp and submerges to escape panicked victim.

- **Front Head-Hold Escape**—If the victim is facing the lifeguard with arms around the lifeguard's head or neck and submersion does not result in release of the hold, place the hands on the hips of the victim and push away while tucking in the chin. If needed, once underwater the rescuer can bring the hands up to victim's elbows and push hard up and away from the victim. Once the release is accomplished, swim backward and away from the victim.

- **Rear Head-Hold Escape**—If the victim grabs the lifeguard's head or neck from behind, the lifeguard should grab a breath of air and submerge, turn the head and tuck the chin to one side. When ready, the lifeguard drops the shoulder to the side where the head is turned and turns quickly to face the victim. Leverage can then be applied to the hips as previously described to break the hold and escape from the victim. If needed the rescuer, once underwater, can bring the rescuer's hands up to victim's elbows and push hard up and away from the rescuer. Once the release is accomplished, swim away from the victim.

Credit: Pete DeQuincy

Rear head hold escape.

Stabilize

Once control has been gained in a rescue, the lifeguard can begin to *stabilize* the victim. In most situations, once support in the form of an RFD has been provided, the panic experienced by the victim will quickly subside. The victim can regain normal breathing, wipe away hair and water from the face, and communicate with the lifeguard. Rational thinking returns, leaving the victim able to listen calmly to the lifeguard.

In most rescue situations, lifeguards should take advantage of this reduction of panic before proceeding with the rescue. It's an excellent chance to explain to the victim what has happened, to assure the victim that the situation is now under control, and to rest before proceeding. Since the immediate crisis has been contained, there's usually no immediate need to proceed with retrieval to shore until extrication is planned and explained to the victim.

Credit: Kekai Brown

Lifeguard practices stabilizing a victim.

Signal & Save

The third and final component of a rescue—*signal and save*—includes five steps:

a. Signal.

b. Retrieve.

c. Remove.

d. Assess.

e. Report.

Credit: Cole Yeatts

Lifeguard gives the *under control* signal after stabilizing the victim.

Signal

The alert initiated by the responding lifeguard at the start of all this begins a backup procedure that directs the attention of other lifeguards to the rescue and may bring other lifeguards or staff to the area near the rescue scene. Once control of the situation has been gained and the victim has been stabilized it's critical to signal to other lifeguards. This is done by using one of the four basic arm signals described in Chapter 11 (*Communication Methods*) and Appendix A. In this way the lifeguard indicates that the victim is under control; or that there is more assistance needed; or that this is a resuscitation case. Of course, if the victim could not be located, the lifeguard signals a Code X.

Retrieve

Once the victim has been stabilized and the signal has been given, the lifeguard will *retrieve* the victim to shore. In calm water conditions, the objective during retrieval is simply to reach water of standing depth. In heavy surf or current conditions, more careful route selection is needed.

If the victim is in a rip current, the lifeguard usually first swims out of the current before swimming toward shore. Rescues off rocky shores or near piers and other obstructions may also require lateral swimming before a turn is made toward the beach. Lifeguards should make every attempt to avoid swimming a victim to the beach through sets of very large surf. Lifeguards can either wait for a lull between sets of waves or swim the victim to deeper water for pickup by a lifeguard rescue boat or rescue helicopter, if available. Another alternative is to swim the victim to an adjacent beach area with less challenging surf conditions. While this may take time and energy, it may also be the safest method.

Once the route is determined, the victim should be informed. In most cases, with lifeguard instruction, the victim will be able to assist by holding firmly onto the rescue buoy and employing a flutter kick or frog kick. By using a backstroke, the lifeguard can maintain constant visual contact with the victim. If a crawl or breaststroke is used, the lifeguard should look back regularly to check on the victim. It's usually immediately apparent if the victim lets go, since there's no longer a pull from the RFD.

Victims should be instructed to continue holding the rescue buoy until told that they can release it. Upon approaching shore, victims often become more confident or simply embarrassed and let go of the rescue buoy. In rip current rescues a victim who releases the rescue buoy prematurely can easily be recirculated back into the rip current.

Credit: California State Parks Lifeguards

Lifeguard keeps a watch on the condition of two victims and incoming waves during retrieval.

While swimming to shore at a surf beach, lifeguards must remember to watch for incoming waves. If the victim will be taken in through large breaking waves, the victim should be advised of this and told how to prepare. The lifeguard gets behind the victim and hugs tightly under the armpits with the rescue buoy against the victim's chest. Just before the wave hits, the lifeguard can pinch the victim's nose with the thumb and forefinger and keep the rest of the hand over the victim's mouth to reduce the chances of water being swallowed or aspirated.

In situations where the victim is extremely weak or unconscious, the lifeguard will have to position the rescue buoy to provide support for the victim before beginning retrieval. Techniques for proper use of rescue buoys in these cases are detailed in Chapter 12 (*Standard Rescue Equipment*).

Remove

Once shallow water is reached, it may be a simple procedure to remove the victim to shore. In most rescues the victim needs little or no further assistance. Some agencies have established policies that require lifeguards to escort all victims completely out of the water to dry sand, even if the victim appears to need little or no assistance. In some situations, victims will need help leaving the water. Perhaps a weak or tired swimmer is having trouble maintaining balance or wading ashore. Other victims may be unconscious or barely lucid. In these situations, lifeguards will have to carry or assist them.

Lifeguards should consider several points important to removing victims from the water. First, lifeguards must have the strength and ability to extricate a victim without assistance. Although there are often other lifeguards, staff, or visitors present to assist

Credit: San Clemente Lifeguards

Lifeguards, with the aid of beach visitors, remove an unconscious victim from the water.

with extrication, there may be times when a lifeguard will have to accomplish removal alone. Second, lifeguards should use extrication techniques that will minimize the possibility of injury to themselves and to the victim, who may be heavy and unable to assist the lifeguard at all.

If a victim is able to assist to some degree during the removal process, a shallow water assist is recommended. To execute this technique, the lifeguard simply drapes one of the victim's arms around the back of the lifeguard's neck, holding the hand or forearm, and supporting the victim's waist with the other arm. Then the victim is gently directed out of the water to dry sand and assisted in sitting or lying down on the beach.

If a victim is unable to assist in the removal process, request additional assistance, if available. If not, a longitudinal drag is recommended. The lifeguard places one hand under each of the victim's armpits from behind and, while attempting to support the head with the forearms, drags victim up the beach. If any spinal injury is suspected, use techniques for stabilizing spinal injuries described in Chapter 18 (*Medical Care in the Aquatic Environment*) unless immediate extrication is needed to provide urgent medical aid or to remove the victim from immediate danger.

Credit: GLC Aquatic Safety Department

Lifeguards remove an unconscious victim from the water during training.

Assess

Assess all victims for possible complications after the rescue. This can be done rather informally in routine cases. Does the person have a steady or unsteady gait? Are the eyes clear? Does the person appear alert? Does the person seem fully oriented? In most cases this will be adequate.

It's a good practice to ask all victims if they are all right upon reaching shore. Can they take a deep breath without pain? Do they think they swallowed or inhaled (aspirated) water? In most cases it will be obvious if a person is feeling poorly, but lifeguards should be aware of the tendency of victims to deny problems. Often after the completion of a rescue everyone on the beach is watching. The victim feels very embarrassed and just wants to leave. Lifeguards should never release victims until reasonably certain they are fine. This is a good time to provide some brief safety advice. For details on assessment and treatment of drowning victims, including when they should be sent to the hospital, see Chapter 18 (*Medical Care in the Aquatic Environment*).

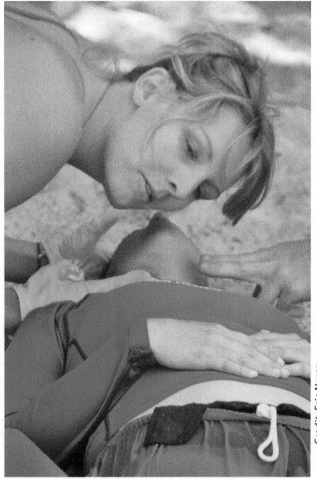

Credit: Eric Nurse

Report

The rescue *report* is critical for all lifeguard provider agencies. Rescue reports, including name and address of the victim, should be completed for every rescue performed by lifeguards. The report form should include information such as the name of the lifeguard, the time of day, and the date. USLA report forms can be downloaded from: www.usla.org/resources.

The USLA defines a water rescue of a swimmer as a case in which someone is judged to be in imminent peril and brought to safety by a lifeguard. This usually involves physical contact. It does not include cases where people are given oral instructions to move to a safer location. For reporting purposes, providing verbal commands or advice to swimmers in the water is considered to be an aspect of preventive lifeguarding, but not a rescue.

Statistics generated through the filing of rescue reports often provide the single most important information in determining the long-term need for lifeguard staffing and the budgets of lifeguard agencies. While stories about rescues are sometimes fascinating, agency administrators need hard facts about the volume of rescue activity when budget-based decisions must be made. This makes the accurate reporting of rescues critical to lifeguards concerned about ensuring that staffing levels at their agency meet the need. Some lifeguard managers remind their personnel that, "If you don't record it, it didn't happen." While in truth the rescue may have taken place, statistically it didn't happen if a rescue report wasn't filed.

The USLA compiles annual statistics on the number of rescues performed at beaches throughout the U.S. These statistics have proven essential in helping justify the value of adequate lifeguard staffing levels throughout the country and the need for lifeguard equipment. They are regularly the basis of media reports and research. Each open water lifeguard agency should report the rescues they perform annually to the USLA, using the USLA national lifesaving statistics form found on the USLA's website at: www.usla.org/statistics. Reports should be submitted within a month after the end of each calendar year. Seasonal agencies should report at the close of the season. United States Lifesaving Association certified agencies are required to report to maintain certification, but all beach lifeguard agencies are strongly encouraged to report. This public database is available to researchers, the policy-makers who decide the budgets of lifeguard agencies, the news media, and anyone else interested in knowing about the work of Americas open water lifeguards.

CHAPTER SUMMARY

In this chapter we have learned about the three components of a rescue and the steps involved in each component. The first component of a rescue is *recognize and respond*, which includes the steps: recognition, alert, equipment selection, and entry. The second component of a rescue is *contact and control*, which includes the steps: approach, contact, and stabilize. The third component is *signal and save*, which includes the steps: signal, retrieve, remove, assess, and report. We have also learned about defenses to prevent being grabbed by a victim and escapes in case this occurs.

DISCUSSION POINTS

- List the critical elements of a rescue.
- Recognize three signs of distress that a lifeguard may observe from an individual in the water.
- List three ways a lifeguard can alert others before initiating the rescue.
- Identify the primary reason to alert others before leaving on a rescue.
- Explain the transition process of a lifeguard entering the water and moving towards a victim.
- Describe how currents impact lifeguards swimming to a victim.
- Explain the process of the lifeguard entering the water transitions from running to swimming.
- Demonstrate the signals used by the on-shore lifeguards to the in-water lifeguards.

- Identify three reasons lifeguards should avoid direct contact with victims in the water.
- Describe how long a lifeguard should take to stabilize a victim before retrieval.
- List three methods of removing a victim from the water.
- Identify three reasons a victim should be assessed before releasing them.
- Explain the best method of releasing yourself from a panicked victim.
- List the critical elements of the front and rear head hold escape.
- Explain the importance of documenting each water rescue.

CHAPTER
14

Specialized Rescue Equipment

In this chapter you will be introduced to some of the specialized rescue equipment employed by lifeguard agencies that can help lifeguards do their jobs more efficiently. Some examples include emergency response vehicles, rescue boats, and aircraft. You will learn the advantages of different types of specialized rescue equipment and how each can be used effectively.

CHAPTER EXCERPT

Motorized rescue boats can often move to a rescue location much more quickly than free-swimming lifeguards, or even those in vehicles, and can cover longer distances with minimal lifeguard fatigue. They are particularly valuable at facilitating a rapid response to emergencies which occur well offshore, to remote beach areas, and to vessels in distress.

EMERGENCY VEHICLES

One of the most useful pieces of emergency equipment employed by lifeguards is the emergency vehicle. Common types of lifeguard emergency vehicles include all-terrain vehicles (ATV) or utility task vehicles (UTV), pickups, and sport utility vehicles (SUV). Emergency lifeguard vehicles are normally equipped with four wheel drive so that they can be driven on sand and other soft terrain. Emergency vehicles are usually equipped with lights and siren for emergency response on the street and on the beach, two-way radios, and public address systems. Standard equipment includes rescue flotation devices, a trauma kit, oxygen or resuscitator, rescue board, spinal immobilization device, and a stretcher (litter). Emergency vehicles may also carry an automatic external defibrillator (AED), flares, wetsuits, extra swim fins, mask and snorkel, and marker buoys for search and recovery. Some agencies also carry scuba, flood rescue, law enforcement, and cliff rescue gear.

Vehicles allow lifeguards to move quickly over significant distances, much faster and more efficiently than running lifeguards. Depending on their size, they can transport a significant number of lifeguards. They can be used to evacuate injured people from the beach and can tow rescue boats on trailers. They can also function as mobile

Credit: Leslie Schwene

A lifeguard rescue vehicle and the equipment it carries.

LEARN MORE

The USLA offers an educational video on beach emergency vehicle operations which you can purchase at: www.usla.org\store.

lifeguard stations. Lifeguard emergency vehicles are essential in many lifeguard systems, especially where large areas must be patrolled by limited numbers of lifeguards.

Operators of lifeguard emergency vehicles should be thoroughly trained in emergency response driving and in safe use of vehicles on the beach. Some lifeguard agencies have specific training courses for emergency vehicle drivers. This is highly recommended. In developing general training in emergency vehicle operations, local public safety agencies may be a source of information; but beach driving requires special skills to address the unusual mix of vehicles and beach patrons. Beach driving is not the same as street driving. There are rarely designated roadways or sidewalks on the beach to separate vehicles from people. Lifeguard agencies with experience in this area should be consulted by those desiring to create beach driving training programs. Of paramount concern in the operation of emergency vehicles is safety. As the size and speed of the rescue vehicle increases, so does the possibility of injury to lifeguards and beach patrons. Some basics of emergency driving are:

- Prioritize safety over speed
- Drive only as quickly as necessary
- If you don't get there, you're of no help
- If you cause injury in the act of responding to an emergency, you've defeated your purpose
- Follow all laws pertaining to emergency vehicle operation

Credit: Lindsey Gerkins

Even routine driving of emergency vehicles in the beach environment can pose hazards. People aren't usually alert for vehicles on the beach. Although the lifeguard vehicle may be big and brightly colored, people may not expect it or notice it. Small children have a tendency to run in front of lifeguard vehicles toward their parents when a vehicle approaches, particularly in emergency response situations. Parents will sometimes bolt in front of the vehicle to protect their children.

Heightened caution is also needed when traveling past pier pilings or other obstructions, such as large rocks. People can suddenly and unexpectedly appear from behind these sight obstructions.

When lifeguard vehicles are parked, beach patrons sometimes lie down right beside them, even in front or behind them. Lifeguards should never assume that because they are sitting in an idling vehicle, no one has sat down in the path of the vehicle while it was parked, even for a brief period of time. Before leaving from a parked position, the driver should exit the vehicle and visually check in front, behind, and beneath the vehicle. This inspection requires only a few seconds and ensures a safe path.

If the vehicle is to be parked on the beach or in a public area, it's a good idea to delineate the vehicle's parking area. This is ideally done by use of ropes and stanchions. It may also be done by use of traffic cones or flags, but people tend to walk right through these areas. Some lifeguard agencies fence off vehicle accessways to discourage pedestrian traffic and indicate areas where vehicles are likely to travel, increasing the likelihood (but not the certainty) that the area remains clear of beach patrons. Cordoning off an area for vehicle parking and access should be done at the start of shift, when beach attendance is low and there's plenty of area to reserve. Signs may also be used. Warning cones may also be placed around a parked vehicle to encourage people to stay back. The area around vehicles on the beach should then be kept clear of people at all times.

An emergency vehicle accessway is marked with cones and a sign which states, "STAY CLEAR, EMERGENCY VEHICLE ACCESS."

Credit: B. Chris Brewster

Lifeguard vehicles on routine beach patrol should be driven at an appropriate speed, which is normally very slow. During urgent or emergency responses beach patrons should be notified by emergency lights and sirens or beepers, as appropriate.

The three most dangerous moves are backing up, right turns, and driving over a berm. During these maneuvers the driver's visibility is impeded. Prior to ascending or descending a berm, the best visibility can be attained if the vehicle is positioned with the berm on the driver's side. Berms should be ascended or descended diagonally. If the driver can't see the path ahead, the driver should stop the vehicle and have the passenger check. If alone, stop and exit the vehicle to check the area before continuing. Lifeguards should never drive in any direction if they are unable to visually ensure a safe path and they should always remember how significant the blind spots are for the driver. Remember, you are not driving on the street where the most likely obstacle is another vehicle as large as yours. You are driving in an environment where a sitting

Credit: San Clemente Lifeguards

child or adult may not be visible due to the sight lines over your hood, to your left and right, and behind you.

RESCUE BOATS

Rescue boats were first used in this country by the original American lifesavers in the 1800s. The variety and sophistication of lifeguard rescue boats have advanced a long way since then. Some agencies still successfully employ variations of traditional manually powered lifesaving craft for purposes of offshore perimeter control and surveillance. As emergency response craft however, the value of these vessels has been eclipsed by motorized rescue boats.

In some states, training is mandated for the operation of motorized rescue boats. Regardless of state law, lifeguards operating rescue boats must first be thoroughly trained in their safe operation, particularly considering the proximity in which they will be operated to swimmers and the potential for injury they pose, including to lifeguards.

Rescue Boat Advantages

Size and Stability

Some rescue boats can support the operator and several victims completely out of the water. Thus, rescue of a victim and removal from the water can take place almost immediately, effectively fully resolving the victim's distress while still offshore. In a multiple victim rescue, lifeguards in a large motorized rescue boat can quickly rescue numerous distressed swimmers from the water, returning them to safety at a later time. This can also assist lifeguards effecting rescues with RFDs. Instead of taking their victims to shore, they can simply swim victims to the waiting rescue boat. In large surf or strong rip conditions, a rescue boat on the outside of the breakers is of particular value.

Credit: California State Parks Lifeguards

Rescue boats can accommodate multiple victims.

Patrol and Observation

Rescue boats, particularly motorized rescue boats, are excellent tools for lifeguard patrols. Lifeguards can patrol from most rescue boats for long periods with limited fatigue. Larger rescue boats can be equipped with much or all of the equipment carried in an emergency vehicle, essentially making it into a mobile, offshore lifeguard station.

Credit: California State Parks Lifeguards

Rescue boats serve as ideal platforms for surveillance from the outer edge of swimming areas.

Rescue boats can provide an observation platform on the outer edge of a swimming area or an offshore recreation area. This provides lifeguards with the ability to monitor these areas and user groups close up. It allows for early intervention and speedy rescue. Although rescue boats should generally not be used as a substitute for observation by a lifeguard on land, there are many situations where a boat-based lifeguard may be more effective. When glare or large surf conditions interfere with water surveillance by shore-based lifeguards, boat-based lifeguards can be of significant help. If there is considerable offshore activity, a rescue boat can provide additional coverage and surveillance. When evaluating the status of people who are offshore swimming, boating, or surfing, the boat based lifeguard can usually speak directly with the person, instead of trying to evaluate status visually from a distance, as must the shore-based lifeguard.

Speed

Motorized rescue boats can often move to a rescue location much more quickly than free-swimming lifeguards, or even those in vehicles, and can cover longer distances with minimal lifeguard fatigue. They are particularly valuable at facilitating a rapid response to emergencies which occur well offshore, at remote beach areas, and those involving vessels in distress. In areas with difficult accessibility to land entry, such as cliffs, or lack of beach or street access, rescue boats can quickly and effectively transport lifeguards to distressed swimmers, avoiding potentially dangerous terrain. Some types of motorized vessels can move through large surf with ease and can be reliably operated inside breaking surf. For lifeguard agencies serving large geographic areas, motorized rescue boats can respond to emergencies many miles away faster than vehicles impeded by traffic problems ashore; and upon arrival, the vessel is already offshore, where the problem is likely to be.

Versatility

Rescue boats can be used for general crowd control when water users need to be separated or swim area boundaries exist. During special events such as open water swimming competitions, lifeguards in motorized rescue vessels can easily monitor the status of swimmers on the course. Rescue boats are also useful in advising water users of shark sightings or other potential marine hazards, while ensuring the safety of the lifeguard. Rescue boats with a deck area allow for emergency medical treatment to begin while still in the water. This can greatly improve patient outcome in some cases.

Boat Rescue, Enforcement, and Firefighting

Credit: Valerie Due

A San Diego Lifeguard Service vessel with full firefighting capabilities that include a fixed nozzle over the wheelhouse, various attachments for firefighting hoses, and a separate engine that powers the pumps.

For some lifeguard agencies, a major responsibility of the rescue boat fleet is response and assistance to boaters in distress. The popularity of personal watercraft, kayaks, and kite surfing has added to the volume of these incidents. Larger rescue boats can be equipped for marine firefighting and using them lifeguards from several American lifeguard agencies are primary responders to boat, marina, and pier fires. Boats are extremely valuable in enforcement of boating regulations. One of the most frustrating experiences for a lifeguard is watching a boater operating dangerously close to a swimming crowd. While the shore-based lifeguard can do little about it, a lifeguard in a motorized rescue boat can quickly address the problem. Lifeguards from some agencies use rescue boats for general law enforcement, including boating safety enforcement and enforcement of environmental laws.

Rescue Boat Limitations

Size

Larger rescue boats must be berthed at a dock or pier. Because of their size and weight, boats can be dangerous in heavy surf and must be handled expertly when navigating the surfline. The boat can become a hazard to swimmers should it be overcome by surf.

Crowded Beaches

Heavy water attendance can cause challenges in effecting rescues from boats because of the area necessary to maneuver. Crowds can also make launching and retrieving a boat from shore difficult. Like motor vehicles on the beach, rescue boats must often be maneuvered very close to people and must therefore be operated with tremendous caution.

Wind and Waves

Because of their high profile in the water, rescue boats are subject to the forces of wind and waves. Although these challenges can usually be overcome with good operating skills, weather conditions can complicate a boat rescue to the point that other rescue equipment may sometimes be a better option. Heavy weather rescue boat operations require special operating skills and should not be undertaken without appropriate training.

Expense

Boats can be expensive to purchase and operate depending on their size and how they are equipped. Training requirements are proportional to the complexity of the vessel.

Personnel Requirements

Boats require operators. This may be obvious, but under most circumstances a rescue boat operator cannot leave the boat to effect a rescue. This is different from a lifeguard in a rescue vehicle, for example, who can park the vehicle and leave it to rescue a victim. On the other hand, in many cases the rescue boat can be brought directly alongside the struggling victim, unlike a vehicle. A properly equipped rescue vessel includes throwable flotation devices in case victims cannot be immediately brought aboard.

Types of Rescue Boats

A wide variety of boats are employed by lifeguards in carrying out their responsibilities. The following are the types most commonly employed by lifeguards at American beaches. Some agencies have boats of several types, employing different boats for different purposes. Lifeguards from these agencies can select the best tool for the job, depending on the circumstances of the rescue. Other agencies focus on a single boat design for purposes of economy and to help limit training time.

Personal Watercraft

Personal watercraft (PWC)—also referred to as personal rescue craft—are typically less than 13 feet in length and have a basic V hull configuration. They are steered through use of a jet of water directed toward the stern by a motorized pump and usually directionally controlled by handlebars. The jet drive avoids the hazard of a propeller and allows the vessel to be operated in relatively shallow water; however, a PWC cannot be effectively steered unless water is coming from the jet. Operators who suddenly back the throttle down to idle can leave themselves unable to control forward direction.

Personal watercraft are very effectively used by many lifeguard agencies. They are highly maneuverable, have a relatively low maintenance cost, are typically unaffected by being capsized (or rolled), and are sometimes

PWC are fast and highly maneuverable.

Credit: Diana Schwene

LEARN MORE

The USLA has developed training and equipment guidelines for rescuers using personal watercraft as a rescue tool, which you can find at: www.usla.org/guidelines.

available from the manufacturers on a loan basis, thus limiting cost. Appropriate training is essential prior to operation and rescue procedures, although learning to master the PWC generally requires less training than larger motorized rescue boats. A single lifeguard without a crewmember can operate a PWC. While these craft typically weigh 500–800 pounds, they can be beach launched with assistance of a properly designed dolly. Personal watercraft are valuable in breaking surf. They can also be very effective in open water swells and even in high wind conditions.

The high speed of PWC makes it essential that the operator vigilantly monitor the surrounding area for swimmers and other craft. They can be operated near large swimming crowds by skilled lifeguards, but their hard hulls are unforgiving if a swimmer is struck. It's also important for the operator to take care not to become launched into the air over a wave. Personal watercraft leave the operator exposed and often wet. They are therefore not well-suited to cold environments.

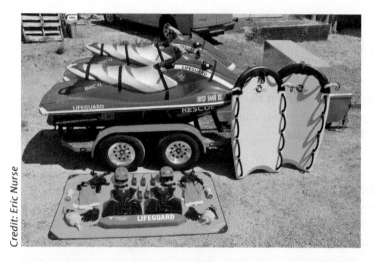

Credit: Eric Nurse

Like other boats, PWC have mandatory equipment requirements according to federal law. These requirements include a lifejacket for each person on board, fire extinguisher, sound producing device, and backfire flame arrester. State regulations may require the wearing of PFDs and may prohibit nighttime operation. Additional personal protection equipment recommended by the USLA includes a helmet, visor, gloves, goggles, exposure suit (wet or drysuit), and footwear. Many PWC have kill switches to ensure that if the operator becomes separated from the PWC, the motor turns off. These are usually activated when a lanyard, attached to the operator, pulls the switch. It's important to always attach this lanyard to the operator prior to operation, as well as to don appropriate personal protective equipment.

Most PWC are designed to hold only an operator and one or two passengers. Thus, rescue capacity is limited. Furthermore, it can be difficult and dangerous to attempt to pull a victim out of the water and aboard a PWC, since they ride high

Credit: Kekai Brown

A PWC with operator and a crewmember aboard a sled

in the water and can be unstable when not underway (which can lead to rollover). The best solution is the rescue sled, which is towed behind the PWC and greatly enhances rescue capabilities. The sled allows for a second lifeguard to ride prone or kneeling behind the PWC. This lifeguard is responsible for the rescue and emergency medical treatment of victims brought aboard the craft, while the PWC operator is responsible for safe operation. Rescues sleds allow for quick and efficient multiple victim rescues and transport of more than one person at a time. The use of a PWC without an appropriate rescue sled is not recommended.

Desirable characteristics in rescue sleds are lightweight, yet rigid (or inflatable) construction, multiple handles along the perimeter of the sled, and a top surface that provides enough friction to keep the crewmember from sliding, but not so much so as to tear wetsuit material or cause abrasions to the lifeguard or victim. It's also advantageous to have reinforced handles that do not protrude through the bottom of the sled. The size and shape of sleds vary by manufacturer. Rescue sleds should have a template that matches, or is narrower than the trough, or wake, created by the PWC when underway. The forward end of the sled should ride high enough to avoid pearling (submersion of the nose of the sled).

The attachment system is an important element in the way the rescue sled integrates with the PWC and its ability to maneuver. If only a single point connection is used (similar to the trailer hitch on a car), the sled can pivot in a wide arc, causing problems of maneuverability and safety. On the other hand, a rigidly attached sled that does not articulate during turns impedes the ability to turn the PWC and decreases the overall turning radius. To avoid this, a three point attachment system is typically used. The center tow point allows the sled to pivot, but the two side points prevent over-articulation to either side.

Inflatable Rescue Boats (IRBs)

Inflatable rescue boats (IRBs), also known as inshore rescue boats, were first employed by the lifesavers of Australia and New Zealand. These boats are typically 12 to 14 feet in length and utilize a small outboard of 25 to 35 horsepower for propulsion. Most often they are staffed by an operator and a crewmember, who sit on opposite gunwales while holding handles. The relatively low weight of these craft (about 300 pounds) allows them to be moved and launched fairly easily by two to four people. To keep the vessels light, fuel cans are replaced with fuel bladders made of a synthetic material. A propeller guard is commonly attached to the outboard for safety. This is highly recommended.

IRBs are versatile boats. Used by trained operators they can successfully handle very large surf conditions and be operated in the surfline for extended periods of time. These boats are relatively fast, because they draw little water as they skim across the surface, but not as fast as a PWC. They can be launched from a beach or

Inflatable Rescue Boat (IRB). Note the propeller guard.

returned to the beach with relative ease. As a result, like the PWC, a nearby harbor is not needed and response is immediate. An IRB can hold several victims. In a mass rescue situation, the IRB can be used as a raft to which many victims can cling until brought to the beach individually by swimming lifeguards. Inflatable rescue boats can be successfully employed in very close proximity to large swimming crowds with limited danger presented.

Inflatable rescue boats have detractions. They are small open boats wherein the operator and crew can be subjected to heavy bouncing over waves and wet conditions. Inflatable rescue boats are less reliable in high wind conditions because of their flat bottoms and light weight. A well trained operator can turn an IRB in a very tight circle, but when used to tow other vessels, IRBs are very difficult to steer due to lack of a deep keel. Inflatable rescue boats can be inexpensively maintained, but require regular maintenance. When caught in the wrong orientation by a breaking wave, IRBs can flip. Even in this circumstance however, they are generally less hazardous than other types of rescue boats because of their soft sides. Properly employed restart procedures can result in complete salvage of an outboard that has been fully doused.

Credit: California State Parks Lifeguards

A lifeguard exits a rescue boat from the stern with fins and rescue tube.

**Hard hull rescue boats come in different configurations. This one is modified with a wave deflector to allow punching through an incoming wave while shipping minimum water.
Note the lip on the wave deflector to minimize water hitting the operator in the face.**

Rigid Hull Vessels

Some lifeguard agencies operate large, motorized rigid hull vessels, equipped for full service response to swimming rescues, boat rescues (including fires and towing services), and other emergencies. These vessels can be equipped with a full complement of rescue and emergency gear such as two-way radios, firefighting equipment, positioning equipment, medical gear, scuba gear, depth finders, and public address equipment. At some agencies, these vessels combine traditional lifeguard duties with those of harbor patrol, general law enforcement, and special rescue missions.

Rigid hull vessels are particularly useful for offshore rescues or for long distance rescues to remote beach areas. They can carry numerous victims from the head of a rip current. They can also accommodate a victim on a stretcher or allow for full CPR. Some lifeguard agencies operate rigid hull rescue boats inside the surf in a manner similar to an IRB; however, this is uncommon and requires special skills. Large, rigid hull rescue boats offer the greatest degree of protection for operator and crew. Depending on their size, most larger rigid hull vessels are either difficult to beach launch or cannot be beach launched at all. A nearby harbor is usually needed, along with docks and storage facilities.

Rowed Boats

In a few areas, such as New Jersey and the Great Lakes, rowed rescue boats remain in use. These boats are most typically known as lifeboats, surfboats, dories, or rowboats. Usually they are rowed by one or two lifeguards.

Manually powered boats include hollow draft surf rescue dories and skiffs designed to cut through the surf. Rescue dories feature a square stern that facilitates foot placement for the rear crewmember, who can propel the boat from a forward facing standing position. The square stern also allows boarding of the victim over the transom. On the surf beaches of the Great Lakes and at many other inland lakes, a wide variety of wood, fiberglass, and aluminum boats are employed.

Rowed vessels are dependable in that they do not rely on motors, which can fail. They are clean, in that they involve no emission of used or unused fuel. Compared to powered vessels however, rowed vessels are very slow and easily delayed or even stopped by surf conditions. In almost every case, a swimming lifeguard responding from the beach will reach a distressed victim more quickly than a vessel which is launched and rowed to the victim. On the other hand, when deployed outside the swimming crowd, the lifeguard aboard a rowed rescue boat can quickly observe and rescue a distressed victim.

Kayaks

The least expensive type of rescue boat is the kayak. Kayaks used for rescue have a sealed floatation chamber—the lifeguard sits atop the craft. While less versatile than a motorized rescue boat, kayaks are light, maneuverable, and in some ways superior to a paddleboard for observation. The open top kayaks used in lifeguarding are typically plastic, highly maneuverable craft that can carry a lifejacket, rescue buoy, and limited medical gear. Kayaks are easily carried to the water's edge by a single lifeguard.

A kayak used by lifeguards on Lake Erie.

Kayaks provide a relatively dry platform for patrol and observation. Lifeguards in kayaks can sit in an erect position, easily observed by swimmers. These craft can be useful for rapid approach, control, and stabilization of a victim or multiple victims. Retrieval though, is more difficult. With minimal skills, lifeguards can propel kayaks quickly through light and moderate surf. Kayaks are particularly useful in choppy light surf conditions that make the use of rescue boards or dories difficult.

Stand-Up Paddleboards

Credit: Stephe McCormick

Lifeguard at a special event using a stand-up paddleboard.

Stand-up paddleboards are primarily used as a platform for observing swimming crowds and special events. They have the capability of being used like a rescue board to assist swimmers in distress. Operators can more easily stand up on them than a rescue board, offering the advantage on an elevated viewing position.

Use of Rescue Boats

The following is an overview of the techniques commonly used to operate lifeguard rescue boats. Actual operation of rescue boats, particularly motorized rescue boats in the surf environment, requires extensive training under the supervision of a skilled and experienced operator.

Alert

The most common source of alert to the need for a rescue boat response is observation by a shore-based lifeguard. A rescue boat may be sent because the victim is a significant distance from shore, because there are multiple victims, or because a patrolling rescue boat is close to the victims. There are a variety of other reasons to utilize a rescue boat, but these are the most common.

Boat operators may also observe distress while on patrol. Lifeguards in a rescue boat are at a lower level than lifeguards in an observation tower and lack the vantage point for broad observation of the entire swim area, but they are also much closer to the swimming crowd and can make more direct evaluations of those who appear to be in distress. At some agencies, lifeguards in rescue boats are expected to patrol unguarded beaches that, due to remoteness and low attendance, lack on-site lifeguard supervision. In these cases they may be the only source of supervision, albeit sporadic.

Lifeguards in rescue boats may be alerted to vessels in distress by observation of a flare, waving flags, whistles, or by a marine radio broadcast. The marine VHF radio band is publicly available to all mariners and many boaters carry them. By monitoring the calling and distress frequency (Channel 16), lifeguard rescue boat operators and crew can keep abreast of emergency calls initiated by boaters. Boaters also carry mobile phones and some prefer them over VHF radios, but 9-1-1 operators are typically not as well prepared to deal with boating emergencies as the U.S. Coast Guard, which monitors Channel 16 at all times.

When lifeguards ashore spot a problem that calls for a rescue boat response, they must have a method to immediately alert a patrolling rescue boat crew. Likewise, when lifeguards in a rescue boat observe people in distress requiring their assistance, they need a reliable method to alert lifeguards ashore of the incident so that proper backup can be sent. Effective use of rescue boats requires two-way radio communication capabilities, both to shore and to other rescue boats. For boats whose operators will be directly exposed to the water, these radios must be waterproof or in waterproof containers. Voice activated microphones on headsets can allow rescue boat operators to transmit and receive radio traffic while navigating the vessel with both hands.

When radio communications break down or in cases that radio communications are not available, it's important to have a backup method. This may include an air horn, flag, etc., but these methods are unreliable and limited in value, in that lifeguards ashore cannot provide details on the nature of the rescue, while lifeguards in the rescue vessel cannot provide information on victim status or other observations.

Entry

When a drowning presentation is detected by lifeguards patrolling in a boat they can move directly from alert to contact and control of the victim. Beach-based boats however, will have to go through an entry. At flatwater beaches, boats can be positioned at water's edge with the bow of the boat in the water, ready for response. At surf beaches, boats will usually be positioned on the beach close to the waterline, but above the uprush. If significant tidal changes are present, the boat will need to be moved regularly to keep it close to the shoreline. Some agencies utilize rollers placed under the hull of the boat or small trailers to facilitate launching.

Boats should be prepared for immediate use, with all equipment aboard and accessible. Proper preparation and maintenance is required to ensure that when an emergency occurs, the boat is fully serviceable. A motorized rescue boat will be of little use, and perhaps seriously impede an expeditious rescue response, if the motor won't start. For this reason, lifeguards should never completely rely on a boat response to a rescue. A lifeguard ashore should always be prepared to effect the rescue if the boat response fails.

Safe entry protocols require that the launch area first be cleared of water users. Flatwater entry is straightforward—lifeguards simply push off from shore and respond; but surf entry can be very challenging, particular in larger surf. It's important to select an area with few or no swimmers around. There's always the possibility of losing control of the boat in the surf and having the boat pushed to shore by incoming waves, striking swimmers. It's also difficult to see over waves to determine whether a swimmer is ahead, and if the operator is focusing on getting through breaking waves, attention can be distracted.

The general rule of operating a rescue vessel in the surfline is that the boat should be kept perpendicular to incoming waves and foam lines of broken waves. This presents the least resistance to the power of the waves and allows the design of the vessel to efficiently deflect wave energy. Skilled operators of motorized craft can learn to take broken waves at almost parallel angles while the vessel is moving forward at significant speed, but this requires advanced training.

Inflatable rescue boats and PWCs normally require two lifeguards, an operator and crewmember (rescuer). Entry with these craft is quite similar. At first, both lifeguards push the boat toward an adequate depth for rowing, for the IRB outboard to be dropped from the cocked position without striking bottom, or so that the PWC jet will not to draw sand and other debris into the jet drive pump. Once this depth is reached, one lifeguard boards the vessel while the other keeps the bow perpendicular to oncoming waves. The

Credit: San Clemente Lifeguards

Launching a PWC using a cart with balloon tires, which will be left behind.

goal is to prepare to exert forward momentum adequate to make way against the waves before the second lifeguard boards the vessel. The PWC operator boards the craft, ensures that the safety lanyard (kill switch) is attached to the operator, then starts the motor. Once the operator gives the command, the second lifeguard boards the rescue sled. The IRB operator starts the engine. Once the lifeguard in either vessel determines that forward progress can be made which will allow the boat to make headway without further assistance from the lifeguard in the water, this lifeguard is advised to climb aboard.

The position of the operator of an IRB is usually sitting on the *port* (left facing forward) pontoon near the stern. The crewmember sits on the *starboard* (right facing forward) pontoon toward the bow. These positions help keep the vessel balanced, with the operator able to steer and adjust the throttle.

Timing is everything when navigating an IRB around the surf break. The operator must exit before the wave breaks (as here) or wait until after the wave breaks. Being on the wave when it breaks can result in capsizing.

An essential role of the lifeguard in command of a rescue boat is to avoid taking a direct hit from a breaking wave. This can injure the crew; it can swamp an IRB, killing the engine; it can significantly impede the progress of a manually powered rescue boat or carry it all the way to shore; and it can knock the operator and crew member off a PWC or rescue sled. In any case, the rescue boat response is slowed or curtailed and people inshore of the boat can be threatened by the incoming boat.

In larger surf, boat operators time their approach to traverse the surfline carefully, often hanging inshore of the breakers until the boat can be moved quickly forward between breaking waves. The inside of the surf break is a difficult area in which to maneuver because the water is moving shoreward so quickly and the water is heavily aerated, providing low buoyancy; but a breaking wave is most dangerous and to be avoided. In large surf, operators of IRBs and PWC may operate the craft back and forth inside the breakers, waiting for the right moment to make it through.

When a two-person rescue boat is clearly about to be caught by a breaking wave which will break directly on top of it, the lifeguard in command of the vessel advises the crewperson. In an IRB, the crewperson braces by grabbing the bow line and lying face down between the bow pontoons, head first. This maneuver adds weight to the bow to reduce the chance of the boat riding up the wave and being flipped.

On a PWC, the best action on the part of the operator is to flatten to the seat. The lifeguard riding on the rescue sled presses tightly to the sled while holding tightly with one hand on a side handle and the other on an opposite forward handle. The crewmember's head position is down and away from the stern of the PWC to avoid impact.

The operator of a motorized craft may decide to try to punch through the wave in a last minute burst of speed. This may allow the boat to avoid much of the power of the wave which would otherwise break directly on the vessel. In any case, a direct perpendicular orientation to the wave is critical or the boat will likely broach, possibly flip, and be pushed ashore.

Credit: Lindsey Gerkins

Great care must be taken if the rescue boat rides up the steep face of a wave about to break and when the bow plunges downward on the other side. Powered vessels are very susceptible to being launched over an incoming wave and becoming airborne. Lifeguards can be seriously injured or even ejected from the boat. Personal watercraft are particularly prone to this problem due to their high power and speed, but any boat can become airborne given the right circumstances. The goal in all cases is to get to the other side of the wave without being caught in the break, but to try to stay in contact with the water at all times. This is done by using no more forward power than is needed to get past the wave and by rapidly decelerating as soon as it is clear that the boat will reach the other side. With all rescue craft, when operating in breaking waves it is critical that operators plan their route to ensure that swimmers, surfers, and others are not placed in peril should the craft be disabled or lose power.

Contact and Control

Safely approaching a victim with a rescue boat, particularly in rough conditions, requires great skill and extensive practice. The obvious goal is to rescue the victim expeditiously without further injury. If the propeller, the boat hull, or an oar strikes the victim, injury is likely. In rescue boats with two lifeguards aboard, if a safe approach will be difficult or the victim's condition is poor, one lifeguard can simply enter the water with an RFD to assist the victim, then swim the victim to the waiting rescue boat.

In flatwater or gentle swells outside the surfline, an IRB is simply brought alongside the victim and the victim is brought in over a pontoon with the assistance of the

Credit: California State Parks Lifeguards

Positioning a victim on a rescue sled.

Credit: Lindsey Gerkins

crewmember (preferably over the mid to forward portion of the port pontoon). The transom is not used because of the hazard presented by the outboard. On a PWC with a lone operator, the victim is helped aboard with a one arm assist from the operator, who must take care not to allow too much weight to shift to one side. If a rescue sled is towed, the boat is positioned so that the victim can be grabbed by the lifeguard on the sled and held there in a prone position, usually under the arms of the lifeguard, who grabs the outer handles of the sled.

The most difficult area to effect a boat-based rescue is inside breaking surf. Generally, only the IRB and PWC are suitable for rescues in this zone because they are able to maintain position inside breaking surf without being overcome. In either case, the idea is to bring the vessel alongside the victim maintaining a constant bow out (toward the breaking surf) position. The victim is then brought abroad as previously explained. It's critical to effect this action quickly when inside the surfline, because maneuverability is limited when operating beside a victim and being caught by a wave beside a victim can be perilous for all involved.

Highly skilled IRB and PWC operators utilize a maneuver in critical rescues between breaking waves which can rapidly extricate a victim. This involves approaching the victim at moderate speed and turning sharply around the victim in a counter-clockwise direction. In the case of the IRB, this brings the port pontoon down to water level. The crewmember leans over from the starboard side and grabs the outstretched arms or armpits of the victim. The victim is then rolled into the boat. For the PWC, the operator maneuvers the craft to locate the rescue sled in a position that the crewmember can grab and roll the victim onto the rescue sled as the operator accelerates away from the breaking wave. Due to the hazard involved, this technique is appropriate only for highly skilled operators in critical situations.

Larger rescue vessels generally approach the surfline from the outside and back down into the waves, keeping the bow out. A crewmember then jumps into the water and brings the victim out to the rescue boat. Great caution is needed in operating large rescue boats near the surf because of the danger involved in having a large hard hull vessel overcome and pushed into the beach toward swimmers. The high gunnels and bow create blind spots somewhat similar to an emergency vehicle on the beach. It's important to ensure that no swimmers have come close to the vessel while it is idling.

Retrieval

Once the victim has been brought aboard the rescue vessel or sled, expeditious retrieval to shore is not normally necessary. Exceptions include cases where the victim needs medical attention or where the rescue vessel is immediately needed for response to other emergencies. Usually however, lifeguards can take the time to carefully consider the return route to shore.

For flatwater, the rescue boat is simply returned to shore. Returning to shore in significant surf conditions requires careful planning and timing. The lifeguard in charge should first select the best area for this return. Considerations include avoiding areas where swimmers are present, selecting areas with less severe surf breaks (if available), and bringing the vessel to a safe shore area (devoid of rocks, debris, etc.).

Beaching a PWC.

Powered vessels that can be beached can normally outrun incoming surf. The operator waits to gauge the incoming sets of waves, then simply drives straight to shore between breaking waves. As an IRB approaches shallow water, the operator kills the engine and raises it to the cocked position. This is very important because striking even a sandy bottom can damage the engine and transom. Personal watercraft can be accelerated over breaking waves and the operator stops the jet prior to running the craft up onto the beach. It's important to ensure the beach area is clear as the craft can travel a considerable distance up the beach depending on the speed of exit.

Rowed boats usually cannot outrun the surf and if caught by the surf may seriously imperil the swim crowd. If there is a significant hazard in retrieval of the victim to the beach, an alternative is to simply swim the victim to shore with a crewmember from the rescue boat or a lifeguard from shore.

Credit: Kekai Brown

Credit: Joel Gitelson

BOAT TOW

The boat tow is one of the simplest and least expensive pieces of rescue equipment a lifeguard will use. It can make the difference in successfully rescuing boats worth tens of thousands of dollars and the occupants. A boat tow is a length of sturdy line approximately six feet long, with a loop spliced in one end and a large snap hook on the other end. When a boat is observed to be in distress, perhaps disabled and drifting toward rocks or surf, the lifeguard runs the boat tow through the rear handle of a rescue buoy and pulls the snap end through the loop end of the line. The snap end of the line is then pulled tight. There is now a six foot piece of line securely fastened to the rear handle of the rescue buoy, with a snap hook on the far end. The lifeguard swims to the boat and clips the hook into the bow eye of the boat. The lifeguard then swims the boat away from danger. This process is surprisingly effective for vessels up to 30' long and larger. Swim fins are highly desirable when using a boat tow. Little progress will be made without them.

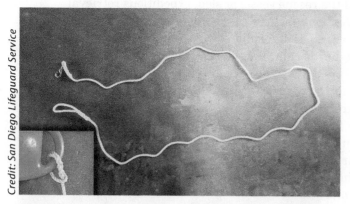

Credit: San Diego Lifeguard Service

A boat tow device is a length of sturdy line with a clasp to allow a lifeguard with a rescue buoy to tow a boat away from danger.

The lifeguard using a boat tow must always be prepared to jettison the rescue buoy if the vessel is caught by surf while the tow is underway. The lifeguard must also maintain a position so that the lifeguard is not caught between an incoming wave and the boat. The goal in using a boat tow is to tow the vessel from immediate danger. Once this is accomplished, if there is an anchor aboard it is used. If a rescue boat is available, it is dispatched to take over the tow.

AIRCRAFT

Few lifeguard agencies have aircraft available for regular use; but many agencies have rescue, medical, and law enforcement aircraft they can call upon when needed. Fixed wing aircraft can be useful for covering wide areas in the case of an offshore search, but are of little value in nearshore work. Of all the forms of transportation available to lifeguard agencies, the helicopter is the fastest, most agile, and most versatile.

Helicopters can transport lifeguards over long distances expeditiously, then drop them to victims. Properly equipped helicopters can lift victims and lifeguards from the water. This is particularly valuable in very large surf conditions where the victim is taken outside the surfline or in rescues of people aboard offshore boats. Larger helicopters can be configured to carry PWC to an offshore location where they can be deployed by being pushed out the door.

Credit: Nicholas Enns

Lifeguards deployed from helicopters can reach difficult locations quickly.

Helicopters are ideal in searches for people lost at sea because of their high vantage point and mobility. When necessary, they can be used to transport medical supplies to offshore locations or drop pumps to sinking vessels. Helicopters can provide night lighting for water and cliff rescues. They can also be extremely valuable in flood rescues, when victims are trapped by moving or rising water. Some lifeguard agencies develop a working agreement with a helicopter provider that results in having a helicopter on standby for large surf conditions, heavy crowds, or inclement weather.

Victim Extrication Using Aircraft

There are two primary methods of extricating victims from the aquatic environment using helicopters—hoist (winch system) and static line. The hoist is typically available on larger helicopters specially equipped for rescue, notably those of the U.S. Coast Guard. The static line method is used by smaller helicopters which lack powered hoists.

The U.S. Coast Guard generally uses a basket into which the victim can crawl or a yoke system (also known as a horse collar) to attach the rescue line to the victim. The yoke is simply a circle of material similar to fire hose. It's placed over the victim's head and under the armpits with the hoist line on the victim's front side. As the victim is hoisted, the circle closes and the victim holds the sides.

Static line rescue systems for helicopters with no hoist typically employ a pouch made of netting attached to the end of the line. The net is lowered into the water and the victim climbs inside. Once the victim is inside, the helicopter pilot lifts off. An injured victim in a stretcher can be evacuated using either the hoist or static system so long as a proper harness is used that will keep the stretcher level and the victim is properly strapped inside.

Credit: Cole Yeatts

US Coast guard hoists rescue swimmer and victim.

A third extrication method, sometimes used in flood rescue, is to have a helicopter actually touch down one skid or even land, allowing the victim to climb inside. The one skid method is extremely challenging for a helicopter pilot in that flight must be maintained simultaneous to touching a stationary object. The simple addition of weight to one side of a helicopter from a victim boarding can cause the aircraft to yaw, creating the potential for a loss of airworthiness.

Helicopters build up static electricity which is discharged upon touching the ground. In order to create a partial discharge without hazard when a metal cable is lowered to the lifeguard or victim, the cable should first be allowed to touch the boat deck, water, or ground. Once this contact is made, there is no further concern for this discharge, as the winch cable will continually act as a ground.

It is vital that a cable or line attached to a helicopter never be secured to a rescue vessel, unless it is a small rescue vessel being hoisted. Helicopters must have the freedom to move according to changing wind currents and cannot in any way be secured to substantial surface craft.

When removing a victim from a boat, helicopter pilots often prefer to head into the wind and maintain minimum airspeed for stability. This requires that the boat be headed in the same direction at the same speed.

Landing on a Beach

If a helicopter must be landed on a beach, lifeguards must create and maintain a secure landing zone (LZ) of adequate size. As a general rule, an LZ which is 100 feet in diameter should be considered a minimum. Helicopter pilots also appreciate the existence of a wind indicator in the immediate area, but outside the LZ. This can simply be a flag atop a lifeguard station, for example, or a smoke bomb. Another option is to draw a large arrow in the sand pointing toward the prevailing wind direction.

The rotor wash of a landing or departing helicopter creates a small windstorm which can carry sand for hundreds of feet. It can also blow beach items like umbrellas and tents, which can injure beachgoers. When a helicopter is expected to land on a beach, beach patrons should be advised to collapse umbrellas and secure light items.

A helicopter landing on a beach always draws a crowd. Adequate crowd control measures should be implemented prior to landing. It's a good practice to summon local police well in advance of landing a helicopter on a crowded beach so that they can assist in securing the LZ. Lifeguards should remember that they are not immune to the problems of rotor wash. Experienced lifeguards take shelter behind emergency vehicles or

Credit: Jon Menzies

other stationary objects to protect themselves during landing and take-off—the times of most intense rotor wash. Helicopters hovering over water can create a tremendous amount of water disturbance and noise which can be very disorienting and curtail verbal communication.

While helicopters are extremely valuable for lifeguard rescue, extensive training is needed before lifeguards can properly employ them. Lifeguards must be very knowledgeable about protocols to be used when approaching a helicopter on the ground, because the blades can be lethal. When working in close quarters with a helicopter it's important to keep eye contact with the pilot if at all possible and to be prepared to back off quickly if necessary.

These concerns notwithstanding, with proper skill and training of the personnel involved, helicopters are an invaluable tool for lifeguards. It is strongly recommended that lifeguard agencies with the local availability of helicopters create appropriate liaisons, develop contingency plans, and conduct regular training exercises.

LANDLINE

The typical landline device is a length of line (usually 200 or more yards), with a snap hook on the lead end and a spliced loop or snap hook on the tail end. It is kept coiled on a reel or laid in an easily transported, open container. Some agencies keep their landlines in inexpensive plastic laundry baskets.

The landline provides a shore-based link to the rescuer as the rescuer swims to the victim. There are safety concerns related to entanglement, so a quick release harness is essential. This must be a release that works effectively under stress. The rescuer dons the harness of the landline or attaches the end of the line to an RFD and swims to the victim. Once control and stabilization are attained, assistants ashore can retrieve both the rescuer and victim(s) by pulling in the line. Therefore, while the rescuer must swim the line to the victim, once the victim is reached, no further swimming is necessary.

While use of the landline is in decline as it is supplanted by lifeguards with swim fins, motorized rescue boats, and other lifesaving tools, it remains in use in a few areas, sometimes required by regulation. In some cases, public safety agencies whose employees may not meet standards recommended by USLA, such as fire department and rescue squads, use landlines, primarily to reduce safety risks to rescuers. Standard protocols in these cases involve rescuers wearing PFDs, swim fins, and, depending on water temperature, wetsuits. (The USLA does not recommend that any person engage in in-water rescue unless trained in accordance with the USLA *Lifeguard Agency Certification Program* or *Aquatic Rescue Response Team* certification program—www.usla. org/certification.)

Landlines contribute drag on the swimming rescuer and therefore slow approach to the victim(s). A lifeguard with swim fins and an RFD will almost always get to the victim more quickly. Landlines require more than one lifeguard to perform a rescue, even of a single swimmer. Landlines require significant training and coordination for effective use. They are not a preferred method of rescue, but where used, lifeguards should be thoroughly trained in their use.

CHAPTER SUMMARY

In this chapter we have learned about some of the specialized rescue equipment used by lifeguards. We have learned about lifeguard emergency vehicles, which can move lifeguards and equipment rapidly over land, but which require careful operation. We have learned about rescue boats of a wide variety, which can enhance lifeguard surveillance, patrol, and response to aquatic emergencies. We have learned about the value of aircraft, particularly helicopters. We have learned about boat tows.

DISCUSSION POINTS

- List five advantages of using a lifeguard emergency vehicle.
- Identify the equipment that should be carried in a lifeguard emergency vehicle.
- Describe three incidents that would involve using an emergency vehicle.
- List five actions that allow lifeguards to avoid injury to beach patrons while operating emergency vehicles.
- Describe the advantages and disadvantages of using a rescue boat.
- What characteristics differentiate a personal watercraft (PWC) from other rescue boats?
- List three advantages of using an inflatable rescue boat.
- Identify the reasons that most hard-hull rescue boats normally stay outside the surfline.
- List five safety considerations when using a helicopter for emergency operations.
- Identify the reasons that a lifeguard using a boat tow must be prepared at all times to disconnect from the RFD harness.

CHAPTER
15

Special Rescues

In this chapter you will learn about special types of rescue situations. The majority of rescues are routine, requiring basic rescue skills covered earlier in this manual. Yet not all rescues are of a routine nature. Here we will learn about a variety of special types of rescues, such as surfer rescues, diver rescues, rescues of people attempting suicide, rescues in fog or darkness, boat rescues, automobiles in the water, rescues of shark bite victims, flood rescues, ice rescues, and cliff rescues. With the exception of rip current rescues at surf beaches, special rescues are less frequent than other rescues and often much more challenging. Thorough training and preparation are essential to ensuring that special rescues are successful.

CHAPTER EXCERPT

Effective use of lifesaving equipment increases the efficiency of rescue, while providing additional safety for the lifeguard. All lifeguards should be provided with the equipment necessary to successfully effect rescues.

Regardless of the complexity of a rescue, the three components of a rescue are always followed. As a reminder, these are:

1. Recognize and Respond
2. Contact and Control
3. Signal and Save

MULTIPLE VICTIM RESCUE

Lifeguards are sometimes faced with two or more victims in a distress or panic presentation. These multiple victim rescues (also known as mass rescues) present unique challenges.

Multiple victim rescues commonly occur when:

- A panicked person grabs onto another for support, but the other person is incapable of providing support or rescue
- A current suddenly sweeps several people into deep water

- A boat capsizes or sinks forcing victims into the water
- An unexpected wave washes bystanders into the water
- A would-be rescuer becomes a victim in a failed attempt at rescue

The two keys to successful rescue of multiple victims are *flotation* and *backup*. Adequate flotation is essential to allow lifeguards to gain control of a rescue. Panic is usually greatly diminished once victims have something to hold on to, which keeps their heads above the water. This also diminishes the immediacy of the need for immediate retrieval. The victims may still be caught in a current and being pulled away from shore, causing significant alarm, but the immediate fear of submersion is eliminated.

If available, a lifeguard selecting equipment for a rescue that may involve several people can take more than one RFD. At beaches where multiple victim rescues occur with regularity, large rescue buoys should be standard equipment, since they can provide flotation to more victims. A rescue board can be extremely valuable for a multiple victim rescue. Although it can be difficult to rescue several people using a rescue board in the surf environment, the speed and superior flotation provided by the rescue board can be utilized until backup lifeguards arrive. Lifeguards using a rescue board should also tow an RFD in the event the rescue board is lost, ensuring that the victim(s) will still have a means of flotation. The rescue board is particularly valuable at a flatwater beach where the lifeguard can quickly access the victims, then slowly move toward shore with all of them holding on.

Credit: Rich Schlatter

Boat staged to assist with multiple victims.

Backup is critical on mass rescues because the responding lifeguard may be unable to complete the rescue alone. Information provided in the initial alert by the lifeguard who first spots the emergency unfolding is very important. If this lifeguard advises of the need for backup, it can be dispatched expeditiously, simultaneous to the first lifeguard entering the water. If no backup is immediately available and the lifeguard is unable to adequately control the situation, other people nearby with flotation devices can be solicited for help. Several victims can hold onto a surfboard or bodyboard, for example, until additional lifeguards arrive to bring them ashore. Caution should be exercised though, when requesting help from untrained citizens. Lifeguards should closely monitor the situation, taking control of the most critical victims.

A rescue boat is an excellent tool for a mass rescue. If large enough, the victims can be brought aboard. If smaller, like an IRB, the boat can simply be used as a raft for flotation until the victims can be ferried ashore by swimming lifeguards.

As a general rule, a lifeguard should not swim past one victim to reach another. If the lifeguard is approaching a victim and sees another further out, the lifeguard may choose to tow the first victim to the second or leave the RFD with the first victim and swim to the second without equipment, physically supporting that victim until backup arrives. Similarly, when using a rescue board the lifeguard may leave the RFD with the first victim, then paddle to the second. In cases where several victims are some distance apart, the lifeguard should try to select the person in the most immediate distress and assist that victim first, then move to the next most distressed person, and so forth. Swim fins are particularly valuable when a lifeguard must support a victim without an RFD and also to swim multiple victims back to shore.

RESCUES WITHOUT EQUIPMENT

Effective use of lifesaving equipment increases the efficiency of rescue, while providing additional safety for the lifeguard. All lifeguards should be provided with the equipment necessary to successfully effect rescues. Nevertheless, lifeguards must be prepared to effect rescues without equipment if none is available. This may occur in a multiple victim rescue if the RFD must be given up to support one victim, while another is aided elsewhere. Another possibility is that rescue equipment may be lost or damaged on a rescue. While off-duty, the lifeguard may be at an unguarded beach when a drowning presentation is recognized. These are just a few examples.

- **Alert**—In the case of an off-duty rescue attempt, it is crucial to ensure that someone, somewhere knows that a rescuer is in the water on a rescue. Call for help. Draw someone's attention. Direct bystanders to call 9-1-1.

- **Equipment Selection**—Look around quickly. Can something nearby be adapted to use as rescue equipment? Are there ring buoys mounted nearby? Does anything nearby float that can be pushed out to the victim? Are others using flotation devices that can be used? Can some object be extended to the victim to prevent direct contact with a panicked victim? A shirt? Rope? How about a surfboard? Many items can be used to improvise rescue equipment.

- **Approach and Contact**—Sometimes victims in distress can make it to shore with encouragement. If so, avoid contact, calm them, and try to talk them in. Even if you can't talk them in, try to calm and assure them that you will help them, so that they are less fearful and less likely to grab you. A rescuer forced to approach a victim without equipment should try to approach from the rear. This can be difficult or impossible because the victim's tendency is to turn to watch the rescuer, if able. Swim wide and circle around the victim or dive underneath the victim and surface behind. Move swiftly to control the situation. If the victim is clothed, try grabbing their collar and tow using sidestroke. If this is not feasible, one of the following three tows may be effective:

  - **Cross-Chest Tow**—Throw one arm over the victim's shoulder and across the chest until your hand is in contact with the victim's side just below the victim's armpit. Immediately secure the victim between the arm and hip (right arm to right hip or left to left). The victim's shoulder should be secured in the rescuer's armpit. Concentrate on keeping the victim's face out of water. While this control method supports the victim and maintains an airway, it may not place the victim in a position that produces a

Credit: Pete DeQuincy

Cross chest tow.

Credit: Pete DeQuincy

Modified cross chest tow.

feeling of security, with the face and head out of the water. Struggling may continue as the victim attempts to lean forward out of the water.

- **Modified Cross-Chest Tow**—Quickly place an arm under the victim's arms and across the lower chest (or upper abdomen) of the victim to secure the victim between the arm and hip (right arm to right hip or left to left). The victim's buttocks should be supported on the rescuer's hip. This position usually provides enough support to allow the victim to lean forward and remove the head from the water. Panic usually subsides more quickly; but this position may result in the lifeguard remaining nearly or fully submerged, due to the added weight being supported out of the water. This position should be used when there is a short retrieval distance to standing depth, since the lifeguard will not be able to maintain this tow for long.

- **Armpit Tow**—The rescuer takes a position facing the victim's back. The hands grasp the victim under the armpits with the thumbs up and the arms slightly bent at the elbow. The rescuer uses a breaststroke kick, rotary kick, or any other effective kick to return to shore. An alternative is to grasp with only one hand, moving to shore with a kick and single stroke. The major advantage of this retrieval method is that the victim is kept high in the water. The major disadvantage is very limited control. It is not normally effective for a surf retrieval.

Credit: Pete DeQuincy

Credit: Pete DeQuincy

Armpit tow with two and one arm.

- **Stabilize**—Attempt to reduce the victim's panic while providing support by using a breaststroke or sidestroke kick. Additional support and momentum can be gained by sculling or pulling the water with the free arm. If the victim struggles, the free arm can be moved to lock onto the supporting arm, pulling the victim more tightly to the supporting hip. If this is unsuccessful, move the free arm to the victim's back and quickly push the victim away. Swim away, reconsider the approach and try again to gain control.

- **Retrieve**—Once control is gained, turn and make progress toward shore using a stroke appropriate to the type of tow.

- **Assess**—Treat or resuscitate the victim if necessary. Be prepared to assist responding personnel in completing necessary reports.

SURFER AND BODYBOARDER RESCUES

Most surfers and bodyboarders have above average water skills. They also have with them an excellent flotation device. In the surf environment, most use leashes so that they don't lose their board. Don't assume however, that a surfer or bodyboarder will not need rescue just because they have flotation. Not all users of these devices are skilled. Bodyboarders without fins can struggle greatly in a rip, since they have only their kick for propulsion. Leashes can break and sometimes injuries occur when a fiberglass surfboard or the skeg strikes a person. Some surfers are novices who end up flailing in a rip current.

Signs of surfer or bodyboarder distress include:

- **Bodyboarders Arm Paddling**—Bodyboards are designed to be propelled by kicking and most users employ swim fins. The use of arm strokes indicates weak ability and possibly distress or panic.

- **Surfers Trying to Kick**—Unlike bodyboarders, surfers propel themselves by arm paddling, not kicking. A surfer who attempts to use a kick may be showing signs of distress or panic. This usually indicates a novice.

- **Surfboard Positioned Sideways**—A surfer who tries to use a swim kick to move forward may find this very difficult because the surfboard keeps the feet above the water. Some will turn the board sideways, so that their feet are in the water, but their body is out of the water. This is a sign of a novice surfer with very limited ability.

- **Imbalanced Surfboard**—Surfers who are not well balanced on their board with either the nose of the board plowing through the water or the nose elevated well above the surface indicates limited experience.

- **Weak Paddling or Kicking**—Surfers making little progress while paddling and bodyboarders with a weak or flailing kick are likely novice and may be in distress.

- **Falling Off**—Surfers and bodyboarders who continually fall off the board are likely novice.

- **Losing or Abandoning the Board**—Surfers and bodyboarders who lose the board or abandon it may not only be novice, they may be poor swimmers in immediate need of rescue. The use of leashes greatly lessens the possibility of drowning and should therefore be encouraged.

- **Caught by a Rip Current**—Experienced surfers and bodyboarders may use a rip current to quickly make their way offshore, just as a lifeguard might; but most avoid these areas once they reach the surfline. Waves usually don't break well in a rip current due to depth of the rip current channel and conflicting water movement. A surfer or bodyboarder who lingers in a rip current is probably a novice and may quickly tire.

- **Struggling in Large Surf Conditions**—Even highly experienced surfers can get into serious trouble in big surf conditions. They may lose their board and be left far offshore. They may be struck by their board or held underwater for an extended period. Don't assume that because surfers are experienced, they will never need assistance.

When surfers or bodyboarders need rescue, the three components of a rescue are employed. In many cases, the board can be used to help stabilize and control the victim prior to retrieval. Caution should be used however, in returning to the shore through the

Credit: California State Parks Lifeguards

Lifeguard retrieves bodyboarder to rescue boat stationed outside surfline.

surfline with a victim who has a surfboard. The board can cause serious injury or be lost to the waves, injuring swimmers toward shore. One alternative is to allow the board to be pushed to shore by the waves in an area where swimmers will not be endangered, then to swim the victim in with an RFD. Another is to use a rescue boat.

Occasionally surfers and bodyboarders become trapped outside the surfline at rocky beaches. This occurs because the victim is able to paddle out through the surf away from shore, but is fearful of being injured on the rocks upon return to shore. The responding lifeguard may also conclude that a safe retrieval is unlikely, particularly in large surf. In these cases, it's usually best to summon a rescue boat or helicopter for assistance outside the surfline.

While rare, surfers using leashes can become entangled in pier pilings, or fish, crab, or lobster trap lines. This has caused drowning deaths. These situations are extremely hazardous, especially in large surf conditions, making the job of responding lifeguards difficult. Agencies with these conditions should train for them and keep equipment on hand to help expeditiously resolve the situation. A hooked safety knife (similar to a seat belt cutter) is an effective tool for cutting surfboard leashes and buoy lines. Preventive actions, when possible, are recommended. In California, the Fish and Game Code (section 9002) was amended at the request of surf lifeguards to allow them to lawfully remove a trap, buoy, or line located in or near breaking surf or adjacent to a public beach if they believe that the trap poses a public safety hazard.

In rescues of wave riders, spinal injury should be considered a possibility. Sometimes the victim will go over the falls—that is, be caught by the breaking wave and dumped in its force. If the victim strikes bottom or is torqued in heavy surf, spinal injury can result.

ROCK, REEF, AND JETTY RESCUE

When compared to smooth, sandy beaches, rescues from rocky shores or reefs can be quite difficult and dangerous for lifeguards, especially in surf conditions where incoming waves can throw a lifeguard into the hard surface. Rocks and reefs often have barnacles, mussels, or other sharp sea-life attached to them that can cause serious lacerations. Urchins may be present in tide pools. Rocks can be very slippery, particularly when seaweed is attached, and it's easy to fall during response and retrieval.

While rescue procedures at rock and reef areas involve the three basic components of all rescues (recognize and respond, contact and control, signal and save), special considerations are in order. The following is a partial list:

- **Protect Your Feet**—Water entry can sometimes be made easier by donning swim fins for foot protection prior to entering the water. Another option is amphibious footwear. The benefits of foot protection should be carefully weighed against maneuverability.

- **Wear a Wetsuit**—Use of a wetsuit can greatly diminish the potential for injury from blunt force injuries or from being abraded.

- **Use Care During Entry Dives**—Shallow diving entries can be made from ledges, docks, and outcroppings, but should be made with great care to avoid head injury. Keep hands extended above the head and plan the shallowest dive possible. In surf conditions, dives should normally be timed for entry into the high point of a wave rather than the trough between waves. Wait for the upsurge of the arriving wave and jump into it.

- **Swim Away Quickly**—Begin swimming as soon as possible upon entry into the water, even in knee to waist-deep water. Continue to keep the hands in front to feel for and fend off rocks.

- **Beware of Underwater Obstructions**—Avoid ducking under incoming waves unless water depth is known.

- **Expect Unexpected Waves**—The surf can break suddenly and unexpectedly due to underwater rocks and reefs that lessen depth. This can cause unpredictable surf breaks.

- **Retrieve to a Safe Area**—Once the victim has been approached and controlled, retrieval should be made away from rock or reef shores if at all possible, especially in surf conditions. This is an excellent circumstance for rescue boat backup. Another option is a long retrieval swim to the relative safety of a neighboring sandy beach. The time and effort involved may greatly reduce the potential for injury.

- **Protect Yourself and the Victim**—A primary rule for lifeguards involved in rescues near rocks is to protect themselves first. The lifeguard will be of no assistance if injured and a serious injury to the lifeguard will greatly delay assistance to the victim. If it's absolutely necessary to make a retrieval to a rocky shore in surf conditions, stay close to the victim rather than towing the victim behind on the RFD. If using a rescue buoy, position it in front of the victim, reach under the arms of the victim (from the victim's back) to grasp the handles, and use the RFD to fend off the rocks or reef during retrieval as needed.

- **Know the Area**—The greatest aid to lifeguard response at rock and reef areas is experience and knowledge of the area. Those who work at these areas should get to know them well by studying them in all weather and tide conditions. Underwater rock and reef formations should be of particular interest.

Credit: California State Parks Lifeguards

Credit: Nicholas Enns

Rock rescue training.

PIER RESCUE

At many surf beaches across the U.S., piers on reinforced pilings extend out past the surfline. Unlike piers at flatwater beaches, surf piers are usually constructed at a considerable height over the water to protect the pier deck and any structures upon it from the highest anticipated surf. Most of the time, they are therefore well above the sea surface. Piers provide fishing opportunities, scenic promenades, and special activity or amusement areas for beach visitors.

Credit: Diana Schwene

Surf piers can pose challenges for lifeguards. Pier pilings contribute to the formation of rip currents and magnify their intensity. They are unyielding to those pushed into them. Pier pilings are a collection point for fishing lines and sea life, presenting the possibility of entanglement to surfers and swimmers. People sometimes fall or jump from piers. Piers can even become attractive, if not dangerous, challenges for imprudent surfers, sailboarders, and boaters who may try to navigate through the pilings.

To save time on a rescue response near a pier, lifeguards may choose to jump from the pier rather than approaching from the water. Special training and regular practice is required for this entry method. To safely accomplish a pier entry, the lifeguard must know the water depths at every point around the pier. These water depths can be influenced by tides, surf, and sand movement. There may also be flotsam in the water that can cause serious injury. Normally, the best option is to enter outside the surf break. The water will be deepest if the lifeguard times the jump to enter the water on an incoming swell.

Entries from piers should only be made where the water is known to be deep enough. They should be made feet first. The proper entry method is to hold the RFD in one hand and swim fins in the other. Jump well clear of the pier, preferably on the side that is shoreward of incoming waves. The RFD is raised over the head vertically in one hand and swim fins in the other. The legs are crossed to protect the groin. Eyes are focused on the horizon to avoid eye injury upon water contact. As the feet hit the water, the lifeguard should let go of the rescue buoy. This helps to avoid shoulder injury as the buoyancy of the RFD might otherwise pull on the arm during submersion. Swim fins that float are of great value in pier entries, because upon hitting the water lifeguards can lose their grip on them.

Lifeguards should pay particular attention to prevent having the RFD lanyard become wrapped around a pier piling. This is especially important in large surf conditions. Injury can result when the force of a wave pushes a trailing RFD around a piling. To avoid this situation, the RFD should be held in front of the lifeguard when maneuvering through pilings, with any excess line in hand.

Panicked victims are sometimes inclined to grasp pier pilings and to try to climb them. Crustaceans and shellfish on the pilings can cause painful wounds, as can water movement, which grates the victim's skin against the rough surface of the piling. Still, it's sometimes difficult to convince victims to release the piling in favor of the support of the RFD. In some situations, it will be necessary to forcibly remove the victim from the piling. Once this has been accomplished, the lifeguard should move the victim a safe distance away from the pier as rapidly as possible, normally to the side of the pier away from the prevailing swell direction, and then to shore or a rescue boat. In the event of entanglement, a knife may be required to free the victim. Careful maneuvering when near pier pilings is crucial, with the RFD placed in a position to be used as a fender. The lifeguard must take care at all times to watch for incoming waves that may drive both lifeguard and victim into the pilings.

BOAT RESCUE

Distressed boats can present life-guards with several rescue situations, ranging from stalled craft needing assistance to serious boat collisions. How a lifeguard agency responds to boat rescues will depend, in part, on the equipment available to lifeguard staff.

At larger agencies, lifeguard rescue vessels can be used for a wide range of boat rescues, including towing and firefighting. At smaller agencies, lifeguards may have to respond to serious boat accidents as first responders, relying on other agencies or individuals to provide the equipment necessary for the safe recovery

Credit: B. Chris Brewster

How a lifeguard agency responds to boat rescues will depend, in part, on the equipment available to lifeguard staff.

of boats and their passengers. Whatever the response policies of a lifeguard agency, there are several points for lifeguards to consider in making boat rescues:

- **Recognition**—Distress clues for boaters can be obvious or subtle. A collision, capsizing, fire, or explosion, for example, indicate a need for immediate assistance. Other presentations may be more subtle. Sailboarders who appear to be in control of a craft may actually be stranded offshore, unable to return against the wind. Small capsized sailboats may be in distress, or involved in training exercises. The following are some indications of possible distress:

  - Smoke or fire
  - People working on a boat engine
  - People on board waving anxiously toward shore
  - A boat positioned broadside to the wind or waves
  - Boats with no one on board or on deck
  - Boats continually circling
  - Sailboats continually *in irons* or with the sail luffing
  - Repeated falling from a sailboard, especially when no progress is made toward shore
  - Any boat approaching a surfline or swim area with obvious lack of control

- A boat that is making no progress, especially if occupants are paddling against the wind
- A kayak sidewise to the wind, current, or waves
- People in the water near the boat
- A boat is low in the water or submerged
- A sail-powered craft with the sail down
- A vessel has flipped and either no one is trying to right it or they are unable to right it
- A boat that is drifting

- **Alert**—In determining if a response is necessary, lifeguards should remember the established area of responsibility. Boat problems outside of it should be immediately reported to the proper agencies for their response, but if lifeguards can provide lifesaving assistance, agency policy usually calls for a lifeguard response regardless. If a lifeguard response is appropriate, the alert should contain enough information to inform backup staff of the situation and required equipment.

- **Equipment Selection**—Rescue boats, rescue buoys, and swim fins are good equipment choices for response to boat rescues. If a swimming approach will be used, a boat tow should be fastened to the rescue buoy. If there is any indication of spilled fuel in the water, face masks should be taken for eye protection.

- **Approach**—Great care should be taken in approaching any motorboat still under power. When approaching a boat drifting toward the surf, avoid an approach from the shoreward side of the vessel. A disabled vessel may overturn at any moment due to wave action. Instead, approach from the seaward side. Warn swimmers in danger of being struck by the boat to move away immediately. During approach, if there are people from the boat who are now in the water, identify those most in need of assistance and aid them first. Ensure, through conversation with the skipper and passengers, that all passengers are accounted for. If you will need to board the boat, explain to the skipper your intentions. If lifeguards will be in the water around the boat, advise the skipper to turn the engine off and remove the key from the ignition (for your personal safety). For sailing vessels, direct the crew to drop the sails. In any case, ask if an anchor is available and can be deployed, since avoiding having the vessel in the surf is a paramount goal. Carefully evaluate the potential for fire. For example, a slick or the smell of gasoline may indicate leaking fuel. If the boat is in a safe condition and a safe position, encourage people to stay with the boat for support and direct them to don lifejackets while awaiting backup assistance.

- **Signal**—Once initial control has been gained and the situation is assessed, signal ashore to indicate if backup response is necessary. In serious boat accidents, lifeguards should continue to stabilize victims while awaiting backup assistance. In flatwater conditions or well offshore from breaking surf, anchors may be dropped. When backup assistance arrives, injured passengers can be immobilized if necessary and extricated to stable vessels for retrieval.

- **Flatwater Retrieval**—In the case of minor problems involving disabled boats or inexperienced operators, the lifeguard can offer to retrieve the boat and passengers. Small, capsized sailboats can often be righted. Swamped or capsized small craft can usually be towed ashore with passengers aboard or holding on. Sailboarders can drop their sail across the board and be towed ashore while riding the board. To assist by towing, clip the boat tow into the bow eye of the craft to be towed. The lifeguard can then swim, paddle, or row, while towing the rescued vessel and passengers.

- **Surf Retrieval**—Disabled vessels approaching the surf present a dangerous situation for passengers, lifeguards, and beach visitors. Should the vessel enter the surfline and be catapulted through it, serious injury and damage can occur. To prevent this, lifeguards will often have to assist by keeping the craft out of the surfline, while awaiting backup assistance from a rescue vessel. Depending on surf conditions, towing a vessel up to about thirty feet in length can usually be accomplished by a single lifeguard equipped with a boat tow and swim fins—see Chapter 14 (*Specialized Rescue Equipment*). Upon approaching a boat (from the seaward side), the lifeguard should gain permission to give assistance and request that lifejackets be donned by the passengers. Request that running engines (if providing no propulsion) be stopped (with the key removed from the ignition) and that sails be dropped. If anchors are being used, but are not effective in stopping progress toward the surfline, they should be retrieved. Clip the end of the boat tow into the bow eye. The lifeguard can now swim the boat away from the surfline to calmer water to await rescue vessel assistance. The lifeguard must always be prepared to jettison the RFD if the boat being towed is overcome by a wave. If towing cannot prevent a disabled boat from entering the surfline or if the boat swamps, passengers should be directed to jump off to the seaward side. Rescue efforts in the water are now focused on people who have abandoned the craft, while efforts ashore focus on clearing the water and minimizing damage to the boat.

- **Ensuring All Are Accounted For**—The lifeguard should query the boat passengers to ensure that no one is missing.

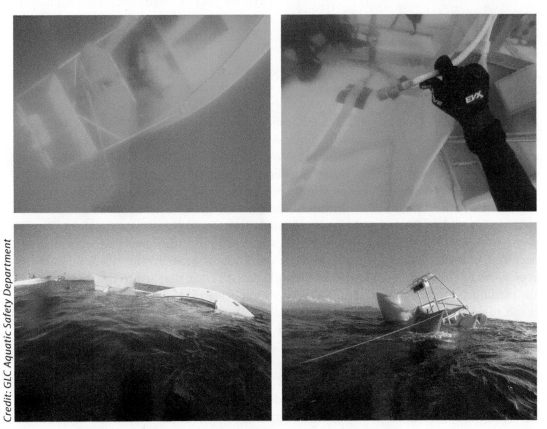

Credit: GLC Aquatic Safety Department

A submerged vessel is raised using inflatable lift-bags, then towed to shore.

DIVER RESCUE

In many beach areas, people skin dive (diving with mask, fins, and snorkel) and scuba dive (using compressed air tanks). Lifeguards are encouraged to become scuba certified. This training provides insight into the sport and helps greatly in understanding scuba rescue techniques, as well as the pathophysiology of diving injuries. For a full discussion of diving injuries, refer to Chapter 19 (*Scuba Related Illness and Treatment*).

Skin diver rescues are no different than those of swimmers, with exception of the fact that a typical source of panic is having the mask fill with water. Often, simply removing the mask resolves the problem. Since skin divers do not breathe compressed air, they are not susceptible to related problems. Rescues of scuba divers are more involved.

Credit: California State Parks Lifeguards

Red flag with white diagonal line alerts other vessels that divers are in the area.

All scuba divers should be trained and certified prior to diving on their own. Several national organizations certify instructors, who certify scuba divers. Reputable dive shops will not provide compressed air refills to people without a training certification card. In addition to a mask, snorkel, swim fins, and often a wetsuit, scuba divers use a tank of compressed air (not pure oxygen) and a regulator. The regulator reduces the pressure of compressed air in the tank to a lesser pressure which can be breathed without damaging the lungs.

Scuba divers also use weights and a *buoyancy compensator* (BC). Weights counteract the natural surface buoyancy of a fully equipped diver so that the diver can submerge more easily. They may be carried around the waist on a weight belt or integrated into the BC. Since scuba divers become progressively less buoyant as they descend, the BC, which is most often an inflatable vest, is gradually inflated by the diver using compressed air from the tank. Divers attempt to maintain neutral buoyancy or to be slightly positively or negatively buoyant to aid in ascending or descending. This requires adjustment of the amount of air in the BC when moving from one depth to another.

As explained in Chapter 19 (*Scuba Related Illness and Treatment*) drowning is the reported cause of over 50% of diving deaths, with cardiovascular disease responsible for over 20% of diving deaths, and arterial gas embolism responsible for about 10%. However, cardiovascular disease is the leading disabling factor that led to death. (It is also the leading cause of death in the U.S.) Many complications of diving underwater might result in death by drowning, including running out of air, entrapment or entanglement, equipment malfunction, or panic. More than half the scuba divers in a national survey reported experiencing panic or near-panic behavior on one or more occasions.

Running out of air is demonstrative of very poor judgment and is a factor completely under the control of the diver (except in the rare case of equipment malfunction). Divers are strongly encouraged to use the buddy system, diving in pairs, so that if one diver has trouble the other can assist. A significant proportion of diving fatalities are sustained by solo divers and divers who have become separated from their buddy. For this reason, a lone diver may be viewed as a high risk taker. When two divers embark from shore and one surfaces alone, lifeguards should be very concerned. This means the buddy is now diving alone and may be in distress.

Divers can become entrapped by entanglement in weeds (particularly kelp) or fishing line or inside a confined space, such as a submerged wreck or cave. Divers are encouraged to carry knives to cut themselves free of entanglement. Diving gear is heavy on the surface and use of it can strain the cardiovascular system. An obese diver should be viewed as a high risk candidate for rescue.

Lifeguards with experience in diver rescue know that preventive lifeguarding involves first sizing up divers before they enter the water. In conversation, lifeguards can learn whether the diver is certified and the level of experience. They can be sure that weights are fastened with quick releases and note the location of the release. They can look for ill-fitting equipment, which may indicate that it is borrowed and the diver is novice. If divers are drinking alcohol before a dive, they should be cautioned not to dive. Good judgment is critical while diving and alcohol impairs judgment. It's a good practice to warn divers of any unusually rough or hazardous conditions. Responsible divers will simply avoid diving on a day that conditions are poor. If appropriate, advise divers of a safer, alternate location. Giving an alternative can often assist in persuading the diver not to venture out in hazardous conditions.

Divers use hand and arm signals to indicate when they are doing all right. The most commonly used is the OK hand signal, made by forming a circle with the thumb and forefinger. Another is the overhead OK signal, which is similar to the USLA approved arm signal for lifeguards. The diver touches one hand to the top of the head, forming a circle with the arm. Divers also use hand and arm signals to indicate distress.

OK   **OK**   **Assistance Needed**

Signs of distress of a diver may include:

- Waving toward shore
- Blowing a whistle
- Surfacing alone with no sign of the buddy
- Surfacing and remaining motionless
- Breaking the surface very suddenly or even explosively

- Hurriedly ripping off a mask or other equipment
- Mask on the forehead or off the face
- Swimming toward shore, but making no progress

Diver rescues follow the three components of all rescues: recognize and respond; contact and control; signal and save. The initial alert to other rescuers prior to entering the water is particularly important in the case of scuba divers. In these rescues there is a heightened potential for physiological complications contributing to the distress and diver rescues are generally more difficult than those of people swimming without equipment.

When approaching a diver in apparent distress, the lifeguard should ask about the nature of the problem, if it's not obvious. Divers have their own source of buoyancy, though they may become panicked and forget to use it. Other sources of distress are a physiological problem related to diving, a current, or separation from the buddy. The presence of the lifeguard usually significantly reduces fear. Approaching from the rear is appropriate as the rescue takes place.

Caution should be used in the approach. Divers often have spears or spearguns with them, which can be lethal. If the diver has a spear or speargun, it should be handled very carefully and always kept pointed away. If necessary to safely complete the rescue, it should be jettisoned.

If the diver is having a buoyancy problem, there are two immediate options.

- Inflate the BC
- Jettison the weight belt or weights in the vest

The BC is usually inflated via breathing into a mouthpiece or by triggering an automatic inflator valve attached to the BC. Some BCs have a CO_2 cartridge which can be triggered too quickly, fully inflate the BC. You can also pull the quick release buckle on the weight belt, jettisoning it. This of course results in loss of equipment and should be avoided unless clearly necessary for rescue. The lifeguard's RFD may provide sufficient buoyancy, but if a diver is negatively weighted, inflating the BC or releasing the weight belt is sometimes necessary and can significantly increase comfort of the diver.

Once buoyancy has been stabilized, any obstruction should be removed from the diver's face. A relaxed diver may prefer to leave the mask on and even continue breathing from the tank. For a panicked diver, it may be necessary to remove the mask and snorkel or regulator from the mouth. Tow the diver by holding onto the top of the tank where the regulator is attached or by having them hold onto the RFD. Diver rescue techniques should be practiced by lifeguards working in areas frequented by divers.

A swimming lifeguard with buoy and fins is ill-equipped to perform an underwater search for a missing diver who may be in very deep water or some distance away. Usually such searches require trained dive teams. Nevertheless, the first responding lifeguard can make a few quick surface dives to perform a hasty search and look for bubbles on the surface.

If a diver is observed beneath the surface who is tangled in something, a surface dive should be performed in an attempt to assist. A knife in the possession of either the diver or lifeguard can be very helpful in such cases, but should be used with caution. Releasing the diver from the entangled equipment by opening quick release buckles may also be effective. If an apparently lifeless diver is observed beneath the surface, the lifeguard should dive down, release the victim's weight belt, and swim to the surface with the victim. The BC should not be inflated unless this is necessary to bring the diver to the surface, since rapid inflation of the BC of a submerged diver can cause the diver to rocket to the surface. Upon reaching the surface, establish positive buoyancy, signal for assistance, and begin rescue breathing.

Credit: B. Chris Brewster

Lifeguard retrieves conscious scuba diver.

Retrieval of a conscious, distressed diver is essentially the same as for any victim, but complicated by the equipment and relative lack of mobility of the diver. Surf rescues of divers can be hazardous because the tank and regulator can strike the lifeguard, causing serious injury including loss of consciousness. Appropriate caution should be utilized and, if necessary, the equipment can be removed.

Rescued divers should be carefully evaluated for physiological complications related to breathing compressed air. Sometimes these problems are instantaneous, other times they become evident after the dive. Such complications can be immediately life-threatening and should be taken very seriously. Sometimes lifeguards learn of such problems when an afflicted diver walks up to the lifeguard for medical advice. For information on recognition and treatment of diving illness, see Chapter 19 (*Scuba Related Illness and Treatment*).

Lifeguards in rescue boats should be made aware of divers submerged in the patrol area so that they can be avoided. Divers sometimes use a flotation device to mark their location and to warn boaters. The most common is an inner tube with a diver flag. The flag is either red with a diagonal white stripe or the alpha flag, which is a white and blue flag with blue dovetails.

FUGITIVE RETRIEVAL

Lifeguards at some agencies have police powers, at others they do not. Regardless, occasionally suspects of crimes attempt to elude arrest by escaping into the water and lifeguards are called upon to retrieve them. How this is handled is a matter of agency protocol. This section provides some general advice.

Often suspects in such cases are actually very poor swimmers and simply desperate to get away. In these cases, superior water skills usually place lifeguards at a distinct advantage. There are several important considerations in these cases:

- **Maintain Personal Safety**—The primary concern of the lifeguard in these cases should be personal safety. Avoid any confrontation likely to result in injury.

- **Wait for Police Backup**—Usually, a suspect has been chased into the water by police and they are nearby. If qualified law enforcement personnel are not at the scene, summon them and wait for their arrival. The situation is better managed by leaving the suspect in the water than by bringing the suspect to shore without someone to take control of them.

- **Is a Weapon Involved?**—Lifeguards should determine if a weapon is involved before any approach. A handgun may be usable even after being submerged and a knife is a hazard regardless.

- **Take Your Time**—While police officers often become very concerned in these cases and desirous of immediate action, rapid intervention is not called for unless the suspect is drowning. Many times, it is best to simply watch the fugitive from nearby and wait. In fact, the more time passes, the more fatigued the suspect becomes, reducing the likelihood of effective resistance. Eventually, the fugitive may actually request assistance. Be prepared though, for immediate rescue as necessary.

If it is decided to approach the victim, it's highly recommended to use at least two lifeguards, as one may be able to approach from the fugitive's rear. Upon approach, lifeguards should first try to talk the fugitive into surrender. A reminder to the fugitive that there is no escape may be successful. Often, the simple fact that people are approaching in the water causes the suspect to give up, realizing the hopelessness of the situation. Lifeguards should always try to avoid direct contact with victims. This is particularly true for fugitives.

If this is unsuccessful, lifeguards should work to a position that requires the fugitive to turn away from one lifeguard. The lifeguard who is able to work behind the fugitive, then immediately throws an arm over the shoulder and across the chest. The wrist of that arm is grabbed by the other hand for additional control.

If the fugitive is a poor swimmer, the control of the lifeguard is likely to cause a cessation of resistance. If not, the lifeguard should try to kick in toward shore while maintaining a grasp of the fugitive. If control is lost, kick away. As in the case of a panicked victim, the best escape if the fugitive grabs the lifeguard is to submerge and wait until the fugitive releases to surface for air.

SUICIDE ATTEMPTS

It's not uncommon for people to try to take their own lives in or near the water. People may jump from piers, cliffs, or bridges. They may swim offshore. They may even attach themselves to weights. They may drive cars into the water. While many suicide attempts will occur at more remote areas or at times when lifeguards are not present, lifeguards may be called to respond.

The most difficult aspect of a suicide presentation is the fact that those attempting suicide may not want to be rescued. They may swim away from approaching lifeguards and refuse to grasp extended RFDs. In these situations, it may be necessary to take physical control using techniques described for fugitive retrieval. Another option is stay nearby, but to wait for the person to tire. This will ultimately help reduce resistance. Stay near enough however, so that if the person intentionally submerges, immediate retrieval from below the surface is possible.

It's recommended that two or more lifeguards participate in approaching a person attempting suicide, as responders can expect resistance from initial contact through and perhaps beyond removal from the water. Response to a suspected suicide attempt should automatically trigger a call for police assistance, since a weapon may be involved and police will eventually be needed to transport the person to a treatment facility.

Responses to suicide attempts involving jumpers attached to weights can be particularly difficult for lifeguards as these presentations are often very sudden and involve immediate submersion presentations. Search procedures should be initiated upon arrival at the scene and may require tools necessary to free victims from attached weights.

Suicide incidents can be very stressful for lifeguards. For more information on dealing with stress see Chapter 16 (*Lifeguard Health and Safety*).

FOG AND NIGHT RESCUE

Fog and darkness have a similar effect of drastically reducing visibility. They also reduce beach activity, so the volume of rescues declines as well. Nonetheless, rescues that do occur in these conditions are typically more difficult for a variety of reasons. Lifeguards need to be prepared for rescues in fog and darkness.

People sometimes travel to the beach from areas where no fog is present, only to find the beach shrouded in fog. Fog may also appear quickly and unexpectedly. In either case, lifeguards may be placed in a position where protection of swimmers must continue when the primary means of victim recognition—visual scanning—is greatly diminished or eliminated.

Credit: Cary Epstein

Lifeguards practice search techniques in foggy conditions.

Some lifeguard agencies elect to close the beach to swimming as a safety precaution in fog conditions or at night. In other areas, foggy conditions will activate special fog patrol procedures. When approaching fog is observed, warnings should be issued to beach visitors. Public address systems can be used to make these warnings and announcements or other audible signals can be made at regular intervals once fog covers the beach, to provide a directional beacon for people still in deep water.

Since visual observation is no longer effective, fog patrols should be commenced to place lifeguards closer to the water's edge in vehicles or on foot. While on patrol, lifeguards should be constantly alert for cries of help or the sound of boat engines from boats mistakenly operated close to shore. Fog patrols are best made in teams of two lifeguards. If a rescue is indicated, one lifeguard can enter the water as the other lifeguard remains ashore to call for backup assistance and to sound an audible device (such as a vehicle horn or siren) at regular intervals. This device serves to help the responding lifeguard determine the direction of shore and helps backup find the location of the response. In surf conditions, shore direction can generally be determined by swell direction and the sound of crashing waves, but lateral position along the beach is more difficult to ascertain.

Lifeguards who become lost in the water in foggy conditions or in the dark should stop and listen for waves, voices, foghorns, vehicle traffic, or other noises that may indicate the direction of shore. In most coastal areas, when wind is present during fog, it is likely to be blowing toward land. The experienced lifeguard knows how important the sound of waves in the darkness or in a fog can be to rescue work. A lifeguard offshore with a victim in the fog can use sound to determine the direction of shore, the timing of the sets, and the type of wave that is breaking, and may thereby be able to use sound to determine the safest route to the beach. Calling for help can also be effective. The lifeguard who starts swimming toward shore should stop frequently to recheck the current position using the clues previously mentioned. Underwater flashlights or waterproof strobes can be attached to RFDs for better identification of lifeguards in the water, in fog and particularly at night.

Fog can be particularly dangerous for boats suddenly caught in a fog bank without electronic positioning equipment. Lifeguards should be prepared for this possibility and continue regular patrols in an effort to locate wrecked vessels.

KITEBOARD RESCUE

Kiteboarders can require rescue for a variety of reasons including exhaustion, loss or direction change of wind, gear failure, currents, and injury. Kiteboarding assistance and rescue can be a technical and demanding process given the variables introduced by the wind powered kite and the long, high-strength lines used for control. A kite can move a parked car under the right conditions and the lines can inflict serious lacerations. Kites that are becalmed can suddenly relaunch, sinking lines can tangle underwater, and tangles can cause total loss of kite control and power. These and other factors dictate the need for careful assessment and informed, practiced procedures in assisting or rescuing kiteboarders.

Kiteboarders offshore may appear to be struggling, but are often able to resolve the problem on their own. It can be challenging to determine when a kiter needs assistance. Special care must be taken by lifeguards to approach from upwind. Kites can suddenly repower. Rescuers and rescue boats can become entangled in lines. The priority should be rescue of the kiter, which may mean opening two quick releases (usually red or orange handles) or even cutting the kite free. In doing so, it's important that the freed kite not be allowed to create a hazardous situation for others downwind.

Uncontrolled kites on land pose an immediate risk. Care must be taken to keep bystanders away and clear of the kite lines. Never grab the lines. Grabbing other aspects of the system can repower the kite or result in injury to the rescuer. If the kiter

A kiteboarder holds the kite inverted.

and kite are stabilized, the kite should be inverted, then deflated, and weighted down with sand so that the wind cannot catch it.

SAND COLLAPSE RESCUE

Beachgoers of all ages love to dig in the sand, but each year people are injured and sometimes killed in accidents involving holes in the sand. Like any trench in the soil, the walls of sand holes can collapse, causing entrapment and possible suffocation, as well as crushing injures. Sand though, is even less stable than the trenches dug in soil.

When a sand hole collapses over a person or persons, it's an immediate, life-threatening emergency. The weight of sand on the chest can prevent breathing and shifting sand granules can fill every void. Exhaling creates a space the sand quickly fills. Depending on the size of the hole, it may be very difficult to determine where the victim is to begin digging and to avoid worsening the situation.

Prevention is key in sand hole collapse. Because rescue is very difficult, preventing the incident from occurring in the first place is the best option. Lifeguards who see people digging holes in the sand can help prevent death or injury by discouraging the activity through warnings and advice. Some jurisdictions

Credit: California State Parks Lifeguards

Digging holes should be discouraged.

Credit: B. Chris Brewster

Sand collapse rescue training. Note the white plastic buckets for sand removal.

ban the activity. Any hole that could collapse and cover a beachgoer of any age is a potential threat to safety. People who dig holes often abandon them, which may mean that others, especially small children, may be endangered. They can also endanger lifeguards operating motorized vehicles on the beach.

When lifeguards become aware of a sand hole collapse that has covered a beachgoer, an immediate emergency should be declared and appropriate backup rescue assistance should be summoned. This is an all-hands-on-deck emergency. Because of the very limited time available to rescue the imperiled beachgoer, immediate efforts at digging, using the best estimate of the victim's location are prudent. Shovels and hard edges have the potential to cause substantial injury. Plastic buckets have been used effectively as an alternative. The assistance of other beachgoers using their hands or other digging materials may prove useful, but do your best to coordinate this assistance effectively.

There are two primary goals:

- Get the victim's chest and airway clear as soon as possible
- Avoid worsening the situation by inadvertently standing atop the covered beachgoer

Be sure to have resuscitation equipment, including suction, en route and summon an ambulance in anticipation of likely need. Time is of the essence in these cases.

AUTOMOBILE ACCIDENTS IN WATER

Roads often parallel or terminate at the beach. The occupants of motor vehicles can accidentally or intentionally find themselves in the water, presenting lifeguards with a sudden submersion. These cases can be complicated by victim entrapment and possible injuries associated with the vehicle accident. Lifeguard response to vehicle submersion accidents often involves a coordinated effort with local police and rescue agencies. There are several objectives in automobile rescue.

- Determine the exact location of the submerged vehicle
- Determine the number and location of vehicle occupants
- Respond necessary equipment and personnel to the scene
- Plan and execute measures to extricate accident victims for resuscitation and treatment
- Protect emergency responders from harm

These types of accidents are relatively rare, so lifeguards are often seen as the water experts expected to handle the situation. Once a submerged vehicle accident has occurred, emergency plans are activated and all responding agencies are notified. These agencies may include police, fire, and rescue agencies, and special responders such as tow trucks. If the lifeguard agency is first on scene, free-diving lifeguards usually attempt to determine the location of the vehicle and make initial attempts at locating and extricating victims. One clue to finding a submerged vehicle is rising bubbles. The ideal tool for rapid dives in these cases is a small scuba tank that can be strapped on the waist and used by lifeguards certified in scuba for a hasty search. Along with a mask and swim fins, an immediate underwater search can then be initiated. The alternative is free diving lifeguards.

Scene safety is paramount when handling a rescue with an automobiles in the water.

If the vehicle is fully submerged, when the vehicle is located a marker buoy should be fastened to it. An RFD is an excellent alternative if the lanyard is long enough. While initial rescue efforts take place, fully equipped dive teams should respond in case the initial responders are unable to execute the rescue. Other responding lifeguards and allied personnel should inspect the scene for victims who may have escaped the vehicle prior to immersion or to interview witnesses in an attempt to determine how many people were in the vehicle.

Because of damage sustained on impact and pressure variances associated with a submerged vehicle, access to victims can be extremely difficult. The best access to a submerged vehicle is normally through the side windows. Side windows are usually made of tempered glass, which is highly resistant to breakage, but which shatters into small, relatively harmless fragments when the glass is pierced. A tool designed for this purpose is the spring-loaded hole punch, but any sharp object, such as an awl, may be effective.

Before breaking windows, attempt to ascertain if there is adequate air in the passenger compartment to sustain life. It may be that there is time to consider alternatives or summon more assistance. Once window glass is punctured, water will suddenly rush in and there will be little time to remove the occupants.

Lifeguards should not assume that all victims are in the vehicle. Some may have been thrown clear during the accident. Checks of the surrounding water, especially pilings or other structures close to the accident scene are important, particularly at night. Lifeguards should also assess prevailing currents to devise a search pattern.

The greatest hazard in rescue of people in submerged vehicles is laceration from exposed metal and jagged glass. Personal protective equipment such as a wetsuit and gloves should be worn by the lifeguard to lessen the chance of injury. There is also potential for entrapment, so lifeguards should not enter a submerged vehicle. RFD harnesses should be removed.

Petroleum products, which can be toxic, particularly to the eyes, are often present in the water. Use a mask and take care not to swallow the water. If there's a current, consider approaching from up-current, since the petroleum will flow down-current.

The likelihood of serious trauma to auto accident victims is high. However, in case of a submersion, the priority is removal to the surface. Spinal injury precautions are important, but not as important as the potential for death from drowning.

The value of pre-planning such responses is high, since they are very unusual, but present an extreme emergency involving potentially trapped and possibly seriously injured victims. The possibility of a person trapped and in imminent danger of death always creates a very high degree of concern on the part of lifeguards and bystanders. It's important to stay calm and to remember to operate as safely as possible, as quickly as possible.

AIRCRAFT ACCIDENTS IN WATER

Aircraft commonly cruise over beaches and adjacent waters. In many areas aircraft traffic is fairly heavy during peak season, with planes towing advertising banners, people sight-seeing from the air, and media or law enforcement helicopters occasionally hovering overhead. Nearshore crashes occur on occasion. Lifeguard response to aircraft accidents should be handled in a manner similar to that of automobile accidents in the water. The aluminum used in aircraft is particularly likely to have jagged edges, so great caution is appropriate.

Some lifeguard agencies are positioned near airports. Over the years, many airliner crashes with multiple casualties have occurred in the water. These cases are particularly challenging due to the number of victims involved. Rescue boats are extremely valuable in these cases. Lifeguard agencies near major airports should have contingency plans worked out with airport authorities and local safety responders. Airports are required to have such plans in place and may be a source of funding for rescue training and equipment.

FLOOD AND SWIFTWATER RESCUE

Flood and particularly swiftwater rescue is extremely dangerous. Unlike surf, which allows for lulls between sets of waves, swiftwater is relentless. A person trapped against a stationary object by swiftwater can easily die and even the strongest swimming skills will be useless. This section is intended as a brief introduction to flood and swiftwater rescue. Any person who will be assigned to these rescues should receive thorough, specialized training and equipment.

One of the most dangerous hazards is the low head dam, which can be natural or human made. A low head dam is an obstruction across the path of a river which increases the upstream water level, but allows the river to flow over the top. In these cases the water flowing over the dam can form a continual cyclical current back toward the dam itself, called a reversal. It thus becomes a relentless drowning machine. A person caught in this cyclical current, even with a personal flotation device, can be trapped and repeatedly recirculated under the water, unable to break free. In 1975, three Binghamton, New York firefighters died in a reversal while attempting to effect a rescue in the Susquehanna River. The gruesome video from the event has been used in training ever since.

Members of the San Diego Lifeguard River Rescue Team. Note the dry suits, helmets, and other safety gear.

Another, similarly hazardous phenomenon in swiftwater is a strainer. This involves debris in the water, like logs or rocks, which the water can easily move through, but to which any large object will be pressed and held by the current. If trapped underwater in a strainer, it can be impossible to extricate oneself. Even trained rescue teams may have great difficulty removing someone from a strainer. In 1991, a member of the San Diego Lifeguard River Rescue Team died in a strainer.

Lifeguards who lack special training in flood rescue should make every effort to avoid attempting a rescue that requires use of a boat or actual entry into the swiftwater environment. Instead, consider methods which allow lifeguards to stay onshore. One simple, but effective method for shore-based rescue is known as the *pendulum technique*. As the victim is swept along by swift moving floodwaters, the rescuer ashore uses a bag of line known as a *throw bag* to toss a line to the victim. The rescuer holds one end of the line while the weight of the line in the loosely open ended bag causes it to uncoil toward the victim. Before throwing, several coils of line are pulled out of the bag out at the rescuer's end to adjust to the force of the load from the weight of the victim and pull of the current. In order to minimize range error, the bag is thrown directly over the victim so the line drops over the victim's head.

When possible, the rescuer should choose a site, both along the water's edge and in the water, that is free of obstructions such as rocks and trees. The optimal site provides the rescuer freedom of movement downstream. This will assist the rescuer in bringing the victim ashore by lessening the risk of being overloaded by the weight of the victim. It will also allow the rescuer to control the exact landing point of the victim along the water's edge. The bag is best thrown underhand. This is easier to learn and has better accuracy results.

Overhand throws may be necessary to clear obstacles. Only one bag should be thrown at a time. Other rescuers should be positioned downstream for other attempts, should the first be unsuccessful. Before the bag is thrown, the rescuer should get the attention of the victim by yelling "rope" or whistling. When the bag is thrown, the rescuer braces and when the victim grabs the line, the force of the current combined with the pull of the line causes the victim to swing to shore (pendulum) on the rescuer's side of the river. If a victim is expected to be swept under an overhang, such as a bridge, netting may be lowered or rescue tubes snapped in the closed position may be dangled to allow the victim an easy purchase.

Other considerations, particularly for victims stranded on objects midstream, is use of a fire department ladder truck, with the ladder extended, or a helicopter. In any case, always wear a highly buoyant lifejacket, a helmet, gloves, and footwear when working around floodwater. Since floodwater is usually contaminated by sewage and other toxins, rescuers should be inoculated against likely maladies, such as hepatitis.

SHARK BITE RESCUE

In 2002, as a result of several high-profile shark bite incidents, the USLA developed the USLA *Shark Bite Prevention and Response* guidelines. This section is taken from that position statement. The most current version can be found at: www.usla.org/guidelines.

Data on sharks suggests that their behavior must always be regarded as *unpredictable*. The USLA is unaware of any proven techniques whereby an unprotected swimming rescuer can successfully or safely intervene when a shark bites another swimmer. However, rescuers are rarely victims of shark attacks. In fact, of 438 unprovoked shark bite incidents investigated by the International Shark Attack File that involved attempted rescue by another person, only 14 (3.2%) resulted in the rescuer being injured. Of those 14, only two (0.5%) involved injury to a beach-based rescuer who responded to assist. One of these two cases was fatal. Since most shark bites occur quickly and can cause serious, sometimes life-threatening lacerations, there is great value in the availability of trained personnel to rescue the injured swimmer, provide emergency medical care, and arrange rapid transport, after a shark bite has occurred.

The best protective equipment for a lifeguard attempting a rescue of a shark bite victim is an enclosed rescue boat with high gunwales. A personal watercraft may be an alternative, but most personal watercraft provide less protection to the lifeguard and may not be adequate to safely evacuate a seriously injured victim. While a rescue board or kayak may elevate the lifeguard from the water, some sharks have bitten surfers and kayakers, apparently after mistaking them for seals or sea lions. In areas where shark bites have occurred with higher than normal frequency, lifeguards should consider stationing a rescue boat in the vicinity that can allow a rapid, safe response to such incidents.

If a lifeguard observes a shark bite in progress, the lifeguard should immediately notify other lifeguards and determine the most appropriate course of action. This should follow the agency's overall emergency response plans and any specific plans that may exist for shark bites. The USLA cannot issue a blanket recommendation that that a lifeguard without protective equipment attempt to intervene during a shark bite incident, due to the potential danger. International Shark Attack File statistics however, suggest that danger to the lifeguard in an attempt to intervene is extremely limited. Moreover, in most cases on record, the shark has bitten, then left the victim alone. Once injury has been inflicted to the victim, heavy bleeding is likely, so rescue from the water and immediate medical aid may be essential to victim survival.

If a rescue boat is not available and if, as is usually the case, the shark bite appears to be a typical single hit and run incident, and if the lifeguard considers it safe and within agency guidelines to enter the water, the lifeguard should perform a rescue and treat the wounds of the victim. Once the victim has been evacuated to shore or to a rescue boat, appropriate emergency medical assistance should be provided in accordance with the lifeguard's training. In addition to normal emergency medical priorities, particular attention should be paid to stop bleeding and treat for shock.

ICE RESCUE

The work of lifeguards normally takes place in warm water; but drowning occurs in cold water too. One of the most dangerous types of rescue is of people who have fallen through the ice. Many who have died have been public safety professionals engaged in efforts to rescue others. While few lifeguards are directly assigned to ice rescue response units, as aquatic rescue professionals, lifeguards are expected to have an above average understanding of aquatic rescue wherever they may find themselves. These rescues require special training and equipment. This section is intended to provide a brief overview of the principles of ice rescue. Those who will be assigned to ice rescue teams will require more thorough information and training.

The majority of accidental ice related deaths occur as a result of recreational activities. These include activities such as ice skating and ice fishing, but may also include simply walking on the ice. Many cases involve multiple victims. For nonswimmers, falling through the ice can be similar to stepping off a drop-off into deep water. Unless able to hold on to the ice or a floating object, the nonswimmer may quickly die by drowning.

For swimmers who fall through the ice and are able to keep themselves afloat, two primary challenges are presented. One is the effects of cold water, including cold shock and hypothermia. Eventually, the victim is no longer able to stay on the surface, submerges, and dies by drowning. The other is the tremendous difficulty in getting out of the water and back onto the ice. Cold limbs and a slippery surface with nothing to grip make self-rescue very difficult.

Lifeguards in areas of the U.S. where waters freeze over in winter should include information about ice safety in their drowning prevention education programs. It's easy to overlook this serious problem when considering the traditional role of a lifeguard, but all lifeguards should be concerned with drowning prevention and any information that can prevent drowning is of value to everyone.

Specialized training and equipment required for ice rescues.

Ice Accident Prevention

- **Keep Kids Away**—Curious children and teenagers are likely victims of ice related accidents. Each year before ice forms on local waters they should be reminded of the dangers, and then reminded again when waters begin to freeze over.
- **Stay Off Unless You're Sure**—Don't venture onto ice unless you can be sure it's safe. For walking, it should be at least four inches thick and fully hardened. Even so, there are no guarantees. No ice is 100% safe.
- **Never Go Alone**—If you're going onto the ice, go with a friend, but stay separated. If one person falls through, the other can call for help and may be able to assist.
- **Wear a Cold Water Immersion Suit**—These suits maximize the amount of time you can survive in cold water and keep you on the surface.

- **Wear a Lifejacket**—If you don't have a thermal protection buoyant suit, wear a lifejacket. This will keep you afloat if you fall through and lengthen survival time.
- **Carry An Ice Staff**—An ice staff can be used to check the ice ahead for integrity.
- **Carry Ice Picks**—Ice picks can be used to pull yourself out of the water and on to the ice. They can be made inexpensively with two four inch sections of a broom handle or dowel, a strong nail driven into the end of each dowel and sharpened on the exposed end, and a string to hang the picks around your neck (drill a hole through the ends of the dowels for the string).
- **Carry Rope**—With rope, you may be able to help yourself or others.
- **Carry a Mobile Phone**—Have a means of summoning help in an emergency.
- **Stay Low and Spread Out**—If you sense instability in the ice, retreat quickly. If you can't, then spread out your weight by lying on the ice and moving slowly to safety by crawling or rolling.

Self-Rescue from Ice Accidents

- **Stay Calm**—Heat loss is a serious problem. Do what you can to avoid over-exertion.
- **Yell for Help**—Don't hesitate to request help if someone is within earshot. It's best to have help on the way in case you can't extricate yourself.
- **Maintain Warmth**—Keep your clothes on, keep yourself as high out of the water as possible by placing your arms on the ice, avoid swimming any more than necessary to stay afloat, and keep your legs together.
- **Don't Let Your Rescuers Become Victims**—Advise them to stay back in a safe area and to attempt to reach you with a pole, rope, or similar device.
- **Use Sharp Objects**—If you have no ice picks, use keys or any other objects you may have on your person to gain a hold on the ice as you try to extricate yourself.
- **Use Wet Bare Hands**—If you have no sharp objects, your wet hands on dry ice can freeze to the ice and allow you to pull yourself out.
- **Kick Out**—Face the direction from which you came, extend arms onto the ice with whatever sharp objects you have, and kick hard to get yourself up on the ice. Keep trying if it doesn't work the first time. Once on the ice, don't stand up! Spread your weight out and roll or slide slowly to safe ice.
- **Get Warm and Dry**—Once out of the water, hypothermia is a very serious concern.

Rescue of Others

- **Protect Yourself**—Ice rescuers become victims very quickly. This can result not only in mortal danger to the rescuer, but may also seal the fate of the original victim. Act thoughtfully and deliberately. Even highly trained rescuers sometimes can't save victims, but rescuer safety is a cardinal rule.
- **Use Personal Safety Equipment**—If available, use a cold water immersion suit and a lifejacket.
- **Tether Yourself**—Tie a stout line around yourself and have others hold it so that you can be pulled to safety if needed. They can pull both you and the victim to safety in a reaching rescue.

- **Low Risk Procedures**—If you can talk the victim to shore by advising of self-rescue techniques or if you can throw a line to the victim or reach the victim with an extended pole or ladder, try this first. Of particular value is a throw-bag or a rope with a lifejacket or RFD attached.

- **High Risk Procedures**—Venturing on the ice to rescue another person is a very high risk decision. If you do so, use great caution. Make sure an alert has been sounded and backup requested. Don all available personal protective gear, including a leash held by others in a safe position. If available, push a boat, such as an IRB or flat bottom aluminum boat ahead of you and toward the victim. The boat should also be tethered to a safety line. Maintain a body position at all times that will cause you to fall into the boat if you break through the ice. If no boat is available, consider any other floatable object, such as a PWC rescue sled, bodyboard, or similar device. If no floating device is available, find something you can use to extend your reach, even a tree branch. Rope yourself in with assistants onshore and crawl slowly toward the victim, flat on the ice, with the extension forward.

- **Treat Hypothermia**—After rescue, hypothermia is a serious problem. Replace wet clothes with dry ones or blankets, find a warm place, and get advanced medical help.

CLIFF RESCUE

Some lifeguard agencies have jurisdiction over areas that include high rock outcroppings or cliff areas adjacent to protected beaches. These areas may experience special rescue presentations involving people who fall or jump from these heights into the water. Cliff rescues can be complicated by difficult extrication routes and the possibility that the victims may be injured as the result of a fall or jump.

Many agencies will plan rescue approaches and retrievals for these presentations from the water, rather than from the cliff. In these cases, responses are made from adjacent beach areas using rescue

Credit: San Diego Lifeguard Service

San Diego lifeguards use a specialized crane unit for coastal cliff rescue.

Credit: Rich Stropky

Lifeguards and firefighters preparing a cliff fall victim for extrication as a helicopter hovers overhead.

boards or boats. Some agencies with nearby cliff areas employ special floating stretchers, which allow entrapped water to drain rapidly while holding the victim firmly inside. These devices are particularly useful when victims have been injured or are suffering from shock. Once victims have been controlled and stabilized, they are extricated to deeper water for retrieval to a waiting vessel or to adjacent beaches.

Some lifeguard agencies are also responsible for rescuing victims trapped on cliffs or who fall from cliffs or rock outcroppings onto dry land. These agencies are outfitted with special extrication tools, equipment, and vehicles for these rescues. The San Diego Lifeguard Service, for example, handles 30 or more rescues each year on cliffs up to 300 feet in height, perhaps more than any other public safety agency in the U.S. This lifeguard service maintains a special rescue vehicle with a crane and mechanical cable to aid in cliff rescue. Coastal cliff rescue is similar to alpine rescue. It requires extensive training which will not be covered in detail in this manual.

CHAPTER SUMMARY

In this chapter we have learned about many special rescue situations. We have learned about multiple victim rescue, rescue without equipment, surfer and bodyboarder rescue, the challenges presented by rescue from rocks, reefs, and jetties, pier rescue, boat rescue, diver rescue, fugitive retrieval, considerations in suicide attempts, fog rescue, kiteboard rescue, sand collapse, automobile accidents in water, aircraft accidents, flood rescue, shark bite rescue, ice rescue, and cliff rescue. Some lifeguards may never encounter many of these circumstances, but being prepared for the unusual is part of being a well-rounded, professional lifeguard.

DISCUSSION POINTS

- Identify how a lifeguard can use the rip current to their advantage in a water rescue.
- Prioritize how you would decide which victim to secure first in a multiple victim rescue.
- List five indicators that a surfer or bodyboarder may be in distress.
- Describe three things a lifeguard may observe that would indicate that a scuba diver is a novice.
- List five signs of distress for a skin or scuba diver.
- Describe the similarities between rescues of fugitives and rescues of people attempting suicide.
- Identify three ways you can protect yourself during a boat rescue.
- Identify two ways you may be able to gain access to occupants of a submerged vehicle.
- Identify five factors that make swiftwater rescue dangerous.
- List five items that could be improvised for an ice rescue.

CHAPTER
16

Lifeguard Health and Safety

In this chapter you will learn about ways to protect yourself. You will learn that lifeguarding is an athletic profession and that lifeguards are therefore susceptible to athletic injuries. You will learn that exposure to the environment is a major aspect of lifeguarding. You will learn about ways to protect yourself and stay healthy, including protecting your skin, your eyes, your ears, and protecting yourself from infection. You will also learn about post-traumatic stress disorder.

CHAPTER EXCERPT

Skin cancer is the most common cancer in the U.S. Skin cancer is highly curable if detected early and treated properly. Nevertheless, it's estimated that more than 17,000 people die of skin cancer in the U.S. each year.

THE LIFEGUARD ATHLETE

Open water lifeguarding is, by its very nature, an athletic profession. The success of a lifeguard in carrying out critical tasks is highly dependent on the lifeguard's athletic skills. It's one of the few areas of employment, other than professional sports, where athletic skills are challenged on a daily basis. While some other professions, such as law enforcement and firefighting, also require athleticism, few rise to the levels required for lifesaving. And like any athlete, the lifeguard is at risk for various types of associated injuries.

Lifeguarding involves several unique hazards. Although performing a rescue can require various skills similar to those involved in sports, such as jumping, running, swimming, paddling, and rowing, it may be impossible to perform them in the prepared, controlled manner of athletic competition. Lifeguards rarely have enough warning to be able to warm up and stretch prior to a rescue. When they must spring into action, they may have been stationary for several hours, and thus forced to make a cold start.

Unlike an athletic competition, when proceeding on a rescue lifeguards usually need to go all out and can't pace themselves. Lifeguards can't avoid their athletic activity. They can't skip an event or a heat because they don't feel up to it. Lifeguards can't drop out in the middle of their "event," since doing so might result in the death of someone in distress.

There are a wide variety of injuries that can be sustained in the course of lifeguard activity. They include death by drowning; trauma from the victim; trauma from equipment, such as rescue boards and boats; trauma from environmental hazards, such as rocks, surf, inshore holes, aquatic life, and cold water; and a wide variety of orthopedic injuries to bones, joints, muscles, and ligaments. Daily exposure to the elements is a factor as well.

Most U.S. lifeguards are employed on a seasonal basis. This adds an extra layer of injury risk. They may be less active in the off-season and time for preseason conditioning may be limited. The sudden increase in physical activity when the season starts can lead to overuse injuries. During the three to four months of the season, these lifeguards may work six to seven days a week. That compounds the physical strains to which they are subject. Full-time lifeguards can also be affected by varying levels of activity associated with the seasons.

Credit: Cary Epstein

Physical conditioning is critical for open water lifeguards.

Trauma, Strains, and Sprains

Overuse injuries occur when the lifeguard has been trying to do something too often, too hard, for too long, or incorrectly, thus over-stressing or straining involved muscles and tendons, leading to inflammation, pain, and decreased function. Back injuries, for example, may occur because lifeguards must lift, push, or carry things, like removing a victim from the water or pushing a rescue boat off the beach.

Perhaps the most common overuse injury of lifeguards is swimmer's shoulder, which represents a tendonitis of the inner shoulder muscles of the rotator cuff. Repetitive use, even in normal overhand swimming, can lead to this condition. It can be further exacerbated by the fact that open water lifeguards are not merely swimming in a pool, but are fighting waves and currents, as well as pulling victims and equipment. This is another reason to use swim fins. With them, the lifeguard can greatly increase speed and strength, while easing strain on the shoulders.

Paddling and general use of rescue boards can cause shoulder tendonitis, but also neck and back strain, elbow problems—such as lateral epicondylitis (tennis elbow)—and trauma from being struck by the rescue board. As compared to surfers, lifeguards typically use longer boards, which are paddled over greater distances, sometimes with a heavy victim aboard, thereby subjecting lifeguards to an increased rate of injury.

Since an integral part of lifeguard work involves running, lifeguards are susceptible to related injuries. These include runner's knee (knee cap discomfort), tendonitis, shin splints, plantar fasciitis (heel spurs), and numerous other injuries, mainly related to overuse. Lifeguard training necessarily involves running, and lifeguards en route to a rescue are usually attempting to keep their eyes on the victim, while running and donning rescue equipment. Due to the instability of the surface, irregularity of the contour, and lack of support, running on the sand can cause various injuries, including Achilles tendonitis, foot problems, sprains, and strains. Walking and running on the sand and beach environment can also lead to a significant number of lacerations and puncture wounds to the foot of a lifeguard. These can be due to natural (e.g. shells, rocks) and human-made (e.g. glass, needles) hazards.

Lifeguard equipment can also be a source of injury. While dismounting from towers or stands, lifeguards can strain their calf, sprain ligaments, or injure joints. A study of lifeguard injuries in the City and County of Honolulu lifeguards found that paddleboards were the number one source of trauma there.

Rescue boats and emergency vehicles of all types can be an injury source. For example, a study of Australian lifesavers identified numerous serious foot and ankle injuries from IRB use.[1] A follow-up study found that impact forces and foot straps were a major source of the injuries. Injuries are also sustained by lifeguards in other types of boats and vehicles.

Even the public can also be a source of injury. Whether or not lifeguards are assigned to law or code enforcement duties, there is always the potential for confrontation.

Preventing Trauma, Strains, and Sprains

Clearly, some injury is inevitable in lifeguarding due to the hazardous nature of the job. Many, though not all of the injuries lifeguards experience can be prevented. The first step is to ensure that lifeguards are physically capable of the job. The USLA recommends that all lifeguards receive a pre-employment physical, and then annually, whether on their own or through their agencies, lifeguards should obtain a preseason physical exam. This helps ensure that they have no medical conditions which would preclude strenuous physical activity or place them at undue risk.

During preseason, lifeguards employed seasonally should gradually increase their training, beginning at least several months prior to starting work activities. An even better approach is to maintain a high level of fitness year-round, thereby avoiding a sudden increase in training and activities. This is certainly the best approach for full-time lifeguards, who may be called upon to employ their athletic talents at any time of year.

It's important that lifeguards acquire and maintain a high level of skills involving proper techniques in all the physical activities associated with the job, proper use of equipment, and appropriate ways of dealing with victims and the environment. The lifeguard must sometimes contend with victims of varying sizes, strengths, and levels of anxiety during emergencies. Carrying out duties in the proper manner can greatly limit injuries.

Workouts should include drills using all items of rescue equipment that will be used in rescue, including RFDs, swim fins, and rescue boards. This produces the combined benefit of physical conditioning and skill building. Coaching and proper technique instruction should be emphasized in regular workouts. Training programs should involve activities to help lifeguards keep up appropriate levels of fitness and strength.

On a daily basis, lifeguards should engage in physical exercise, including cardiovascular workouts which stress the respiratory and circulatory systems. These activities should be carried out for periods of at least 30 minutes at a time and should significantly increase the heart rate to gain full benefit. This can improve speed and stamina.

Strength workouts should be carried out several times a week. This type of exercise involves stressing individual muscle groups to increase strength. Strength exercises typically involve various groups including arms, shoulders, back, and legs. If an athlete has increased strength, muscles will fatigue slower, perform better, and will be less subject to injury.

Lifeguard athletes are advised to cross-train. They should not solely perform a single sport or exercise, such as swimming, but also carry out other activities such as running and biking. The goal is to be able to continue to increase cardiovascular fitness and muscular strength, but to avoid using one body part or muscle-set to the exclusion of others. This will greatly reduce the risk of overuse to these areas.

Lifeguards are subject to immediate and unexpected intense physical activity on a regular basis, responding to rescues and other emergencies. This may increase the likelihood of injury. Therefore, it is recommended that lifeguards try to keep their muscles loose and warmed up throughout the day.

When carrying out activities about the beach, whether rescues, equipment movement, or training, proper ergonomics should be used. Heavy lifting should be accomplished using proper body mechanics in which one employs the legs, and not the back, to lift. Heavy items should be moved by several lifeguards or using vehicles or rollers. These recommendations also extend to the moving of victims. Hazing and show-off activities involving movement of stands, boats, etc., should be condemned.

To avoid foot injuries, lifeguards should always be vigilant about the state of the surface upon which they are running or walking, particularly in bare feet. The beach area should be checked on a daily basis and, if possible, footwear should be worn when walking on the beach. If injury to the foot occurs, proper wound care should be carried out as well as further treatment and follow-up as indicated. Infection is a particular concern in foot wounds.

Since equipment is a source of injury, maintaining equipment in proper condition and ensuring it is safely used can be expected to minimize injury. To avoid dismounting injuries from towers, safe options need to be made available and lifeguards trained in their use. This includes ladders, stairs, and ramps. A prevention strategy employed by some lifeguard agencies is to mound sand in front of towers to minimize dismounting injuries and allow lifeguards to focus on victims. Use of these strategies can help prevent the strained calf injury, known as lifeguard's calf, as well as other leg injuries. The time or expense involved in this is easily offset, not only by reduced injuries, but also by savings in worker's compensation costs.

Equipment should be properly maintained to prevent damage, breakdown, or failure, any of which may result in injury. Proper training should be provided for all motorized equipment and appropriate safety measures required. For example, the use of helmets can be expected to limit head injuries. Rescue boards should be properly maintained and their handles designed to avoid hand injuries.

The environment is a common injury source that generally can't be modified. Training and knowledge of the environment, including location of hazards, such as rocks, jetties, piers, and inshore holes, will help lifeguards prevent injuries to themselves and others.

Finally, with respect to law enforcement and interactions with the public, injuries can be minimized through training and through judicious decision-making by the lifeguard as to when to intervene and when to stand back. Lifeguards should be trained in how to avoid violent situations, how to defuse them, and how to respond appropriately.

SKIN PROTECTION

The skin is the largest organ of the body. It's a protective sheath, but in providing protection, it's susceptible to many types of injury. One of these is skin cancer. Skin cancer is the most common cancer in the U.S.[2] Skin cancer is highly curable if detected early and treated properly. Nevertheless, it's estimated that more than 17,000 people die of skin cancer in the U.S. each year.[2]

The type of skin cancer that kills the most people is melanoma. It's the most common form of cancer (of all types) for young adults 25–29 years old and the second most common form of cancer for young people 15–29 years old.[3] Skin cancer can and has killed lifeguards, *even at a young age*. Exposure to the sun is not the only problem. Those who use a tanning bed before age 35 increase their risk for melanoma by 75%.[3]

> **LEARN MORE**
>
> Read the International Life Saving Federation Medical Commission's Sun Protection statement at: www.ilsf.org

Skin Cancer Facts

- Over the past three decades, more people have had skin cancer than all other cancers combined.
- One in five Americans will develop skin cancer in the course of a lifetime.
- One person dies of melanoma every hour.
- The vast majority of melanomas are caused by the sun.
- On average, a person's risk for melanoma doubles if he or she has had more than five sunburns.
- Regular daily use of an SPF 15 or higher sunscreen reduces the risk of developing squamous cell carcinoma by about 40% and the risk of developing melanoma by 50%.
- More than 419,000 cases of skin cancer in the U.S. each year are linked to indoor tanning.

Source: The Skin Cancer Foundation[3]

Lifeguards are particularly vulnerable to skin cancer because of the high levels of sun exposure they sustain and because of the strength of the sun's rays at the beach. The intensity of these rays can be tripled by reflection off the water and sand. The most serious threat comes from a spectrum of sunlight called ultraviolet (UV) light.

There's no such thing as a safe tan. Even gradual tanning damages the skin. Sunburn greatly increases the risk of melanoma, doubling the risk for those who have had more than five sunburns.[3] Exposure to UV rays adequate to produce tanning or burning actually harms the skin at the cellular level, causing direct injury to DNA. As the body begins a process of trying to repair the damage, it produces melanin, a protective pigment which darkens (tans) the skin. Most people's bodies can partially repair the damage; but the repair is never complete and long term injury accumulates over the years. Skin exposed to the sun ages at a significantly accelerated rate. Generally, people with darker skin color have more natural defense against sunburn than people with lighter skin. Darker skin however, only provides increased protection, not complete immunity from sun related skin damage.

LEARN MORE

You can learn more about skin cancer on the website of the Skin Cancer Foundation at: www.skincancer.org

While melanoma is the deadliest form of skin cancer, non-melanoma skin cancers are also a concern. Squamous-cell and basal cell carcinoma can be disfiguring and even fatal.[3] If caught early, the deadly forms of skin cancer can usually be removed and their spread often stopped. For example, the estimated five year survival rate for patients whose melanoma is detected early is about 98% in the U.S.[3] The USLA recommends awareness training for lifeguards, to help them better understand the problem and to check themselves for skin cancer, as well as annual evaluations by qualified medical experts.

Skin Cancer Symptoms

Symptoms of skin cancer which should be evaluated by a physician:

- An existing mole which enlarges irregularly or takes on a notched border
- Red, blue, or white areas in a mole
- Itching or bleeding in a mole
- The appearance of a new mole in an adult
- A scaly or crusty raised area
- Raised hard red bumps with a translucent quality to their surface

Protecting yourself from skin cancer includes avoiding intense sunlight for long periods of time and practicing sun safety when you know you will be exposed. One element of sun safety is use of sunscreen. Daily sunscreen use reduces the incidence of melanoma by over 50%.[4] Not only that, but those who use sunscreen with an SPF of 15 or higher daily show 24% less skin aging than those who do not use sunscreen daily.[5]

In an effort to describe the level of protection offered by different sunscreens, the *sun protection factor* (SPF) was developed. A higher SPF number indicates greater protection, but this is not as simple as it may seem. An SPF 15 sunscreen blocks 93% of UVB radiation, while SPF 30 blocks about 97%.[3] SPF above that level offers a very marginal value and may be much more costly. The most important part of ensuring that sunscreen is effective is to apply it thoroughly and often.

The makers of sunscreen have historically made various claims about their effectiveness. Some of this is marketing. The Federal Drug Administration has prohibited manufacturers from making claims that sunscreens are "waterproof" or "sweatproof" or to identify their products as a "sunblock." [6] The FDA allows sunscreen to be labelled as "water resistant" (effective for up to 40 minutes in water) or "very water resistant" (effective for up to 80 minutes in water).[6] The best advice is to concentrate on the SPF factor and reapply regularly.

A concern of some dermatologists is that sunscreen may create an air of permissiveness about sun exposure. By using sunscreen, many people seem to believe they eliminate damage from the sun's rays and therefore don't have to worry about sun exposure. This may make them more likely to stay out in the sun. The reality is that there is damage to the skin even with sunscreen. Damage is simply less than it would be without any sunscreen.

Good sun precautions protect a lifeguard's health.

Credit: Eric Nurse

Sunscreen should be applied to dry skin, 20 to 30 minutes before sun exposure. It should be used even on cloudy days because up to 80% of UV rays penetrate clouds. Attention should be paid to ensure an even distribution over all exposed areas. Particular heed should be paid to the lips, ears, nose, shoulders, and head, since these areas are highly susceptible to burning.

Clothing also provides protection from the sun. There are a variety of types of hats, shirts, and other garments that are promoted as offering an *ultraviolet protection factor* (UPF) with an associated number. Consumer Reports found that even a heavy T-shirt offers a high level of protection approaching that of garments with a high UPF.[7]

The USLA recommends that all lifeguard agencies require their lifeguards to wear shirts and hats to help protect them from the sun, mandate use of sunscreen, and provide shade and protection. It has been demonstrated that mandating use of sunscreen and protective clothing by lifeguards reduces the incidence of skin cancer and related workers compensation claims.[8]

EYE PROTECTION

Keen eyesight is essential to lifeguards and the swimmers they watch over. Unfortunately, eyesight can be seriously damaged by sun exposure. With proper protective steps however, the chances of eye damage can be significantly reduced.

Serious eye problems associated with sun exposure include:

- **Cataracts**—A clouding of the lens of the eye
- **Macular Degeneration**—Loss of central vision
- **Photokeratitis**—Damage to the cornea of the eye from exposure to intense light
- **Pterygium**—A callous-like growth that can spread over the white of the eye

Cataracts and macular degeneration generally occur over a period of years and primarily affect people later in life. They can cause full or partial blindness and require surgery. Pterygiums, caused by exposure to sun, wind, and dust, occur over a period of years and are often sustained by lifeguards. These three conditions typically require surgery. Photokeratitis can develop shortly after overexposure to intense UV light and can be very painful. Recovery occurs over several days and sometimes requires bandaging the eyes. Sunglasses and wide brimmed hat greatly reduce the amount of UV rays reaching the eyes.

Selecting Sunglasses

Sunglasses come in a wide variety of price ranges. Marketing claims to the contrary, many inexpensive sunglasses offer excellent protection and high cost sunglasses may not. Lifeguards should insist on sunglasses which filter out 99% to 100% of both UV-A and UV-B light. UV protection is unrelated to darkness (tint) of the glasses. Even eyeglasses with no tint can be manufactured to provide full protection from UV light. However, wearing dark glasses that do not screen UV rays can actually cause more damage than not wearing glasses at all, since the screening of visible light causes the eyes to dilate, letting in more UV rays. The effects of UV light are cumulative. UV light can cause cataracts, retinal degeneration, and damage to the front surface of the eye.

USLA Buying Guide for Sunglasses

Feature	Recommendation
UVA Protection	99–100%
UVB Protection	99–100%
Lens Material	Polycarbonate
Lens Color	Brown, Grey, Green, or Amber Recommended
Screening of Visible Light	75–95%
Meets FDA Breakage Requirement	Required
Polarized	Highly Recommended
Wrap Around Style	Recommended

In general, the best lens colors for lifeguards are gray, brown, green, or amber. Blue lenses should be avoided. Choose sunglasses of an adequate tint to allow observation of the water and sand without discomfort on days with bright sunlight. Lenses that block between 75% and 95% of visible light are probably a good choice. One rule of thumb is that if the eyes can be seen when looking in a mirror, the glasses are probably not dark enough, although if the glasses are too dark, vision may be inhibited.

Good quality lenses are generally made of high quality optical glass, plastic, or polycarbonate. Optical glass is more distortion free and resistant to scratching than polycarbonate or plastic, but glass is heavier and usually more costly. Polycarbonate lenses are more impact resistant, thus safer. Make sure the lenses pass the FDA requirement for breakage. Choose a design that covers as much of the area around the eyes as possible (wrap-around sunglasses) without affecting peripheral vision. This helps

Credit: James Ginley

Polarized, wrap-around sunglasses provide protection and glare reduction.

protect from side light and from the blowing sand that may cause growths on the surface of the eyes.

Polarized sunglasses dramatically reduce reflected glare—a major problem for lifeguards trying to watch a swim crowd. While tinted glasses darken glare, polarized glasses reduce glare with a filter in the lenses. Lifeguards should insist on polarized sunglasses to help reduce eye fatigue and improve observation.

EAR PROTECTION

Chronic irritation and inflammation of the ear is a frequent problem for lifeguards and other swimmers. The most common afflictions are known as swimmer's ear and surfer's ear. The causes are similar. In both cases, the middle ear is affected.

A healthy ear is coated with earwax. The wax not only forms a water-repellent coating, it also contains antimicrobial substances. Unfortunately, continual contact with the water washes earwax away, removing the protection. This problem is exacerbated when people stick fingers or other items in the ear to remove water, scraping away the earwax. Sometimes surgical removal is necessary.

The most common symptoms of these afflictions are pain, inflammation, and itching. Hearing loss may be experienced in some cases and there can be a fluid discharge from the ear. Lifeguards with these symptoms should see a doctor.

Prevention of ear problems primarily involves keeping the ear canal dry and clean. Standard wax earplugs are not a good choice. Instead, use silicone earplugs. Wearing tight fitting swim caps and wetsuit hoods can help reduce cold water induced injury and debris impaction. After swimming, tilting the head and jumping vigorously, as well as gently drying the outer ear with a towel are helpful. Lifeguards should make every effort to avoid reaching into the ear with anything. Physicians can recommend drying agents, as well as cleaning agents that help remove impacted debris.

Disposable gloves and a pocket mask are essential pieces of personal protective equipment (PPE).

INFECTION CONTROL

Infection of a healthcare worker through exposure to the bodily fluids of another person (known as cross-infection) is very rare. Nonetheless, it can occur. These secretions can carry pathogens—agents, particularly living microorganisms, which cause disease. Whenever medical aid is rendered by a lifeguard, contact with the victim's bodily fluids is possible. In some cases, it's likely.

Most other healthcare and public safety professionals can take the necessary steps to prevent any contact with potentially infectious bodily fluids. This is not always so for lifeguards.[9] Lifeguards may need to enter water that has been contaminated with blood or other bodily fluids; or may be offshore in a situation where mouth-to-mouth may be needed without the immediate availability of a barrier device. While the USLA is unaware of any case of a lifeguard having contracted a serious infectious disease from a victim, lifeguards should be taught the proper blood and bodily fluid procedures.

The best way to avoid infection from bloodborne pathogens which the victim may be carrying is to employ universal precautions: All human blood and certain human bodily fluids are treated as if known to be infectious for human immunodeficiency virus (HIV), hepatitis viruses (including B & C), and other bloodborne pathogens.

LEARN MORE

Read the International Life Saving Federation Medical Commission's Infection Control statement at: www.ilsf.org

General Recommendations on Exposure

Vaccinations

The U.S. Centers for Disease Control and Prevention recommend the following vaccinations for healthcare workers.[10] Although Hepatitis A is not listed, one of the primary transmission routes is contaminated water, so it should also be considered.

- **Hepatitis B**
- **Flu (Influenza)**—annually
- **MMR (Measles, Mumps, & Rubella)**—If you were born in 1957 or later and have not had the MMR vaccine, or if you don't have an up-to-date blood test that shows you are immune to measles or mumps
- **Varicella (Chickenpox)**—If you have not had chickenpox (varicella), if you haven't had varicella vaccine, or if you don't have an up-to-date blood test that shows you are immune
- **Tdap (Tetanus, Diphtheria, Pertussis)**—And get boosters every 10 years thereafter
- **Meningococcal**—Those who are routinely exposed to isolates of N. meningitis should get one dose

Credit: Eric Nurse

During Water Rescue of a Bleeding Victim

- Avoid contact with the victim if possible.
- Avoid contact with bleeding areas when removing the victim from the water.
- Wash off any blood as soon as possible.
- During in-water resuscitation attempts, wash any blood or body fluids away from the victim's mouth before contact. If exposed, the rescuer's mouth should be washed out after contact.
- If possible, move the victim to dry sand to prevent further in-water exposure.

During Medical Treatment of a Victim Ashore

- Assume that all blood and other bodily fluids are infectious and treat them as such.
- Use mechanical ventilation, such as a bag-valve-mask (BVM) when possible.
- Use disposable resuscitation masks with a system that prevents body fluids from passing through the mask.
- Use oxygen delivery systems with disposable masks whenever possible.
- Wear occlusive gloves for handling bleeding victims.
- If the victim is bleeding profusely, especially from an artery, wear a mask, goggles, and an occlusive gown in addition to occlusive gloves.
- Wash the hands with soap and water after contacting blood, even if gloves are worn. Use diluted bleach or Betadine if blood directly contacts skin.
- Clean up blood and body fluids on equipment with a germicide containing household bleach and then air dry. Wear gloves while performing this task. Place used blades and needles in a disposable, puncture-proof container.

When Infected Items Are Found on the Beach

- Remove the items using universal precautions.
- Dispose of the items in a manner which avoids exposure to others, consistent with agency and regulatory protocol.

In Case of Possible Infection

- Lifeguards who are involved in contact with potentially infectious material should follow agency protocol. If no protocol exists, the lifeguard should contact a physician.
- Lifeguards exposed in a blood-to-blood inoculation with known or suspected fluids should follow agency protocol, which should include contact with a physician. Testing and drug regimens may be initiated.

OSHA Requirements

The Occupational Health and Safety Administration (OSHA) in 1991 (29 CFR Part 1910.1030) requires that certain steps must be taken by all employers to help employees avoid cross-infection. The OSHA rule specifically states, "This section applies to all occupational exposure to blood or other potentially infectious materials ... Occupational exposure means reasonably anticipated skin, eye, mucous membrane, or parenteral contact with blood or other potentially infectious materials that may result from the performance of an employee's duties." Lifeguards clearly fall under the requirements of this rule and the USLA requires that all agencies seeking national certification provide equipment consistent with OSHA guidelines.

OSHA Requirement Excerpts

- **Hepatitis B Vaccine**—The employer shall make available the Hepatitis B vaccine and vaccination series to all employees who have occupational exposure. There will be no cost to the employee.
- **Protective Equipment**—The employer shall provide at no cost to the employee and make readily accessible to the employee appropriate personal protective equipment.
- **Use of Protective Equipment**—The employer shall ensure that the employee uses appropriate personal protective equipment unless the employer shows that the employee temporarily and briefly declined to use personal protective equipment due to unusual circumstances.
- **Exposure Control Plan**—Employers must establish a written Exposure Control Plan designed to eliminate or minimize employee exposure.

> **LEARN MORE**
>
> You can check the latest OSHA standards at:
> www.osha.gov

DAILY PREVENTIVE HEALTH

All athletes take prudent steps to stay healthy. In the case of lifeguards, the lives of others depend on your health. Eat a balanced diet. Avoid alcohol and drugs. As we have explained in the Chapter 10 (*Water Surveillance*), the use of recreational drugs has been scientifically demonstrated to affect vigilance, even when the user is not under the influence. There is a lingering effect. The residual effects of alcohol will also impact your readiness. Sleep deprivation has also been shown to decrease vigilance, even after a recovery night of sleep, so it's important for lifeguards to have a full night's sleep before assuming lifeguard duties.[11] The lives of others depend on you.

When on the beach, even while sitting still, but particularly when involved in heavy physical activity, lifeguards should maintain hydration. When involved in strenuous activity in hot weather, one can lose up to a quart of fluids in a half-hour period. As a lifeguard becomes dehydrated, performance decreases, judgment skills decline, vigilance can be negatively impacted, and the risk of serious injury increases. Fluid should always be available. Water is usually sufficient. If exercising for over an hour or during high temperature days with prolonged sweating, a sport drink that replenishes essential minerals (electrolytes), but is non-carbonated, non-caffeinated, and low in sugar may be helpful. Sugared drinks have been shown to negatively impact vigilance.[12]

POST-TRAUMATIC STRESS DISORDER

Like other public safety providers, open water lifeguards are regularly subjected to situations involving high stress. A harrowing rescue, for example, is a stressful event involving a person in mortal danger and an effort on the part of the lifeguard to save them from death; but even the frantic parent of a lost child can provoke great stress in lifeguards. These cases are normally resolved positively. Occasionally though, events occur that are potentially much more troubling.

Post-traumatic stress disorder (PTSD) is a psychiatric condition which may occur after a stressful event. In the aftermath, people suffering from PTSD may have a number of troubling experiences like depression, flashbacks, difficulty sleeping, and feelings of detachment.

Public safety workers were once expected to simply deal with these stresses, but it is now widely accepted that helping people deal with the high stress of public safety work is an obligation of employers, supervisors, and coworkers. PTSD can affect anyone. Some people are able to deal with terribly stressful circumstances for years without experiencing PTSD, only to suddenly and unexpectedly be affected. Others may have a reaction the first time they experience a highly traumatic, life-threatening event. Since it is impossible to know who will be affected and when, the best approach is to anticipate the problem and take proactive steps to address it.

Every lifeguard agency should develop protocols for dealing with PTSD. These can take into account available resources, such as counseling services, employee assistance programs, and mental health experts associated with the employer. Supervisors and coworkers are essential in helping manage PTSD. Recognizing and accepting that PTSD is a part of life in emergency services is an important step in avoiding stigmatizing a member of the team, which could worsen the effects. It helps to make those affected comfortable with seeking assistance.

After an event that might be expected to cause PTSD, particularly a highly stressful event that is significantly out of the ordinary for some lifeguards or for the organization, the best approach is to assume that a member or members of the team could be affected. Many public safety organizations address this first by conducting a *debriefing*. All people directly involved in the event are gathered to discuss it. Each person is provided a chance to ask questions and bring up concerns. Those with information about the event and a sense of perspective are expected to provide them.

Debriefings are intended to be confidential, and all involved should be given a sense that what they have to say will be kept within the group. Moreover, debriefings should not be used to assign blame or point fingers. If something has been done improperly, it may well need to be addressed, but the debriefing process is intended to help people deal with stress, not to fix blame. It sometimes helps to focus on how the organization might better respond to a similar situation in the future. After all, every organization can always improve.

Depending on the circumstances and magnitude of the event, a more formal *critical incident stress debriefing* (CISD) may later be appropriate. These debriefings are normally led by mental health professionals, sometimes several days after the event. This allows for a more thorough approach by people whose expertise is in dealing with psychiatric issues and helping people cope with dramatic events in their lives.

CHAPTER SUMMARY

In this chapter we have learned that the lifeguard is an athlete who can be affected by injuries in a manner similar to other professional athletes, and we have learned ways to prevent those injuries. We have learned ways to protect our skin, particularly from skin cancer. We have learned about eye protection and how to select sunglasses appropriate for lifesaving. We have learned about ear protection. We have learned about infection control, including OSHA requirements. And we have learned how post-traumatic stress disorder can impact lifeguards.

DISCUSSION POINTS

- Identify the importance of lifeguards maintaining a high degree of physical conditioning.
- Discuss the similarities between lifeguards and professional athletes.
- List five ways lifeguards can avoid injuries.
- List five ways lifeguards can protect themselves from skin cancer.
- List three considerations in selecting a good pair of sunglasses.
- Describe how ears can be affected by the open water aquatic environment.
- List three preventive actions that lifeguards can take to protect their ears.
- List five universal precautions for protecting yourself from infection.
- Identify the types of inoculation that are recommended for healthcare workers like lifeguards.
- Explain how an individual can be affected by post-traumatic stress disorder.
- List three steps that can be taken to assist lifeguards with post-traumatic stress disorder.

CHAPTER

17

Aquatic Life and Related Hazards

In this chapter you will learn about various types of aquatic life, as well as the impact of humans on the aquatic environment. Aquatic life includes organisms (plants and animals) that live partially or fully in water. Some aquatic life can injure water users, but in most cases that injury is temporary, like a painful sting. You will learn that sharks are a feared, but statistically minimal threat. You will also learn about a wide variety of other aquatic life such as schooling fish, stingrays, and jellyfish. Since aquatic life differs widely between saltwater (marine) and freshwater environments, it will be discussed separately for those two areas. Treatment of injuries associated with aquatic life is discussed in Chapter 18 (*Medical Care in the Aquatic Environment*).

CHAPTER EXCERPT

Shark attack is viewed by many as the most feared risk associated with swimming in the ocean. In fact, on average there is less than one fatal shark attack each year in all U.S. waters. Lightning fatalities are far more frequent.

One of the keys to understanding the dynamics of open water beaches lies in the fact that they represent components of much greater ecosystems. A host of highly adapted organisms, many of which can injure or be injured by humans, live in these ecosystems. Aquatic injuries associated with aquatic life typically include bites, stings, lacerations, and abrasions. Death can result, but is very rare, and far less of a threat than drowning.

MARINE LIFE

Usually, when one thinks of dangerous marine life, such notorious animals as sharks, barracuda, and Portuguese man-of-war come to mind, but even seemingly non-threatening organisms such as barnacles and kelp can cause injury. Conducting a complete inventory of all hazardous marine life inhabiting American coastal waters is beyond the scope of this text. We will therefore discuss some of the most common.

From a lifeguard's perspective, the initial consideration when dealing with any form of potentially dangerous marine life is early, accurate identification. Complicating this, some dangerous marine animals can be confused with those not generally considered dangerous. For example, several kinds of large fish and mammals may be confused with sharks. Proper identification is essential, because clearing the water due to presence of a non-threatening species may cause panic and later non-compliance when a real danger exists. To prevent this, some agencies use a key—a small sheet with pictures—to help lifeguards make correct identifications.

Sharks

Shark attack is viewed by many as the most feared risk associated with swimming in the ocean. In fact, on average there is less than one fatal shark attack each year in all U.S. waters. Lightning fatalities are far more frequent.[1] Administrators of the International Shark Attack File, maintained by the Florida Museum of Natural History under the auspices of the American Elasmobranch Society, were able to confirm an average of less than 70 unprovoked shark attacks per year on humans worldwide from 2000–2009, with less than six of them fatal.[1] (Unprovoked attacks are defined as incidents where an attack on a live human occurs in the shark's natural habitat with no human provocation of the shark.)

> **LEARN MORE**
>
> You can view statistics on shark attacks and other information about sharks in the International Shark Attack File at: www.flmnh.ufl.edu/fish/isaf

People recreating on a surfboard or other flotation device are the most common victims of shark attacks, followed by swimmers, divers, and waders, in that order. From 2001 to 2014, the U.S. states with the highest numbers of documented, unprovoked shark attacks, averaged per year, were Florida (23), Hawaii (5), South Carolina (3), California (3), North Carolina (2), and Texas (1). While Florida leads in attacks, only 0.93% of the Florida attacks resulted in death, whereas 11.63% of the California attack victims died.[1]

Experts recognize over 200 species of sharks, but only a few are considered a serious threat to people. Three shark species are the most frequent attackers of humans. These are the white shark (known as the great white shark), the tiger shark, and the bull shark, in that order.[1]

Most shark attacks occur in nearshore areas. This includes the area between sandbars, where sharks are sometimes trapped at low tide, and in areas with steep drop-offs. Sharks are drawn to such areas because their natural prey can be found there. Attacks occur more commonly when waters are murky. This condition increases the chance of a shark making a *prey identification mistake*.

A prey identification mistake occurs when the shark accidentally attacks something other than its natural prey. It is

Credit: San Clemente Lifeguards

Identifying sharks can be challenging. Here a shark swims near a surfer.

generally believed that most shark attacks occur for this reason, rather than an intention on the part of the shark to attack or eat a human. Differing sizes and types of shark prey in various areas of the world may help explain variations in the likelihood of an attack being fatal to a human.

In Florida, the predominant food items of sharks are fish. In this area, shark bites seem to occur when sharks confuse the splashing of surfers and swimmers in murky nearshore waters as being from schooling fish. Most attacks in Florida result in a single bite or slash, with no repeat passes at the victim.

Along the California coast, the threat to humans engaged in aquatic recreation is essentially confined to one species: white sharks. Attacks in this area are believed to occur when the shark confuses the size, shape, and actions of a person with a seal or sea lion—a major indigenous food item. Great whites attack this prey with a ferocity intended to maim or kill an animal of that size, so their initial bite sometimes proves fatal even if they don't continue the attack.

In Hawaii, attacks largely involve the tiger shark. This species is known to attack humans and life-threatening injuries can result. Surfers are the most likely victims. A favorite haunt of the tiger shark is the area where the surf breaks over reefs, which is also an area where surfers congregate.

Dolphin and porpoise are often mistaken for sharks, but are normally harmless to swimmers. These small whales have a horizontal tail fin, so they usually expose only their dorsal fin when swimming near the surface. Dolphins, particularly the common bottlenose dolphin, regularly swim in groups, continually surfacing and submerging in forward arcs. Sharks, on the other hand, have a vertical tail fin. When swimming along the surface, the dorsal fin cuts through the water, while the tail fin moves back and forth. Sharks do not swim in an arcing motion. Instead, when swimming along the surface, they cruise at a fairly consistent depth, with their fins exposed for longer periods than porpoises. Such observations are rare on the West Coast, but occasionally seen on the Gulf Coast and East Coast, particularly in Florida.

The trailing edge of a shark's dorsal fin is mostly vertical, as is the case for this hammerhead shark.

The trailing edge of a dolphin's dorsal fin is mostly curved, and dolphins tend to swim on the surface in an arcing motion.

Periods that shark attack is more likely along the West Coast include times of heavy seal and sea lion activity, especially during the annual birthing period. Under these conditions, white sharks are more likely to move into the surf zone. Along the East Coast and Gulf Coast, where shark bites are sometimes sustained near schooling fish, it may be prudent to warn swimmers away from heavy concentrations of fish—often indicated by sea bird diving. In addition, periods of onshore winds along the east coast of Florida can result in concentrations of fish and sharks in poor visibility water—a bad combination when humans are added to the mix. In Hawaii, surfers and swimmers should avoid dawn and dusk periods when tiger sharks are particularly active and the areas around the mouths of rivers, especially after heavy rains, where tiger sharks may scavenge.

For further information on preventing and responding to shark bite incidents, please refer to Chapters 9 (*Preventive Lifeguarding*) and Chapter 15 (*Special Rescues*). Lifeguards are strongly encouraged to report shark attacks to the International Shark Attack File, so that information can be gathered for future reference. For information on reporting, see the organization's website at: www.flmnh.ufl.edu/fish/isaf.

Barracuda

Barracuda are large, streamlined predator fish usually found in tropical and subtropical waters. Biologists classify at least 20 species of barracuda. Only one of these species, the Great Barracuda, is considered dangerous to people. Although attacks are rare, there have been authenticated reports. Most of these attacks are associated with blood in the water; either from an injured fish or a human. There are also reports which suggest that bites may result from swimmers wearing bright and shiny objects during times of poor water visibility. When a barracuda, especially a large one, is observed near a swimming area, it should be monitored carefully. Some agencies will establish a barracuda sighting as criteria for the water to be cleared of swimmers, especially if it appears that there are also baitfish in the area.

Barracuda.

Schooling Fish

Most schooling fish don't represent a problem. A few species, under certain circumstances, can inflict injury. Some of these include jacks, tarpon, mackerel, and bluefish. Bluefish in particular, while schooling nearshore, have inflicted serious lacerations and avulsions. Other fish may inflict injury by biting or even brushing up against swimmers and waders. Schooling fish can also attract larger predatory fish (e.g. sharks and barracuda). Whenever schools of large fish are observed, they should be carefully monitored. Some lifeguard agencies clear the water of swimmers immediately. This is an agency by agency decision based on past experience.

Schooling fish.

Credit: GLC Aquatic Safety Department

Venomous Fish

Venomous fish are classified in the family *Scorpaenidae*. There are hundreds of species in the family widely distributed along coasts of the U.S. Most biologists divide these fish into two groups: scorpionfish and stonefish. Stonefish are found in tropical waters, including those adjacent to the continental U.S. Some of the common names for members of the two groups include: lionfish, rockfish, turkeyfish, and sculpin.

These fish are usually bottom feeders. Many are found in or around coral reefs or kelp beds, in which they blend quite well due to their protective coloration. Some species prefer sandy bottom habitats. They often lie motionless on the bottom for long periods of time.

The venom of the scorpionfish is stored in special sacs located in hypodermic-like dorsal spines. When a swimmer steps on these fish, venom is injected into the wound. The result is intense, sharp, and shooting pain. Besides pain, the victim may suffer convulsions and nervous disturbances. Although there have been reports of deaths from the scorpionfish sting, none have been confirmed. A few deaths have been confirmed for stonefish.[2]

Scorpionfish.

Credit: Dave Foxwell

Marine Mammals

Marine mammals are common visitors to nearshore waters, usually on a seasonal basis. Marine mammals living in coastal waters of the U.S. include whales, manatees, dolphins, porpoises, seals, sea lions, and sea otters, among others. Under normal conditions, these mammals are not dangerous. When sick, injured, or stressed however, some can present a considerable danger. Consequently, whenever a marine mammal is observed behaving abnormally or is hauled out on a beach, people should be kept at a distance. Many areas have local marine mammal stranding networks capable of responding to a sick or injured animal.

LEARN MORE

You can read about legal protections for marine mammals, including the Marine Mammal Protection Act, on the website of the National Marine Fisheries Service at: www.nmfs.noaa.gov/pr/laws/mmpa/.

Various federal and state laws protect marine mammals from harm or harassment. The most notable is the Marine Mammal Protection Act, which became law in 1972 and has been amended since. According to the act, it is unlawful, "… to harass, hunt, capture, or kill, or attempt to harass, hunt, capture, or kill any marine mammal." The term "harass" is defined as any act of pursuit, torment, or even annoyance that has the potential to disturb or injure a marine mammal in the wild.

Credit: San Clemente Lifeguards

Curious seal pup.

Credit: Christopher Roxon

Dolphins feeding.

Credit: Ed Vodrazka

Dolphin rescue.

Lifeguards are sometimes called upon to protect marine mammals being harassed. While local protocols consistent with federal law should be followed, it's generally best to keep the public away from marine mammals and to consult authorities with expertise in handling marine mammal incidents. This will most typically involve agents of the National Marine Fisheries Service, along with state fish and wildlife officers.

Stingray

Only a few members of the ray family are considered dangerous. The most common is the stingray, whose tail has a venomous barb or barbs. Stingrays are not aggressive animals and are easily frightened; but they often bury themselves in the sand in shallow water. If accidentally stepped on by a hapless wader or otherwise struck, stingrays reflexively flip their tail. This flip of the tail can result in the barb or barbs lacerating the skin and venom entering the victim's body. A recommended method for avoiding the sting of a stingray is to do the "stingray

Stingrays lie on the bottom using camouflage to hide.

shuffle." In areas where stingrays are common, by shuffling your feet instead of leaping forward in shallow water, you may lessen the chance of surprising a stingray, stepping on it, and being stung.

Serious bleeding can result in these cases and deaths have been caused from exsanguination (massive blood loss), but the most noticeable result is typically intense, sharp, shooting pain in the affected area. If left untreated, the pain may intensify for up to 90 minutes, then slowly subside. Besides pain, the victim may experience rapidly declining blood pressure, vomiting, diarrhea, sweating, arrhythmia, and muscular paralysis leading to death in rare cases. Wounds to the chest or abdomen are particularly serious and have resulted in death. In 2006, famed wildlife expert and television personality Steve Irwin died when an unusually large stingray struck him in the chest. The usual site of a sting from a stingray however, is the foot or ankle.

Jellyfish

Most jellyfish are free swimming, colorless, and range in size from a few inches to three feet in diameter. Their appearance on surf beaches tends to be seasonal—spring and summer is when they are most common. Jellyfish feed on small marine animals caught in their dangling tentacles and stung by nematocysts in those tentacles. Humans are stung in the same way when they come into contact with the tentacles.

Although there are hundreds of species of jellyfish, only a few are considered to pose a serious danger.

Perhaps the best known is the box jellyfish, which can cause death to a human within a few minutes after contact, but this is extremely rare in the U.S., with only one reported death. Jellyfish species in U.S. waters typically cause pain and stinging, but no long-term effects.

Portuguese Man-of-War

The Portuguese man-of-war is sometimes confused with the jellyfish, to which it is related. It is a colony of animals called hydroids, which appear to be a single animal. Portuguese man-of-war are found in many warm water areas, but also drift north with warm currents to cooler zones. In marine waters of the U.S., they are found most often in the Gulf Stream of the Atlantic Ocean.

Credit: Dave Foxwell

Portuguese man-of-war beached.

The Portuguese man-of-war is most readily identified in water by a brilliant blue, pink, or violet float, usually floating on the surface, which is gas filled and bladder-like. The float is typically about two to eight inches in length. Atop the float is a crest which functions somewhat like a sail, allowing the man-of-war to move with the wind. Hanging below are tentacles which serve the same function as in jellyfish, and which have a similar stinging effect on humans. These tentacles can be many feet in length.

Other Marine Life and Hazards

There are a host of other marine organisms capable of inflicting injury to humans. Some of these include barnacles, crabs, marine worms, coral, sea urchins, marine shells, eels, catfish, and sea turtles. Due to the limited distribution of many of these animals and the limited danger they represent, only a few are covered here.

Sea urchin.

Sea Urchins

Sea urchins are spiny marine invertebrates, found in rocky crevices in the intertidal area. Urchin wounds are usually sustained when people step on urchin spines. The spines from these creatures are have multiple venom organs. They can penetrate the skin, even through protective clothing, to cause a wound with intense burning sensations followed by redness, swelling, and aching. More severe reactions to urchin wounds include weakness, loss of body sensation, facial swelling, and irregular pulse. Rare cases involving paralysis and respiratory distress have occurred. A problem with sea urchin spines is that they can be hard to remove and can break off below the surface of the skin, and can thus be very difficult to remove. Advanced medical care may be required in some cases.

Muscles and barnacles.

Mollusks and Crustaceans

Mussels, oysters, and other mollusks, along with crustaceans, such as barnacles, can cause lacerations that are easily infected.

Microscopic Stingers

Various marine organisms, commonly referred to as *sea lice*, are prevalent in the warm waters off Florida, the Gulf of Mexico, and the Caribbean Sea, but can also be present on both the east and west coasts of the U.S. during summer months. (The term "sea lice" in this case is a misnomer. True sea lice affect freshwater fish.)

These larvae of jellyfish and other ocean stingers contain the same nematocysts (stinging cells) as their respective parent organisms. In many areas of the Gulf and Caribbean the primary culprit causing infestations is the larvae of the thimble jellyfish. These larvae, sometimes half a millimeter in length or smaller, can become trapped between the bathing suit and skin, or in crevices like the armpit, and compressed, causing the stinging cells to fire.

During summer months high concentrations of these stinging larvae may float in "clouds" or "blooms" that affect large areas of the ocean. Common symptoms of stings include an intensely itchy red rash with small blisters and elevated areas of skin. Severe reactions to exposure may include fever, chills, headaches, nausea and vomiting, especially in children. Extreme allergic reactions may include anaphylactic shock and require hospitalization in rare cases. The infestation season generally runs from April through August.

Sea Snakes

Certain species of sea snakes can bite. Toxic signs, appearing within twenty minutes, can include malaise, anxiety, euphoria, muscle spasm, respiratory problems, convulsions, unconsciousness, and all signs of shock.

Kelp

Kelp is leafy seaweed, which can grow in water as deep as 60 feet and beyond. Kelp attaches itself to rocks on the bottom and grows upward to the surface. Its trunk-like main stem can be very strong. It exists in the cool ocean waters off Alaska,

Credit: California State Parks Lifeguards

Lifeguards training over a kelp forest.

New England, and the entire West Coast. Kelp is home to many species of marine life. The hazard posed by kelp is entanglement, particularly of scuba divers whose protruding equipment may become wrapped in the kelp. A panicked diver may die by drowning or abandon underwater breathing apparatus and shoot for the surface, producing diving related injuries.

Coral

Coral can cause cuts, abrasions, welts, pain, and itching. Severe reactions are unusual.

FRESHWATER LIFE

Although the number of animal species capable of inflicting harm on swimmers is much larger in saltwater than in freshwater, lifeguards at lakes, rivers, and ponds should take the time during their training to become familiar with local species and assess the possible risks to visitors. Some types of the potentially problematic freshwater aquatic life are listed here.

Leeches

Leeches are bloodsucking worms. They typically have a flattened, segmented body with a sucker at both ends, used to bore into flesh and draw out blood. Leeches are found in many freshwater bodies throughout the U.S. Although leeches are not life threatening, the presence of a leech on a person usually evokes a strong emotional response and requests for assistance.

Snapping Turtles

Several species of turtles frequent the freshwater bodies of the U.S. Most pose no danger whatsoever. One type of turtle that may present limited concern is the snapping turtle. These turtles have a rough shell and powerful jaws. Although most are not particularly dangerous, some species have been known to deliver painful bites to people who knowingly or unintentionally corner or trap them. Lifeguards should become familiar with the turtles specific to their area and which, if any, display aggressive behavior. Lifeguards can then work to minimize possible confrontations between them and humans. With this knowledge, lifeguards can also reassure those who may become needlessly concerned.

Mussels

Freshwater mussels are bivalve mollusks found in many areas of the U.S. These mussels usually have a dark, elongated shell and dwell on the bottom in the mud. The edges of their shells can be very sharp and lacerate the feet of beach visitors. This is particularly likely in the case of half-shells from dead mussels. Some species of mussels are invasive and cause significant economic impacts on the ecosystem, so in some areas observation should be reported to appropriate authorities.

Fish

Although many species of fish are found throughout freshwater bodies of the U.S., few pose any threat to swimmers. Some areas report problems with different species of cat-fish due to their tactile barbs, but injuries involving fish usually occur when people fishing remove them from the hook.

Snakes

Some types of freshwater snakes or snakes that travel on water can be dangerous or poisonous, particularly in warmer climates. Snake problems are regional in nature and should be addressed through local training programs.

Other Reptiles

Some species of reptiles can prove dangerous to beach visitors, particularly in the South. Alligators, for example, can be extremely dangerous in a freshwater body that also includes a swimming beach. Alligator problems are regional in nature and should be addressed through local training programs.

Credit: Jim Jordan

Alligators are mostly freshwater creatures, but also exist in brackish water and even at saltwater beaches.

Semi-Aquatic Animals

Semi-aquatic animals are animals that, while not adapted to living underwater, spend a great portion of their time in the water environment. Examples of semi-aquatic animals include beaver, otter, muskrat, and various species of waterfowl.

Credit: San Clemente Lifeguards

Most of these animals will pose no threat to swimmers at freshwater beaches, as they usually actively avoid contact with humans. There may be situations, however, when a semi-aquatic animal approaches or even enters a swim area unsuspectingly. Waterfowl may be drawn into a swim area when visitors attempt to feed them. While waterfowl are not usually dangerous, they may be hosts to various parasites that can cause conditions in visitors like *swimmer's itch*. This occurs when water with the parasites that infest waterfowl dries on the skin of humans. It can cause an allergic reaction that primarily involves itching and redness. The best avoidance measures are to keep swimmers away from waterfowl and to encourage those who swim in such areas to wash themselves thoroughly immediately upon leaving the water.

Non-Native Freshwater Plants

As is the case in the marine environment, non-native weeds have been introduced into the freshwater environment, sometimes causing serious environmental impacts that may close aquatic areas to recreation. One of these, *Hydrilla vericillata* has infested aquatic areas throughout the U.S. It was apparently spread through use in aquariums, water from which may have been dumped into lakes. Lifeguards are a frontline resource in identifying the presence of these weeds, reporting them, and discouraging the dumping of aquaria into the waters they protect.

A Florida lake infested with *Hydrilla vericillata*.

CHAPTER SUMMARY

In this chapter we have learned that a wide variety of aquatic life can impact humans, just as humans can impact aquatic life. We have learned that the danger of sharks, though they are greatly feared, is minimal. We have also learned about the types of sharks involved in shark attacks and the areas where different types of sharks are more common. In addition to sharks, we have learned about the many types of other fish, mammals, mollusks, reptiles, and jellyfish that can injure humans, most in a minor way that is easily treated.

DISCUSSION POINTS

- Identify the types of sharks that frequent the beaches in your region.
- Explain why reports of shark attacks draw so much public interest.
- Identify the reason that great white shark bites are more likely to cause death compared to some other shark bites.
- List three measures that can be used by beachgoers to avoid envenomation by a stingray.
- Identify the part of the jellyfish that causes stinging.
- Explain how marine mammals are protected by federal law.

CHAPTER
18

Medical Care in the Aquatic Environment

I n this chapter you will learn some special considerations for providing medical care in the aquatic environment. These include recommended training and equipment, as well as general treatment guidelines. You will learn methods for treating injuries from drowning, aquatic life, spinal trauma, and cold water. This chapter is intended as a supplement to your medical aid training and focuses on issues specific to the aquatic environment.

━━━━━━━━━━ **CHAPTER EXCERPT** ━━━━━━━━━━

Lifeguards must be capable of supporting life, sometimes for an extended period of time, until a higher medical authority can take over.

The beach and open water comprise a natural, ever-changing environment with many dynamic forces at work. These forces, human made structures, and the wide variety of physical recreational activities in which beach users participate, make injury and illness inevitable, even commonplace. Injuries which happen away from the beach, such as traffic or in-home accidents, typically result in the response of emergency medical aid providers to the scene, sometimes from significant distances; but when people are injured at the beach, lifeguards are an immediate source of emergency medical attention. Lifeguards are almost always the *first responders* to medical aid needs at the beach. It has therefore long been recognized that open water lifeguards must have appropriate medical aid training to provide immediate medical care and to evaluate the need for further medical care.

In the case of minor injuries, the care rendered by lifeguards is usually adequate to fully resolve the immediate needs of the victim. These are the vast majority of cases handled by lifeguards. More serious injuries, such as difficulty breathing or serious trauma, require both the immediate care of lifeguards and assistance from providers with more advanced medical training and equipment. This will typically involve the response of ambulance personnel and transportation to a medical facility; however, lifeguards must be capable of supporting life, sometimes for an extended period of time, until a higher medical authority can take over.

The information provided in this chapter and elsewhere in this manual regarding the treatment of injury and illness is intended to supplement approved courses in emergency medical aid. These courses usually do not go into great depth on issues specific to the aquatic environment, and may not address them at all. Lifeguards may find the information in this chapter a valuable supplement to other medical aid training they have received; however this is not a complete medical aid course and lifeguards should never practice any emergency medical aid technique beyond their level of training and qualifications.

In providing medical aid to others, lifeguards may garner information that is highly personal and private in nature. Lifeguards have an obligation to protect the confidentiality of this information. It's important that the trust placed in the lifeguard is maintained. Federal law and agency policy will guide the lifeguard's actions. You will learn more about this in Chapter 23 (*The Responsible Lifeguard*).

LIFEGUARD MEDICAL TRAINING

To ensure that all open water lifeguards are prepared to perform at appropriate levels, the USLA sets minimum recommended standards for emergency medical training. Those standards are detailed in Chapter 4 (*Open Water Lifeguard Qualifications and Training*) and are updated from time to time. The latest standards are available at: www.usla.org/certification. Lifeguard agencies should ensure that lifeguard personnel receive ongoing, in-service emergency medical care training to supplement their basic training. This helps ensure that skills are maintained, that lifeguards can work as a team in an emergency, and that all established protocols are carefully followed. This training should include the types of medical incidents lifeguards are likely to encounter.

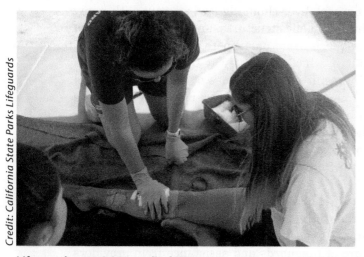

Credit: California State Parks Lifeguards

Lifeguards practicing medical care.

LIFEGUARD MEDICAL EQUIPMENT

To ensure that all open water lifeguards are properly equipped to provide medical care, the USLA sets minimum recommended standards for emergency medical equipment. Those standards are detailed in Chapter 24 (*Lifeguard Facilities and Equipment*) and are updated from time to time. The latest standards are available at: www.usla.org/certification.

Medical aid supplies and each medical aid kit should be clean and properly stocked at all times. As supplies are depleted during the day they should be restocked as necessary. Oxygen and other medical equipment should also be inspected daily, and maintained in a ready condition at all times.

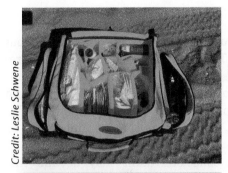

Credit: Leslie Schwene

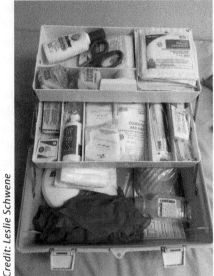

Credit: Leslie Schwene

Credit GLC Aquatic Safety Department

PROVIDING MEDICAL CARE

Lifeguards should provide care in accordance with their training, agency policies, agency protocols, and any applicable regulations.

Levels of Injury

For purposes of classification and communication, injuries that lifeguards commonly encounter can be divided into three levels.

Minor Injury

Minor injuries are conditions unlikely to require medical treatment beyond primary care. The vast majority of injuries sustained at beaches involve minor abrasions, cuts, and scrapes which can be quickly and effectively treated by lifeguards.

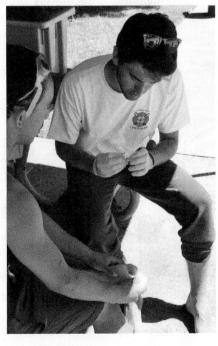

Credit: Eric Nurse

Moderate Injury and Illness

Moderate injury and illness are those which are not immediately life-threatening, but which require further care at a medical facility. These are injuries like minor lacerations that require sutures, minor puncture wounds to the extremities, and other similar injuries. Moderate injuries present a dilemma. Should an ambulance be called or should the victim be allowed to leave with only an admonition that a doctor be consulted? The best advice may be to err on the side of caution, encouraging that an ambulance be summoned.

Credit: Kyle Maxwell

A conscious adult may decline this level of care, but for minors, release from care in the case of a moderate injury is not recommended and may be prohibited by law or regulation. If an adult declines further care beyond what the lifeguard offers, lifeguards should first stabilize the injury to the greatest extent possible, then document both their recommendation for further medical care and the patient's refusal. See Chapter 22 (*Records and Reports*) for appropriate forms. Preprinted maps with directions to the nearest medical care facilities can be very helpful in these cases.

Acute Injury and Illness

An acute injury or illness is one that requires urgent care at a medical facility. This includes immediately life-threatening injuries, such as uncontrolled bleeding, as well as those which are not immediately life-threatening, such as a simple, closed fracture. The recognition and assessment of some major injuries will indicate the need to activate an emergency operation plan, which is described in Chapter 25 (*Emergency Planning and Management*).

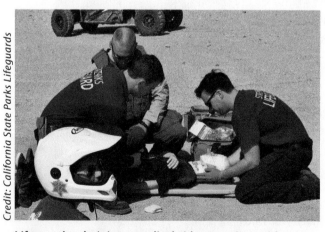

Credit: California State Parks Lifeguards

Lifeguards administer medical aid to a patient with an acute trauma injury to the head.

Treatment Guidelines

The following are some general guidelines for treating injuries and illness, which may be modified in accordance with the severity and other circumstances:

1. Determine whether the area where the victim is found is safe to enter without further risk to lifeguards or the victim, and mitigate any continuing threat to safety.

2. Summon necessary backup.

3. Use universal precautions for infection control.

4. Treat immediate problems according to level of medical training, including:

   A. Airway

   B. Breathing

   C. Circulation

   D. Bleeding

5. Determine mechanism of injury.

6. Conduct a full patient assessment for any and all injuries and determine the acuity of the patient's injuries or illness.

7. Stabilize injuries or illness according to medical protocol and level of training.

8. Avoid moving the victim until the full extent of injury or illness is determined.

9. Monitor and record vital signs.

10. Protect body temperature.

11. Make the victim as comfortable as possible.

12. Recommend further treatment in cases that victim is not transported to the hospital. (See *Treatment Principles* below.)

13. Document your actions.

Treatment Principles

In addition to general guidelines for treating injuries, the following principles should help lifeguards address issues they will commonly encounter.

- **Prioritize Responsibilities**—Treating a minor injury that does not require immediate care may not take precedence over water surveillance. Ensure that drowning prevention activities are not unduly interrupted. If necessary, call for backup.

- **Inspect and Treat the Injury**—Beach users occasionally request medical supplies for self-treatment of minor injuries without revealing the injury. This should be discouraged. Lifeguards are typically better trained and qualified to provide this assistance. Furthermore, a request for medical supplies is often, in reality, a veiled request for medical assistance. Lifeguards should offer to assist in treatment and take reasonable steps to ensure that the injury is no more serious than the person believes. Direct treatment by the lifeguard helps ensure that wounds are treated properly and demonstrates the concern and capabilities of lifeguard personnel.

- **Assess Carefully**—The assessment of injuries requires good judgment and skills on the part of the lifeguard. The victim may be in a state of denial, but once lifeguard care is initiated, it is critical to conduct a thorough evaluation and to give good advice.

- **Treat Carefully and Thoroughly**—Whenever a lifeguard initiates medical treatment for an injury, the lifeguard undertakes a responsibility to treat properly. A carelessly treated laceration, for example, may become infected later, resulting in serious complications well beyond the severity of the initial injury.

- **Treat Minors with Care**—If there is a parent or an adult supervisor of the minor readily available, the lifeguard should make sure that the adult knows of the injury, preferably before treatment. If the adult wishes to treat the child using lifeguard supplies, it may be allowed. In the unusual event that a parent or guardian refuses treatment for a child who is clearly in need, a higher level of medical authority should be summoned. Police should also be summoned, as this may constitute neglect or abuse. (See *Release from Care* below.)

- **Keep Bystanders Back**—A pushing crowd can aggravate the fear and anxiety of an injured person. It also intrudes upon privacy. Keeping onlookers away and calming bystanders can greatly assist the victim. In this effort, a courteous, but firm approach is best. Attempt to gain compliance if possible, but make it clear in a low key manner that compliance with the perimeter that has been established will be necessary. Police officers may be needed in some cases.

- **Maintain Control**—In a medical emergency, other beach visitors may offer assistance, suggest treatment, and try to take over care. It is not rare to have bystanders state, "I am a nurse," or "I am an EMT." These cases can be difficult. The lifeguard doesn't know the person or their actual level of training, but doesn't want to prevent care from a qualified medical provider with a higher level of training. Nonetheless, there are many examples of individuals professing to have high levels of medical qualifications who are later found to be impostors. While trained bystanders can often assist with stabilizing the victim, it is important for lifeguards to maintain control of the situation and keep treatment within the lines of established protocols.

- **Use Discretion**—The beach is a very public place. If treatment of a wound will require removal of clothing, it may be best to bring the victim inside, if possible. Privacy is a secondary issue in the case of a life-threatening injury, but it should be taken into account. When clothing must be removed or private areas of the body must be treated, it is best to try to have a lifeguard of the same sex as the victim handle treatment. If this is not possible, it is best to have another lifeguard present. While this may seem to create an additional violation of the person's privacy, it may be prudent to avoid a later complaint of inappropriate conduct.

- **Release from Care**—Lifeguards must be careful not to release a person whose status may quickly deteriorate. A person with blood loss from a head laceration, for example, might lose consciousness while driving to the hospital for sutures. It is therefore wise to establish guidelines to aid in this decision. (Please see the section on *Resuscitation of Drowning Victims* in this chapter for specific advice on release of drowning victims.) Some lifeguard agencies prefer to simply avoid such judgment calls due to the level of responsibility placed on the lifeguard. At these agencies, a higher level of care is always sought before the victim is released. Release of a minor from care without prior notification of a parent or guardian should be avoided. This is an issue which agency policies should address. As a general rule, minors with moderate or acute injury or illness should never be released after treatment. Either parents should be summoned to the scene or the minor should be turned over to an ambulance for transportation to the hospital. On the other hand, if lifeguards were required to summon a parent for every stubbed toe treated, lifeguard stations would be full of minors waiting for parents. Nevertheless, in some areas parental notification prior to release of a minor from care is a requirement of law.

- **Encourage Follow-Up Treatment**—For all but the most minor injuries, it is wise to recommend that victims follow-up with their physicians. Even minor cuts can become major problems later. It's useful for lifeguard agencies to maintain a printed list of the nearest emergency medical facilities, including addresses and phone numbers. This may include clinics that provide walk-in care, as well as hospitals. For those who decline an ambulance, a typical question is for directions to the nearest medical facility. Lifeguards should be prepared to provide this.

- **Document Treatment and Advice**—The treatment provided, advice rendered, and all recommendations for further treatment of injuries should be carefully documented on appropriate report forms. The USLA offers example forms on our website at: www.usla.org/resources.

RESUSCITATION OF DROWNING VICTIMS

Drowning victims may be conscious and alert or they may be unconscious. They may have a heartbeat with no respirations or they may have neither. To supplement the medical training of lifeguards, this section offers guidance specific to the treatment of drowning victims.

The hypoxia caused by immersion or submersion, if not corrected, results first in respiratory arrest. The tissues of the body become starved for oxygen. If respiratory arrest is not corrected, it is followed by cardiac arrest within a variable, but short time interval, which is determined by the physical condition of the victim, water temperature, previous hypoxia, emotional state, and associated diseases.

American Heart Association (AHA) guidelines for treating drowning have consistently made clear that drowning resuscitation priorities differ in key ways from standard CPR for sudden cardiac arrest (a heart attack). For example, although the sequence of CPR normally begins with chest compressions in a compression, airway, breathing (C-A-B) sequence, the AHA states: "Healthcare provider CPR for drowning victims should use the traditional A-B-C approach in view of the hypoxic nature of the arrest ... The first and most important treatment of the drowning victim is the immediate provision of ventilation. Prompt initiation of rescue breathing increases the victim's chance of survival ... Rescue breathing is usually performed once the unresponsive victim is in shallow water or out of the water. Mouth-to-nose ventilation may be used as an alternative to mouth-to-mouth ventilation if it is difficult for the rescuer to pinch the victim's nose, support the head, and open the airway in the water."[1] One additional advantage to beginning with ventilation is that, "Victims with only respiratory arrest usually respond after a few artificial breaths are given."[1]

It is generally recommended to use a barrier device when performing rescue breathing, but such devices are not always available or practical in drowning resuscitation. About this the AHA states, "Despite its safety, some healthcare providers and lay rescuers may hesitate to give mouth-to-mouth rescue breathing without a barrier device." Barrier devices have not been shown to reduce the low risk of transmission of infection, and some may increase resistance to air flow. "If you use a barrier device, do not delay rescue breathing."[1, 2]

Credit: Eric Nurse

Lifeguard provides ventilations with a pocket mask.

The International Life Saving Federation emphasizes this point, stating, "Studies suggest that the chance of contracting a communicable disease via mouth-to-mouth resuscitation attempts is extremely small. On the other hand, the chance of saving a life in these cases is high. Rescuers should take this into account in deciding the best course of action. If the rescuer has a barrier device, it may be used, but these devices are usually very difficult to use in-water and attempts to use them may add further delays."[3]

While some drowning victims aspirate no water due to laryngospasm, more often there is some degree of aspiration of water (into the lungs). There is no need to clear the airway of this water because only a modest amount is aspirated by the majority of drowning victims, and aspirated water is rapidly absorbed by the body. Attempts to remove water from the breathing passages by any means other than suction (e.g., abdominal thrusts or the Heimlich maneuver) are unnecessary and potentially dangerous.[1]

Drowning victims do commonly vomit. A 10 year Australian study found that two-thirds of drowning victims who received rescue breathing and 86% of those who required compressions and ventilations vomited.[4] The AHA states, "If vomiting occurs, turn the victim to the side and remove the vomitus using your finger, a cloth, or suction."[1]

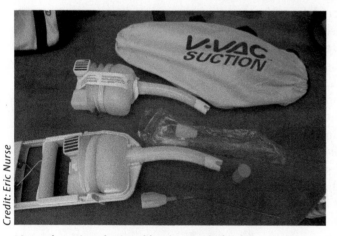

Credit: Eric Nurse

Manual suction devices like this can help clear vomitus.

When a victim is recovered in deep water (overhead) the lifeguard should take the following actions consistent with recommendations of the International Life Saving Federation:[3]

Position the victim face up, extending the neck to open the airway. This can be accomplished by a single trained rescuer with the aid of appropriate lifesaving equipment (a rescue tube, rescue can, rescue board, bodyboard, etc.) or by two or more trained rescuers without lifesaving equipment. In either case, swim fins are highly recommended and will greatly facilitate these procedures. If there is no spontaneous breathing, the rescuer should attempt to ventilate for approximately one minute (12 to 16 ventilations), and then proceed depending on circumstances. If ventilation is restored, proceed toward shore intermittently stopping to check that the victim is still breathing. If breathing is not restored after one minute of ventilation, the rescuer should consider if it is a long (over five minutes) or a short swim to a dry or shallow place. If a short swim, rescue the victim while ventilations are continued or stop every one or two minutes to ventilate again for approximately one minute (12 to 16 ventilations). If a long swim, continue ventilation one additional minute in place and check for movement or reaction to ventilation. If present, use the same procedures as with the short swim. If movement or reaction to ventilation is absent, the rescuer should bring the victim to shore without further ventilations.

When performed in deep water, this is a difficult procedure, requiring extreme fitness, swimming ability, a flotation device and prior training. Do not check victim's pulse or attempt compressions while in the water. These are difficult and inefficient, and will slow the rescue process. In case of a suspected back or neck injury the rescuer should check breathing before extending the victim's neck, then if there is no breathing, tilt the victim's neck backwards to check for breathing again. If there is no spontaneous breathing the rescuer should immediately start ventilations consistent with the rescuer's training protocol. Suspicions of back/neck injury should be greater in shallow water. The rescuer should always keep the victim under observation during the rescue, even if the victim is breathing spontaneously, since during the first 5 to 10 minutes the victim could again cease breathing.

Steps to Retrieval and Resuscitation of a Viable Victim

1. The victim is brought to the surface and the lifeguard signals to shore with the USLA approved arm signal for a resuscitation case—wave one arm back and forth overhead several times.

2. The lifeguard turns the victim to a face-up position and thrusts one arm under both of the victim's armpits, behind the victim's back.

3. The lifeguard passes the RFD to the hand of the lifeguard's arm which is under the victim's armpits. The victim is now supported on one side by the lifeguard's body and on the other by the grasped RFD. The lifeguard's other hand is free.

4. The airway is opened and the lifeguard checks for breathing.

5. If there is no spontaneous breathing, the lifeguard should attempt to ventilate for approximately one minute (12 to 16 ventilations).

6. If breathing is not restored after one minute of ventilation, and the swim to shore is expected to be five minutes or less, rescue the victim while ventilations are continued or stop every one or two minutes to ventilate again for approximately one minute (12 to 16 ventilations). If the rescue to shore is more than five minutes, continue ventilation one additional minute in place and check for movement or reaction to ventilations, then follow the same protocols as for a swim of five minutes or less.

7. If breathing is restored, rescue the victim to shore while carefully monitoring that spontaneous breathing continues. If spontaneous breathing stops, return to step #6.

Note: These steps should be followed for recent submersion victims who are recovered within 15 minutes of submersion in warm water or when total submersion time is uncertain.

Positioning the Drowning Victim Onshore

On a sloping beach, the victim should be placed in a position parallel to the waterline, lying supine (face up), so that the body is level. Do not position the victim head-down on the slope of the beach, as this will increase the likelihood of vomiting. Be sure to bring the victim far enough up the beach to avoid uprush, especially considering anticipated wave and tidal action. The first lifeguard takes a kneeling position on the side of the victim closest to the water. By leaning up the slope of the beach instead of down the slope of the beach while providing medical care, the lifeguard can work without falling forward over the victim, and can protect the victim from unexpected uprush.[5]

Credit: Pete DeQuincy

Lifeguard performs an airway assessment and begins ventilations.

Oxygen

When a drowning victim is recovered from the water, the person is typically experiencing hypoxia. Immediate resuscitation efforts are therefore needed if hypoxia is severe, ideally with administration of oxygen and, if possible, positive pressure ventilation.[6] The administration of oxygen requires appropriate training, which all open water lifeguards should receive. You can provide oxygen in several ways, depending upon the equipment provided by your agency, including:

- **Mouth-to-Mouth or Mouth-to-Mask**—Mouth-to-mouth and mouth-to-mask breathing, without use of supplemental oxygen, provides an approximately 16% concentration of oxygen.

- **Oronasal Mask**—By using a supplemental bottle of oxygen attached to an oronasal mask as you provide rescue breaths, you raise the oxygen concentration from 16% to as high as 50% or more.

- **Non-Rebreather Mask**—By providing supplemental oxygen through a non-rebreather mask to a person who is breathing spontaneously, you can deliver 60% oxygen or more depending on the delivery system.

- **Demand Valve**—By providing supplemental oxygen through a demand valve, you can provide 100% oxygen to a breathing or non-breathing victim. This method also provides positive pressure.

- **Bag-Valve-Mask**—By providing ventilations with supplemental oxygen through a BVM, you can provide 100% oxygen to a non-breathing victim. This method also provides positive pressure.

Oxygen units require regular service and inspection, whether they have been used or not. If left unused, the equipment can deteriorate and leak. Equipment that is used or moved frequently will be subjected to bumps, falls, and other accidents that can cause mechanical problems. Lifeguard agencies should maintain enough oxygen cylinders for reasonably anticipated demand. Empty bottles should be clearly marked and expeditiously filled. The oxygen regulator should receive an annual service check.

Defibrillators

Automatic external defibrillators (AED) are a common tool of lifeguards. They are primarily intended to treat sudden cardiac arrest. AEDs can sometimes stop *ventricular fibrillation*—an uncoordinated beating of the heart—and other serious arrhythmias. Ineffective heartbeats that can be corrected by an AED are rare in submersion victims.[6] Most drowning victims have healthy hearts that simply cease to function due to hypoxia. If available, an AED should be used in accordance with the manufacturer's instructions, in the relatively unlikely case the victim is experiencing ventricular fibrillation. CPR should always take precedence over the use of a defibrillator in treating a drowning victim. AEDs have been shown to be safe for use in a wet (not immersed) environment.

Release of Drowning Victims from Care

Whenever a victim has inhaled water in a drowning incident, but is conscious, the lifeguard must make a determination whether further treatment is needed or the victim can be released from care. This may be an issue of local or agency protocol, which the lifeguard should follow. The International Life Saving Federation has developed the following guidelines to help lifeguards determine who should be sent to the hospital as a result of complications from drowning.[7] Such determinations should be made with great care. If in doubt, consult a higher medical authority. As previously explained, minors require special consideration.

1. The following people should be sent to the hospital in most cases:

   - Any victim who lost consciousness even for a brief period.
   - Any victim who required rescue breathing.
   - Any victim who required cardiopulmonary resuscitation.
   - Any victim in whom a serious condition is suspected such as heart attack, spinal injury, other injury, asthma, epilepsy, stinger, intoxication, delirium, etc.

Credit: Leslie Schwene

Oxygen delivery kit.

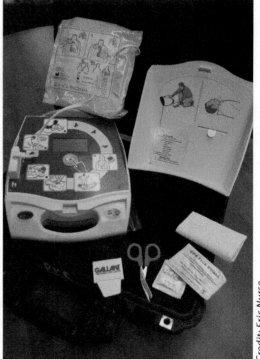

Credit: Eric Nurse

Automatic external defibrillator (AED).

2. The following people may be considered for release from care at the scene if, after 10–15 minutes of careful observation, while being warmed with blankets or other coverings as required, the victim meets *all* of the requirements listed below. In such cases, it is unwise for the victim to drive a vehicle and the victim should be so advised. If any of these conditions do not apply or if the lifeguard has any doubt, then the victim should be transported to the hospital or advised to seek early medical attention.

   - No cough
   - Normal rate of breathing
   - Normal circulation as measured by pulse in strength and rate and blood pressure (if available)
   - Normal color and skin perfusion
   - No shivering
   - Fully conscious, awake and alert
   - An oxyhemoglobin saturation level over 95% (if a pulse oximeter is available)

3. There is always a risk of delayed lung complications. All immersion victims should therefore be warned that if they later develop cough, breathlessness, fever, or any other worrying symptom, they should seek medical advice immediately. It is preferable that these individuals not return to a home environment where they are alone for the next 24 hours. Special care and observation should be given to child victims.

INJURIES FROM AQUATIC LIFE

Various types of aquatic life, discussed in Chapter 17 (*Aquatic Life and Related Hazards*), can cause injuries ranging from minor to major. This section includes specific treatment recommendations for common injuries from these sources.

Bites

If a swimmer is bitten by a predatory fish, it's important to get the victim out of the water. This will help prevent blood from entering the water, potentially provoking additional bites. (For shark bites, see Chapter 15: *Special Rescues*.) Minor wounds should be cleansed and disinfected. Major wounds require immediate transport to a medical facility. A tetanus shot should be recommended.

Stings

Lifeguard treatment procedures for wounds from stings vary, based on the level of medical training, locally prevalent species, and local medical protocols. The victim should first be evaluated for any reaction that extends beyond pain and any bleeding controlled. Advanced medical care and transportation to the hospital should be carefully considered for more serious reactions or for stings to areas other than the foot or ankle. Procedures to protect against shock should be employed as appropriate.

Jellyfish and Portuguese Man-of-War

For most jellyfish and Portuguese man-of-war stings in the U.S., unless there are medical complications beyond pain, the lifeguard's primary role is calming the victim and providing pain relief. First check to see if there are any tentacles remaining on the victim's skin. If so, they may contain nematocysts that have yet to sting. They should be washed off using seawater (freshwater will cause the nematocysts to sting), then removed with the fingers.

Ideally, the lifeguard should use a medical glove to remove the tentacles. If none is available, the pads of the fingers are thick and only a slight tingling will normally be felt. The lifeguard's hands must be washed immediately afterward though, because touching other areas of the body with the hands may produce painful stinging.[8]

Hot water immersion of the affected area, a hot shower, or application of a heat pack have been demonstrated in various scientific trials to provide the best pain relief.[9–11] The water temperature should be the highest that can be applied safely and that is tolerable and applied until the pain resolves.[9] If heat treatment is not available, cold packs have also been shown to be effective for pain relief, but less so than hot water immersion or heat packs.[10]

Numerous commercial products and solutions have been advocated over the years to treat these stings. They include urine, lemon juice, papaya, ammonia, vinegar, meat tenderizer, sodium bicarbonate, and commercial products, which are typically a derivative of these. None have been scientifically proven to work.[8, 12] Vinegar has been shown, in some cases, to worsen the discharges and the sting with some species. Often the logic used in advocating these solutions is that they will stop the nematocysts from further stinging, but if the lifeguard properly removes tentacles and rinses the area with seawater, there should be no remaining nematocysts. Therefore, at this point the only concern is to treat the pain of the sting, not to prevent further stinging.[8]

As in all cases of medical aid, the victim's condition should be monitored closely. Special precautions, which may include transport to a medical facility, should be considered for those with a history of reactions to insect bites and stings. Any person with extensive stings or stings to the face, particularly in the case of children, may require hospital transport.

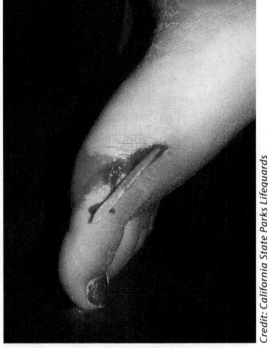

Credit: California State Parks Lifeguards

Stingray sheath and barb still in victim.

Stingray

In some areas, stingray envenomation is a regular occurrence. Lifeguards in these areas routinely treat and release people who have been stung in the foot or ankle, and who display no unusual complications. The wound should first be checked to make sure that the sheath and barb are completely removed. Otherwise, envenomation may continue. Thereafter, the injury site should be immersed in water as hot as the victim can tolerate without producing further injury to the tissue.

In most cases, hot water immersion reduces the pain dramatically.[8, 9] The affected area is then left in the hot water until it can be removed without the pain returning. This sometimes takes an hour or more. During treatment, as the water cools, add more hot water to maintain temperature. In remote areas, where hot water is unavailable, hot sand or hot packs have been used with some success. Once pain subsides, the wound is dressed and bandaged, as appropriate to the lifeguard's medical training and presentation of the wound.

Penetrating wounds often become infected. The lifeguard should counsel a victim who is released from care to see a physician and to watch for any signs of infection. A tetanus shot should be considered, as death from tetanus after stingray envenomation has occurred.[13] In rare cases, deaths have been reported due to these stings.

Scorpionfish

Stepping on the spines of a scorpionfish can cause immediate and severe pain. Generally, this can be treated in a manner similar to that for a stingray; however, serious complications are more likely. All victims of scorpionfish envenomation should be monitored closely for reactions and should be referred to a doctor or sent to the hospital via ambulance. The doctor may need to remove remaining parts of the spine and provide a tetanus inoculation.

Sea Urchins

The spines of sea urchins cause penetrating wounds, and the spines often break off beneath the skin. More severe reactions to urchin wounds include weakness, loss of body sensation, facial swelling, and irregular pulse. Rare cases involving paralysis and respiratory distress have occurred.

Treatment for urchin wounds differs from agency to agency, but often includes the application of hot water immersion or hot compresses. Follow-up with a doctor should be recommended, particularly if spines remain in the skin or infection develops. A tetanus shot may be appropriate.

Mollusks

The shells of a variety of mollusks can cause abrasions and lacerations. The wound should be cleansed and a sterile dressing applied. Serious cases may require transport to a medical facility. In cases where the victim is treated and released, the victim should be advised to seek further medical care if infection develops and to ensure current tetanus inoculation.

Coral

If necessary, coral cuts should be rinsed with seawater, as stinging nematocysts may be left on the skin and freshwater may cause them to sting. These cuts often become infected, requiring a physician's care and antibiotics. The victim should be counseled about this. A tetanus shot may be appropriate.

Snakes

Toxic signs, appearing within twenty minutes, can include malaise, anxiety, euphoria, muscle spasm, respiratory problems, convulsions, unconsciousness, and all signs of shock. Treatment appropriate to the presentation and immediate transport to a medical facility is generally appropriate.

Leeches

Many agencies on beaches with leech problems provide lifeguards with equipment to help detach and dispose of leeches. A common practice is to simply place salt directly on the leech, which typically causes it to release. Treatment for minor bleeding is usually sufficient.

SPINAL INJURIES

In cases of nonbreathing victims or those with compromised breathing, resuscitation is the priority. The American Heart Association reports that, "The reported incidence of cervical spine injury in drowning victims is low (0.009%). Unnecessary cervical spine immobilization can impede adequate opening of the airway and delay delivery of rescue breaths."[1] However, spinal injuries are a reality in the aquatic environment and so long as resuscitation is prioritized, lifeguards should address spinal injuries in accordance with their training. In this section we offer some options specific to the challenges of the open water environment.

The first step in treatment of spinal injury victims is recognition. Any neck or back pain after injury (even trivial injury) or head trauma needs to be treated appropriately. Numbness, pins and needles, or weakness, even if temporary, are all signs of possible spinal injury requiring further evaluation and treatment.

Unless the victim is in imminent mortal danger and must be moved quickly, all actions should be taken slowly, carefully, and in unison. The ultimate goal is to successfully rescue the person to a point where an ambulance can transport to the hospital, while doing no harm. The aim is to stabilize the spine and maintain the neck and back from further motion, usually in a neutral (straight) position or in the position of comfort. Proper immobilization can limit the possibility of further damage and facilitate moving the victim. It will allow for efficient, more permanent immobilization. Specifics should be taught and regularly practiced in accordance with the lifeguard's level of medical training.

The best methods to use will depend on several factors:

- **Location**—Onshore or offshore, deep or shallow water, surf or flatwater, distance from shore
- **Available Lifeguards**—Strength, training, and numbers
- **Victim**—Size and condition (i.e. walking or sitting, face up or face down, breathing or non-breathing, other injuries)
- **Available Equipment and Transportation**

Beach Presentation

Many of the spinal injuries a lifeguard will see involve people who walk up to the lifeguard complaining of neck or back injury sustained during water recreation, such as bodysurfing or a shallow water dive in which the bottom was struck. Lifeguards should not assume that because the victim is able to walk, there is no injury to the spine. The very fact that the person has consulted with the lifeguard suggests significant concern. This victim should not be allowed to lie down. The *standing spineboard technique* can be used.

Credit: Eric Nurse

Lowering a standing spinal injury patient to the ground using a spineboard.

One lifeguard moves to the rear of the victim and stabilizes the head and neck with one hand on each side. While the first lifeguard maintains neck stabilization, the spineboard is slid in between the first lifeguard and the victim. At least two other lifeguards then stand facing the victim and grasp opposite sides of the spineboard through the victim's armpits and gently lower the board to the sand. Standard protocols for securing the victim to the spineboard are then followed.

Water Presentation

Victims found in the surf or floating in shallow water, or those seen diving, need appropriate precautionary care for possible spinal injury. Upon approaching a victim in the water with suspected spinal injury, avoid unnecessary turbulence. If the victim is not breathing, the face needs to be carefully removed from the water and rescue breathing begun as soon as possible, using appropriate techniques. The modified jaw thrust or jaw thrust maneuvers are the recommended airway methods. They allow the lifeguard to maintain the neck in as neutral a position as possible.

Three in-water spinal immobilization techniques are offered below. It's best to be skilled in more than one. Some are better under different conditions and none fit all circumstances ideally. Although names for these maneuvers vary, for purposes of standardization the names used in this section should be used for each technique.

Spineboards which float have been available for many years. Lifeguard agencies are encouraged to acquire these devices, since they can improve the quality of victim care by allowing stabilization of the victim, even in deep water. They also make extrication from the water of a victim with compromised movement much easier.

Vice Grip

The lifeguard approaches from the victim's side, places the lifeguard's dominant arm along the victim's sternum (upper chest), and stabilizes the chin with the hand. The lifeguard's other arm is then placed along the spine with this hand cupping the back of the victim's head. The arms are squeezed together forming a vice which provides stabilization. Care must be taken to avoid excessive pressure on the airway. If the victim is face down, the vice grip is applied as described and the lifeguard submerges and rotates underneath the victim.

This method is quickly and readily applied by any size lifeguard to any size victim. It works well in deep to medium depth water, but it is not practical if the victim is face down in water less than three feet deep. It leaves the lifeguard in a good position to check respiratory status and carry out rescue breathing.

Body Hug

The lifeguard approaches the face-up victim from behind and partially submerges. The lifeguard then places the lifeguard's arms through the victim's armpits from the back and places the lifeguard's hands over the victim's ears, thus stabilizing the head. The lifeguard's face is placed next to the victim's head.

For a face-down victim, the technique is applied in a similar manner. The lifeguard reaches over the back and through the armpits of the victim and places the lifeguard's hands over the victim's ears. The lifeguard then rolls the victim toward the lifeguard, with the lifeguard submerging momentarily and then surfacing in the position described for a face-up victim. In this way, stabilization is maintained while the victim is turned to a face-up position.

This method provides exceptional immobilization. It may be impractical in shallow

Vice Grip.

Credit: Sandra McCormick

water. It may not be applicable if there is a significant size mismatch between lifeguard and victim. A lone lifeguard cannot adequately perform rescue breathing using the body

Body hug.

Credit: Kekai Brown

hug, although some modifications are used by some agencies. A change in the immobilization method is required before placing the victim on a spineboard.

Extended Arm Grip

Of the three methods, this method (also known the head splint) is probably the most versatile method. The lifeguard takes a position at the victim's side and grabs the victim's arms just above the elbow right to right and left to left. The lifeguard then carefully raises the victim's arms above the victim's head, pressing them together against the ears. This immobilizes the victim's head and neck. This head grip can be maintained by the lifeguard with only one hand holding the victim's two arms together. Further stability can be obtained if the lifeguard uses two hands with the lifeguard's thumbs supporting the back of the victim's head. A face-down victim has the method applied as above. The victim is then gently glided head first and slowly rolled toward the lifeguard, thus positioning the victim in the crook of the lifeguard's arm.

Credit: Sandra McCormick

Extended arm grip.

This method can allow the lifeguard a free hand to support the body or to check for respirations and begin rescue breathing. It can even allow a free arm for sidestroke or backstroke to assist in moving the victim toward shore or recovering the victim from a submerged position. It works in deep or shallow water and is perhaps the only method for a single lifeguard to roll a victim in the surf zone or extremely shallow water. This is done using one hand to apply the overhead arm pressure and the other to roll the victim's hips. It further allows for easy transition to a spineboard.

Rescue to Shore

If in deep water and if a floating spineboard is available, carefully submerge it under the victim and secure the victim to it with the least amount of movement possible. If not, the victim should be carefully moved toward shore or a rescue boat. As a last resort, the lifeguard could place a rescue tube under the lifeguard's armpits and continue the immobilization until further help arrives, possibly kicking toward shore in the meantime. Each lifeguard agency should have all lifeguards practice coordinated transition from these methods to spineboard stabilization. All appropriate equipment needs to be readily available and frequently checked, including straps and head immobilization.

Placing a victim on a spineboard is not possible with one lifeguard and difficult with less than three. More are helpful. The victim should be kept in shallow water until further help and equipment arrive, unless waves, cold water, or the immediate need for resuscitation preclude this option. When holding or moving a victim in surf conditions, attempt to keep the victim's body perpendicular to incoming waves, in order to limit movement.

COLD WATER INJURIES

All cold water immersion victims should be quickly rescued. Those victims who have been in cold water for a considerable time, and who are breathing, should be rescued in a near horizontal attitude, if possible, to prevent a potentially adverse fall in blood pressure.[14] Those whose airways are threatened should be rescued by the quickest method, regardless of body attitude.

Victims who are not in need of resuscitation and who are not severely hypothermic should have wet clothing removed and replaced with dry clothing, if available. They should then be wrapped in warm, dry blankets, making sure their airway is clear and supported. Conscious shivering survivors will usually rewarm themselves reasonably quickly, but the process can be accelerated by immersion in a bath of warm water or a warm shower (active rewarming). As they recover, they should be removed from the bath to avoid overwarming. In cases of severe hypothermia active rewarming should be avoided until the patient is in a hospital setting. Victims suddenly immersed in cold water and those who are severely hypothermic are at risk for cardiac arrhythmias.

In case of unconsciousness or apparent cardiac arrest, the airway should be cleared and appropriate procedures should be employed according to CPR protocols. It may be difficult to assess whether the unconscious victim of hypothermia has a heartbeat, because the heartbeat may be extremely slow and a pulse hard to assess. Since drowning victims are typically starved of oxygen, pay particular attention to ventilating the victim, ideally with oxygen. Arrange rapid transfer to the hospital.

In those who are apparently dead, avoid a hasty diagnosis. The maxim *no one is dead until they are warm and dead* is appropriate provided you are not too remote from medical support. Follow resuscitation protocols and arrange rapid transport to the hospital. People, especially small children, who have been submerged for up to an hour in ice-cold water have been successfully resuscitated in the hospital.[15] People who have experienced serious hypothermia, even if successfully revived, should always be sent to the hospital to be checked for pulmonary complications.

One very rare complication of contact with cold water is *cold urticaria*. It can occur in water as warm as 60 degrees, perhaps warmer. This condition is an allergy-like reaction to contact with cold water, as well as other sources of cold.[16] Within minutes, the skin may become itchy, red, and swollen. Fainting, very low blood pressure, and shock-like symptoms can present. In cases of apparent cold water urticaria, removal from the source of cold is essential. Treatment is similar to that for any allergic reaction, with priority being given to maintaining breathing and circulation.[16, 17]

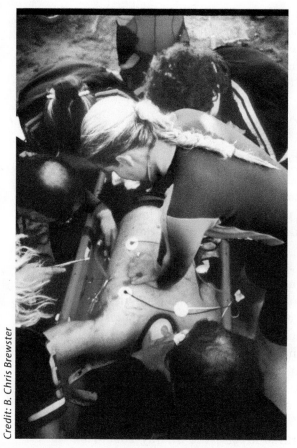

Credit: B. Chris Brewster

A lifeguard performs chest compressions during a drowning resuscitation.

CHAPTER SUMMARY

In this chapter we have learned the minimum medical training and equipment levels appropriate for open water lifeguards. We have learned to classify levels of injuries, along with some general medical care guidelines and tips. We have learned about resuscitation of drowning victims, including proper positioning, the value of oxygen, and when it is appropriate to release a drowning victim from care. We have learned about treating injuries inflicted by aquatic life, including bites, stings, and other injuries. We have learned about treatment of spinal injuries, both on the beach and in the water. We have learned how to treat victims of cold water injuries.

DISCUSSION POINTS

- Identify the reasons that open water lifeguards should have training in CPR/AED and emergency medical response.
- Explain the value of having medical aid equipment readily available.
- Explain the need for people who have been provided medical care to do a follow up with a doctor.
- List the critical elements in the resuscitation of a drowning victim.
- Explain the value of applying heat for a jellyfish sting.
- Identify the importance of the standing spineboard technique for potential spinal injuries.
- List five considerations in stabilizing a spinal injury victim in the water.
- List three techniques in re-warming a victim of cold water immersion.

Scuba Related Illness and Treatment

I n this chapter you will learn about how scuba works and the associated risks. The development of modern scuba equipment has helped diving grow into one of the more widely practiced aquatic sports. You will learn about diving illnesses, including why they occur, how to identify them, and how to treat them. You will also learn about proper reporting of diving accidents.

CHAPTER EXCERPT

Some very important information to document and convey to the receiving emergency department is the patient's dive profile. Some key questions the lifeguard can elicit are: How deep for how long? How many dives in the last 24-hours? Was there a rapid ascent? If the diver is unable to provide this information, the diver's depth gauge or dive computer may provide it. The dive buddy is another excellent source. The lifeguard can then call the emergency department physician with this information. Since many doctors are unfamiliar with the Divers Alert Network, the lifeguard should advise of DAN's free medical consultation services and *provide the DAN emergency telephone number.*

Divers Alert Network (DAN) 24-hour emergency hotline number: (919) 684-9111

HOW SCUBA WORKS

Most scuba divers breathe air, which is compressed in two different ways—mechanically and by water pressure. Air (not pure oxygen) is compressed into a scuba tank by a mechanical air compressor. This increases the air capacity of the tank. A regulator with a hose and mouthpiece attached is then used to breathe air from the tank. The regulator reduces the delivery pressure of the compressed air in the tank to ambient (surrounding) pressure, so that it can be inhaled normally without damaging the lungs.

Credit: Eric Nurse

Divers may also use mixed or altered breathing gases. These include nitrogen-oxygen (nitrox), helium-oxygen (heliox), or helium-nitrogen-oxygen (trimix). The use of mixed gases, which requires special training, generally allows the diver to avoid lengthy decompression stops when returning to the surface.

When air (or mixed gas) is made available through the regulator during a dive, it is inhaled at a pressure consistent with the depth of the diver. This is because as a diver descends, the ambient pressure becomes greater due to the increasing pressure of the water above. This pressure is expressed in *atmospheres*. Surface atmospheric pressure at sea level is 14.7 pounds per square inch (psi). This is known as one atmosphere of pressure. For every 33 feet a diver descends, an additional atmosphere of pressure is added. Therefore, a diver at 33 feet experiences two atmospheres of pressure, at 66 feet three atmospheres, at 99 feet four atmospheres, and so on.

As pressure of the water above increases, the volume of a given quantity of air decreases. For example, if a bubble of air at the surface were taken to two atmospheres (33 feet in depth), it would be reduced to one half its surface volume; at three atmospheres, one third its surface volume; at four atmospheres, one fourth its surface volume; and so on.

A diver at 33 feet can breathe normally through a properly functioning regulator, but the air is still compressed so that it is twice as dense as it would have been on the surface. However, the volume remains the same because regulators are designed to deliver air at the surrounding pressure. If this diver were to hold a breath while ascending to the surface, the volume of air in the lungs would double. Therefore, while the regulator reduces the pressure of compressed air from the scuba tank to a comfortable, breathable level, air breathed below the surface remains compressed by water pressure, compared to what its volume would be on the surface. For example, at 33 feet air is two times (2X) as dense and at 66 feet it is three times (3X) as dense.

RISKS ASSOCIATED WITH SCUBA DIVING

It's difficult to judge the rate of injury associated with diving because the number of participants is unknown. Most estimates of the number of active scuba divers in the U.S. easily exceed one million. The Divers Alert Network (DAN), a nonprofit, membership organization dedicated to the safety of recreational scuba diving, provides annual statistics based on the number of reported injuries and deaths associated with scuba diving. DAN collects this information primarily from hyperbaric chambers used to treat scuba related illness and claims filed with DAN insurance. Most of the statistical information in this chapter is provided by DAN.

There are over 1,000 emergency department admissions reported for scuba related injuries each year

LEARN MORE

Divers Alert Network:
www.diversalertnetwork.org

in the U.S.[1] The number of fatalities has been gradually declining, but in the years 2010–2013 DAN received notification of an average of 58.[1] Death occurs due to a number of factors. Drowning is the reported cause of over 50% of diving deaths, with cardiovascular disease responsible for over 20% of diving deaths, and arterial gas embolism responsible for about 10%.[1] However, cardiovascular disease is the leading disabling factor that led to death.[1] (It is also the leading cause of death in the U.S.) Many complications of diving underwater might result in death by drowning, including running out of

Lifeguard scuba training.

Credit: California State Parks Lifeguards

air, entrapment or entanglement, equipment malfunction, or panic. More than half the scuba divers in a national survey reported experiencing panic or near-panic behavior on one or more occasions. This included both novice and experienced divers.[2]

Divers in the 50–59 year age range are most likely to be involved in fatal accidents, followed by divers in the 60–69 year age range and the 40–49 year age range.[1] Men are over 80% of the victims.[1] It's important to note however, that these numbers could simply be reflective of the dive population at large, since there are no hard numbers regarding the age and sex of participants in diving. According to DAN, "The diving community is aging steadily … and … the average age of newly certified divers has also increased since the early days of recreational scuba."[1]

DECOMPRESSION ILLNESS

Decompression illness (DCI) is the result of a bubble phenomenon which occurs in the body's tissues as the diver ascends to the surface or at some point after the dive. There are two types of decompression illness: decompression sickness (DCS) and arterial gas embolism (AGE). The vast majority of reported scuba injuries involve DCS, but AGE is the cause of over 85% of fatalities in bubble related disease.[1]

Decompression sickness, often called *the bends*, involves changes to dissolved nitrogen in the body. Nitrogen is an inert gas and plays no role in the body's metabolism, but it makes up about 79% of the air we breathe. It is carried through the bloodstream to the body's tissues as a normal process of circulation. As a diver breathes compressed gas underwater, the increased pressure during diving causes more nitrogen to be delivered to the body's tissues, thus, increasing the dissolved nitrogen content within the body's cells. As the diver slowly returns to the surface, nitrogen is eliminated by a gradual release back into the bloodstream where it can be eliminated by the lungs through respiration. If a diver ascends too rapidly to allow for the gradual release of nitrogen, bubbles can form in the bloodstream and body tissues, which can inhibit normal circulation. Decompression sickness most often occurs as a result of dives deeper than 80 feet and is strongly associated with repetitive, deep, and/or prolonged dives.

Credit: California State Parks Lifeguards

Lifeguard divers enter the water from a lifeguard rescue vessel.

Dive tables were created many years ago to help scuba divers avoid DCS. Through calculations based on these tables, divers can determine maximum depth and time profiles, as well as the number of dives they can make with relative safety in a day. Dive tables also help determine if in-water decompression stops must be made while ascending from various depths. These stops are intended to prolong the diver's ascent and allow the release of nitrogen from the tissues before it produces bubbles. This is known as *off-gassing*.

Many divers use small, computerized gauges attached to their scuba gear or on their wrists. Use of dive computers has been shown to reduce the likelihood of injury. According to DAN, "A diagnosis of AGE or barotraumas was two to three times more likely for divers who used dive tables and dive guides than for those who used dive computers."[3] This is likely due to error avoidance in dive table calculations by divers and to ascent indicators found on dive computers that alert divers to an ascent that is too rapid.

Arterial gas embolism, also known as air embolism, occurs when compressed air is trapped in the alveoli—the small sacs in the lungs where exchange of carbon dioxide and oxygen take place. Arterial gas embolism most often results from a rapid ascent, which may occur when the diver runs low on air or is out of air. In a panicked ascent, divers may hold their breath, which closes the airway, effectively trapping compressed gas within the lungs. As the diver ascends toward the surface, the decreasing ambient pressure allows gas to expand and over-inflate lung tissue. When a scuba diver ascends, the excess gas must be exhaled. Otherwise the lungs will progressively increase in volume until the elastic limit of the alveoli is exceeded, and rupture occurs. This process may force gas bubbles into the pulmonary circulation from the capillaries via the pulmonary veins to the left side of the heart, and then to the carotid or basilar arteries.

Arterial gas embolism can happen at any depth, although it is more likely to occur in shallow waters of less than 33 feet. Cases have been reported in water as shallow as four feet. The percentage of AGE cases has been declining. The Divers Alert Network believes that this is due to slower ascent rates, better training, safety stops near the surface before exiting the water, and possibly the practice of spending the last minutes of the dive near the surface where divers are less likely to run out of air. Nevertheless, out of air or insufficient breathing gas remains a large contributor to diving injuries and fatalities.

Symptoms of Decompression Illness

Onset of symptoms of DCS is usually somewhat gradual, although they may be present immediately upon surfacing. They commonly include, in particular, pain in the joints and numbness or tingling. The pain is often described as a dull ache, perhaps slowly getting worse. Pain, when present, is most often felt first in the joints, such as elbows, shoulders and knees. Other frequently reported symptoms are dizziness, headache, extreme fatigue, weakness, nausea, visual disturbance, and difficulty walking.

Divers tend to deny symptoms of DCS, which delays treatment. DAN reports that only 25% to 30% divers with symptoms of DCS request assistance within four hours after symptom onset. This is a critical issue in treatment of DCS because the longer the delay in providing proper treatment, the greater the likelihood of long-term health

Credit: Leslie Schwene

Scuba diver in a kelp forest.

complications which may not fully resolve. For this reason, *even a slight hint of decompression illness symptoms should be taken very seriously by the lifeguard*. Transport to the hospital should be strongly encouraged, as well as consultation with DAN.

Onset of symptoms of AGE is typically more rapid than those of DCS. They can be immediate and extreme. A diver who suddenly loses consciousness upon surfacing should be assumed to have AGE.[4] Symptoms similar to an acute stroke can be one of the most serious results of AGE.[4] These cases usually involve a dive profile with a very rapid ascent.

Treatment of Decompression Illness

Lifeguards need not spend extensive amounts of time deciding whether a diving case involves DCS or AGE. Both can be very serious. If either are suspected, the diver should be treated for ABCs, given *high oxygen concentrations (via either a demand inhalator valve or non-rebreather mask at 15 liters per minute)*, and transported to an emergency department, ideally under care of trained ambulance personnel. DAN should be consulted.

At one time, emergency responders were taught to place divers in a radical head down position, perhaps on their side. This is no longer recommended and may actually worsen the problem.[4] Instead the patient should be transported supine or in the recovery position. To position the patient in the recovery position, turn the patient onto either side and support the head, assuring the airway is open. Avoid crossing the extremities because circulation may be compromised for diving injuries.

Full resolution of a DCI generally requires treatment in a recompression chamber. A recompression chamber uses atmospheric air pressure to comfortably return the patient to a pressure environment while breathing 100% oxygen. Any remaining bubble growth

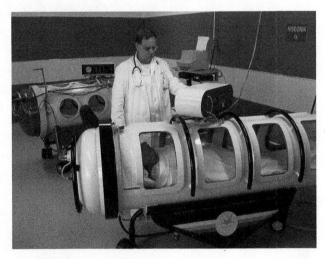

Recompression chamber.

may be reduced in volume and effectively diffused into the surrounding tissue where it can be off-gassed by the body's perfusion. The patient is then slowly reintroduced to normal surface air pressure.

Recompression chambers are not always readily available near a diving accident site. Even if a recompression chamber is nearby, it may be unattended or in use for other medical reasons. Therefore, in most cases it is important to transport the patient to the nearest emergency department for evaluation and stabilization, where the nearest recompression chamber can be notified as early as possible. In some areas, lifeguards call the recompression chamber immediately to advise them of the case, to inform them of the possibility they will be receiving a patient, and to elicit advice. Transport by helicopter may be necessary, depending on severity of the illness and the proximity of the recompression chamber. The aircraft should be pressurized to sea-level and fly at the minimum safe altitude, preferably below 1,000 feet.[4] DAN will assist in coordination of evacuation of injured divers.

Some very important information to document and convey to the receiving emergency department is the patient's dive profile. Some key questions the lifeguard can elicit are: How deep for how long? How many dives in the last 24-hours? Was there a rapid ascent? If the diver is unable to provide this information, the diver's depth gauge or dive computer may provide it. The dive buddy is another excellent source. The lifeguard can then call the emergency department physician with this information. Since many doctors are unfamiliar with DAN, the lifeguard should advise of DAN's free medical consultation services and *provide the DAN emergency telephone number.* It is generally recommended to keep the equipment in an as-is condition for later review and investigation.

A diver with DCI symptoms who refuses treatment should be advised to seek further medical assistance, especially if there is any worsening of symptoms. One other important consideration in a DCI case is the dive buddy. If two divers have followed similar dive profiles and one exhibits complications, the other should be carefully evaluated. Even if symptoms are not readily apparent, they may appear within a short period of time.

REPORTING DIVING ACCIDENTS

Credit: California State Parks Lifeguards

Scuba rescue diver training.

The Divers Alert Network maintains a 24-hour diving medical emergency hotline. This hotline provides injured divers and health care providers with expert consultation and referrals. The DAN Emergency Services hotline number is (919) 684-9111. DAN also maintains a telephone information line to provide answers to commonly asked questions about scuba diving medicine, health, and safety. This number, (919) 684-2948, is answered during business hours, Eastern Time, on regular business days.

All scuba diving injuries should be reported to DAN. This allows DAN to produce information aimed at increasing diver safety. You can report online at: www.diversalert-network.org. You can also find valuable information about preserving evidence, autopsy protocols, health risk, and other diving related issues.

Lifeguards and lifeguard agencies are encouraged to join DAN and help support this organization. Oxygen training courses are also available through DAN for lifeguards, divers, and emergency medical personnel. Membership and training information is available at: www.diversalertnetwork.org.

CHAPTER SUMMARY

In this chapter we have learned about risks associated with diving, including drowning, diving illness, and cardiac arrest. We have learned about how surface air is mechanically compressed in scuba tanks and by the weight of water, and how a regulator allows divers to breathe compressed air. We have learned about decompression illness, including decompression sickness and arterial gas embolism. We have learned about the dive tables and how they help divers avoid diving injuries. We have learned some of the symptoms and treatments of diving injuries. And we have learned about reporting diving accidents.

DISCUSSION POINTS

- Identify three circumstances that could lead to a scuba diving death.
- List five causes of scuba diving deaths.
- Identify the two ways in which the air divers breathe is compressed.
- Explain the importance of scuba divers following the dive tables.
- List five symptoms of decompression illness.
- Identify ways a lifeguard can treat a scuba diving illness.
- List all the information that should be gathered from a scuba diver that has suffered a diving injury.
- Identify the organization that can be called to provide information on diving illness and treatment.

CHAPTER
20

Underwater Search and Recovery

I n this chapter you will learn about the steps to take if a victim submerges and is lost beneath the water. This includes searching for the victim, recovering the victim, and what to do afterward. This is a rare occurrence, but search and recovery of missing victims are essential functions of a lifeguard. They must be conducted quickly and efficiently if the victim is to have a chance of survival.

◼◼◼◼ CHAPTER EXCERPT ◼◼◼◼

If a lifeguard onshore observes a submersion or receives a credible report of a submersion, the alert to other personnel is essential. Extensive backup should be immediately responded.

When a victim submerges and is unable to return to the surface, the final stage of the drowning process begins. Breathing is no longer possible. Without freshly oxygenated blood, the heart will eventually stop beating and pumping blood. Brain death usually begins in five to six minutes after adequately oxygenated blood stops circulating, although in some very unusual cold water drownings this may be greatly delayed. This oxygen starvation is why immediate resuscitation efforts, ideally with use of supplemental oxygen, are so critical for a drowning victim. It is also why the protocols for CPR in drowning cases are different, emphasizing early ventilation of the victim. It's different from a sudden cardiac arrest where the heart has stopped beating suddenly, not as a result of lack of oxygen. Please see Chapter 8 (*Drowning*) for more information on the pathophysiology of drowning and Chapter 18 (*Medical Care in the Aquatic Environment*) for detailed recommendations on resuscitation.

The standard practice for search and rescue of victims who have submerged underwater in water of a temperature normally used for swimming is to continue an *emergency search* for one hour. The term emergency search refers to the period during which personnel and equipment are heavily committed in an effort to recover a victim who may be able to be successfully resuscitated. During this window of time, resuscitation procedures are normally attempted if the victim is recovered. Once this hour has passed, the emergency portion of the search is typically terminated, although efforts to find the body of the victim may be continued.

This one hour standard intentionally involves a period of time far greater than a successful resuscitation is typically likely. One reason is the extremely remote possibility of a successful resuscitation up to one hour after submersion. Another is the possibility of an error in the time submersion is estimated to have occurred. Lifeguards must also consider the concerns of family and friends of the victim, who may find it extremely difficult to accept a briefer emergency search.

The need for a reasonable emergency search period must also be balanced against the importance of protecting other beach users. Lifeguards have an ongoing responsibility for those continuing to use the water area for recreation. Considering that a human being is presumed lost underwater, it's fully appropriate to devote significant resources in an attempt to recover and resuscitate the victim, but all beach users need protection. If a second person is lost while lifeguard resources are diverted in an effort to recover the first, the tragedy is compounded. This is a primary reason that many lifeguard agencies clear the water during a search effort.

Despite the one hour standard for emergency search and resuscitation efforts, the USLA believes that in open water, there is a *two minute window* of enhanced opportunity for successful recovery and resuscitation of submerged victims. During the initial two minutes, responding lifeguards may be able to make quick dives at the last seen point, bring the victim to the surface, perform initial in-water ventilation, and retrieve the victim to shore for further medical assistance. After the two minute window has closed, the chances of successful recovery and resuscitation decline rapidly. Water currents and surf can quickly move the body, poor water visibility can complicate the search attempt, and the last seen point of the victim can be obscured on waters with no immediate landmarks. In the flatwater environment, some of these factors may not enter the equation, but successful recovery of a viable victim remains very challenging. This brief opportunity is yet another reason that prevention is such a critical aspect of open water lifesaving. Nevertheless, all lifeguards must be prepared to instantaneously and effectively implement search and recovery procedures.

Certain equipment is essential to conduct effective search and recovery. Under USLA guidelines, all beach areas must have masks and snorkels readily accessible to mount an underwater search and rescue, and all must have marker buoys readily accessible to mark the last seen point. Swim fins are essential when searches must be conducted. Marker dye may be useful in indicating the speed and prevailing direction of the current.

Reports of missing persons do not always call for an in-water search. Often the missing person is simply lost on the beach. Chapter 25 (*Emergency Planning and Management*) provides guidelines for interviewing people reporting a missing person and determining whether an in-water search is appropriate. This chapter is intended to detail search and recovery procedures once it is determined that a full emergency search should be conducted for a reportedly submerged victim.

SEARCH

An apparently valid report of a submerged swimmer should immediately trigger an agency's existing emergency operation plan and implementation of steps on a checklist designed to help to ensure that all normal steps are considered by the incident commander in a logical, priority order. This should include automatically sending backup personnel to the scene for assistance, along with any available search equipment. Lifeguards from adjacent beaches and allied agencies may also be summoned. Refer to Chapter 25 (*Emergency Planning and Management*) for more on this.

The estimated time of the victim's submersion should be established and documented as soon as possible. This information is critical to determining the time available to summon additional personnel for the search and ultimately for determining when to conclude the emergency portion of the search. If available, it's a good practice to summon ambulance personnel at the start of a search for a submerged victim. In this way, advanced life support will not be delayed upon recovery of a victim. In addition, police may be useful to provide crowd control.

Initial Search

If a lifeguard onshore observes a submersion or receives a credible report of a submersion, the alert to other personnel is essential. Extensive backup should be immediately responded. If a victim submerges as a lifeguard approaches in the water, lifeguards onshore can be alerted by the lifeguard in the water using the internationally approved arm signal of a submerged victim. The lifeguard looks toward shore and crosses both arms overhead in the form of an X (the Code X signal). As with all arm signals, lifeguards ashore should respond with the same signal to show that the signal has been received and understood.

Perhaps the most critical task in initiating a search for a submerged victim is to fix a *last seen point*. Without landmarks, the surface of the water can make it virtually impossible to fix a specific point. The best executed searches will be foiled if the place the victim was last seen prior to submersion is not correctly fixed or if it is not marked in a manner to ensure that it is not forgotten. Extensive resources are normally devoted to missing victim searches and great care should be taken to ensure that they are based on the best possible location of initial submersion. If the submersion was witnessed by a non-lifeguard, the witness should be interviewed thoroughly, but expeditiously, in order to obtain an accurate last seen point. If the initial report by the witness is made away from the area of the reported submersion, the witness should be returned to the area and a lifeguard placed in the water to pinpoint the last seen point to the best recollection of the reporting party.

As soon as the best known last seen point is identified, bearings should be taken to attempt to fix the point. Use cross-bearings by lining up two stationary objects onshore in two separate locations, the imaginary lines for which form an X at the last seen point. The first lifeguard arriving at the last seen point should make several immediate surface dives in an attempt to locate the victim. The RFD can be left floating on the surface if it will impede diving.

The second lifeguard in the water should carry a marker buoy, along with a mask, snorkel, and swim fins. The value of a marker buoy cannot be understated. It is essential to keeping the search in the proper area. The buoy anchor should be strong enough to remain stationary in reasonably anticipated water conditions, but the cross-bearings should be regularly checked during the search to ensure that the buoy has not moved. The second lifeguard drops the marker buoy at the last seen point and assists the first lifeguard in surface dives until the victim is found or a more organized search can be mounted. If a marker buoy is not immediately available, response of the second lifeguard should not be delayed while waiting for this equipment. The clock is ticking. The buoy should be placed as soon as it becomes available.

Credit: San Clemente Lifeguards

A lifeguard enters with a marker buoy, a mask, a snorkel, and swim fins.

During the search, personnel allowing, at least one experienced lifeguard should be left ashore to act as the *incident commander* (IC) to coordinate the search and ensure safety of the searchers. (Learn more about the role of an incident commander in Chapter 25). As soon as possible, a *safety officer* should be assigned to focus solely on rescuer safety. The safety officer ensures that any rescue boats summoned to the scene stay clear of swimmers and divers, for example, and that all divers are accounted for. Communication must be maintained with arriving lifeguards and other public safety agencies.

Full Search

Prior to initiation of a full search, a search zone should be established by the IC or someone designated by the IC. This provides search personnel with boundaries. Ideally, the search zone should be marked to give search teams a reference point during water searches. Markers may include buoys or cross-bearing landmarks. Like the buoy to mark the last seen point, these buoys, particularly when used in a surf environment, should be weighted heavily enough to keep them stationary in reasonably anticipated conditions.

Search Methods

In the flatwater environment, if no currents are present, searches can concentrate on the last seen point with an expectation that the victim is most likely near this area, assuming the last seen point is reliable. In the surf environment and other environments with significant currents, submerged, unconscious victims may move significantly from the last seen point. Those overseeing a search in such conditions must make reasonable, educated guesses as to how the body of the victim might move underwater. In doing so, it's important to consider that currents beneath the surface of the water may be significantly different than those above.

There are three general search methods:

- **In-Water Search**—Wading and swimming lifeguards search the water. In shallow water, lifeguards may systematically wade back and forth along the shore in a line that extends perpendicular to the beach, searching the water with eyes, legs, and arms. In deeper water, lifeguards use face masks and snorkels, along with swim fins, observing from the surface. These searchers should make surface dives if the bottom cannot be seen from the surface.

Lifeguards practice a missing person line search.

Credit: Eric Nurse

- **Surface Search**—Lifeguards are deployed in boats or on paddleboards and use those craft as platforms from which the water is searched. Helicopters provide a superior vantage point for this purpose, especially if the water is clear. Emergency operation plans and checklists for agencies with helicopters available should involve an immediate request for a helicopter when a Code X is confirmed. Since submersion victims normally sink, the value of a surface search is dependent on water depth and clarity.

- **Underwater Search**—Lifeguards equipped with scuba can dive below depths of free divers and can stay down. Trained divers are extremely valuable during the emergency portion of a

Lifeguards conducting a missing person search.

Credit: Eric Nurse

search, but only if scuba equipment is readily available. Advanced lifeguard agencies maintain scuba equipment at their beaches and in their emergency vehicles (and boats) for this purpose.

Search Patterns

The IC or a person designated by the IC should establish a search pattern to ensure systematic coverage of the search zone. The three most common search patterns are the line search (also known as the parallel search), the circular search, and the fan search (sweep). The line search is the most effective option in the surf environment. Any of the three may be used effectively in flatwater. Surface search teams may start in deeper water, working a pattern toward shore, while in-water search teams may work from shallow to deep. Searchers using mask and snorkel should be spaced to maximize coverage, but close enough to see anything between them.

- **Circular Search**—In the circular search, a buoy is placed at the last seen point and an anchor guard holds a line, if available, at that point. Lifeguards then space out an appropriate distance from the anchor guard and swim a circular pattern. Once a full circle has been turned, the lifeguard farthest from center maintains position, while the other searchers move to points beyond on the line. The searchers then swim another full circle. This is repeated until the area is thoroughly covered or the victim is found. If the victim is not found at first, the pattern may be started over again.

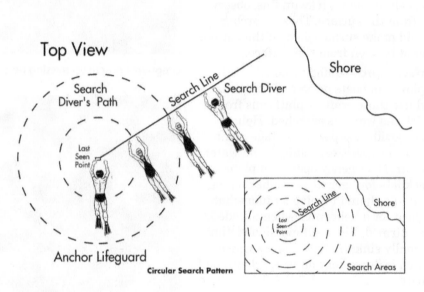

Circular Search.

- **Fan Search**—A buoy is placed at the last seen point. The fan search is used with a line tender on shore or in a boat. Searchers on the line move back and forth in a fan pattern, extending outward as occurs in a circular search. The starting point of the search will be determined by the last seen point. As searchers complete each arc, the fan gets bigger.
- **Parallel Search**—A buoy is placed at the last seen point. In the parallel search (also known as the line search or grid search), it is best to start by defining your search area using landmarks or other methods. A line of lifeguards, spaced appropriately, swim parallel to each other along one end of the rectangle, from one side to the other. They then move sideways along the side of the rectangle and swim back to the other side. This back and forth pattern can be continued until the area is fully searched. An option, depending on conditions, is use of a line, which searchers grasp to help ensure proper spacing and alignment. At this point the IC can order that the area be searched again, or create a new area adjacent to the area searched. Once the second area has been thoroughly covered, a new one can be created and so forth. It's a good practice to designate one offshore lifeguard to take charge of the search line. This helps ensure that order is maintained. If possible, this lifeguard should be on a rescue board or rescue boat.

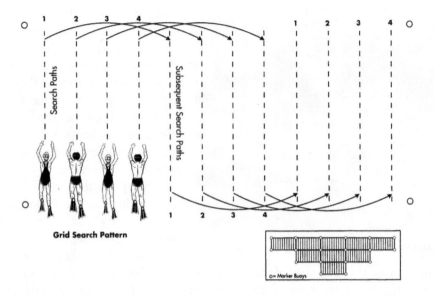

Grid Search Pattern

O= Marker Buoys

Line Search.

To cover an area of limited water visibility more quickly, a team of lifeguards may use the following procedure to complete a parallel search pattern. Lifeguards are spaced in a line close enough to see, or touch, each other while on the bottom. Prior to each dive the team leader checks that everyone is lined up and ready, announces the dive count and starts the dive. For example, directions may go something like, "Everyone OK? Line up on me. Dive for a ten count, ready... go." Lifeguards then begin the dive while counting to themselves, "One and two and three," etc. They should dive straight down, while equalizing air pressure in their ears, and then begin their search along the bottom. In water with zero visibility, searchers should touch hands as they feel along the bottom. Lifeguards should closely monitor each other while underwater, surfacing when the diver next to them does. This improves safety while minimizing the time spent on the surface reorganizing for the next dive. As lifeguards surface, they should identify who covered the least distance. The line should be reformed a few feet behind this lifeguard. On the leader's direction, dives should be repeated until the search area is covered or the victim is located.

Rescue boats are extremely valuable in searches and should always be used if available. They allow on-scene supervision, support of the searchers, and facilitate communication to shore. Rescue boats with global positioning systems (GPS) can help maintain proper positioning and report coordinates to other resources, such as helicopters. Rescue

Credit: Eric Nurse

Lifeguards reforming their line search after a dive.

Credit: California State Parks Lifeguards

Using a rescue boat to assist with a search.

boats may also offer sonar capabilities and deliver underwater search technology. If a victim is recovered, rescue boats provide a rapid method of retrieval to shore. Some include a deck large enough for CPR, along with advanced medical equipment. When rescue boats are used, caution must be employed to avoid striking a submerged searcher.

The potential for success of a search is largely dependent upon water clarity and currents. In clear water, a few lifeguards can cover a large area in a short time. As water clarity decreases, the difficulty of mounting a successful search increases dramatically.

If the victim is not recovered within a one hour period, or longer if so designated by the incident commander or agency protocol, the search may be changed from one of an emergency search to that of a body recovery. When the emergency portion of the search is terminated, lifeguard personnel can be returned to preventive lifeguarding duties, but it is a good practice to continue the search at a lower staffing level. While family members or friends of the missing victim may be able to understand the need to protect other swimmers, they are likely to view complete termination of the search as callous abandonment. A life has been lost and the shock can be profound for all involved. The investment of further time and resources is well justified if available.

RECOVERY

The goal of a search for a submerged victim is to recover a viable victim who can be resuscitated. This is not always achieved. Lifeguards must be prepared for either outcome.

Recovery of a Viable Victim

If a victim is recovered within an established time-frame after submersion (usually one hour) resuscitation efforts should be initiated immediately. Special considerations for the resuscitation of drowning victims and what to do if you recover a non-breathing victim offshore are detailed in Chapter 18 (*Medical Care in the Aquatic Environment*).

Body Recovery

Agency protocols and individual circumstances will dictate a period of time after which an emergency search phase terminates and becomes a body recovery phase. The presumption of a body recovery search phase is that no resuscitation attempt on the recovered victim would be successful. At this point, priorities change. Concerns for rescuer safety and the safety of beach users is heightened. Some lifeguards may be released from the search to return to regular duties, including incident investigation. These changes should be discussed with searching lifeguards. As well, friends and family members of the missing person should be informed carefully and sensitively.

Depending on local protocol, upon recovering a body lifeguards may be expected to make careful observations on land and underwater, collect evidence, and complete reports for those legally responsible for investigating the death. Body position, location, and water depth are three basic facts that will need to be recorded. Once the scene investigation is complete and actual recovery is to take place, consideration for the sensitivities

Rescue divers recovering a body.

Credit: GLC Aquatic Safety Department

of others at the scene should be addressed. The law in many U.S. states regarding a human body dictate that the body is to be left in the position found until the coroner or medical examiner approves moving it. This is often impractical in lifeguarding, since a body left in the water might be lost to currents or sinking, for example. Local protocols will dictate the most appropriate action.

Body recovery requires preparation and discretion. The body should be handled with respect. To the greatest degree possible, the body should be protected from public view. Use of a body bag, blanket, or other covering is appropriate as soon as the body is removed from the water. (If feasible, this should occur prior to removal.) Crowd control is important, as is the sensitive treatment of family members and other people close to the deceased person who may be present at the recovery. Depending on local protocol, police, a coroner, or medical examiner should be notified as soon as a body is recovered and summoned to the scene. Police officers often have experience notifying and working with next of kin of deceased persons. They can be a helpful resource in this area.

CRISIS INTERVENTION

In many communities, people are trained and assigned to help relatives and friends of the deceased cope with their loss. Some lifeguard agencies train designated lifeguards to perform this function. These services are of particular importance in unexpected deaths, especially those involving children. Part of an emergency operation plan for dealing with a submersion incident (as well as other incidents that might result in death) should include these resources. They may be summoned early in the recovery attempt, so that they are available as soon as possible. If such resources are not available, a lifeguard should be designated to provide any and all possible support to the family. This is true both for recovered victims who do not survive and in cases where the victim is not recovered and presumed to have died.

DEBRIEFING AND COUNSELING

Once search and rescue procedures are concluded, the incident commander (IC) should terminate command and return lifeguards to regular duty assignments as needed. Careful documentation of the event should be made for further investigation.

In addition to standard incident reports, many agencies will require all involved life-guards to prepare a narrative report and to participate in a debriefing session or operational critique. A major emphasis of this process should be development of ideas that will help do an even better job in the future. Any drowning death in a lifeguarded area should be fully investigated.

Like all emergency personnel, lifeguards are susceptible to psychological trauma. Each person handles these situations in their own way. Supervisors should be prepared to offer support. See Chapter 16 (*Lifeguard Health and Safety*) for more on this topic.

CHAPTER SUMMARY

In this chapter we have learned about the steps to take when a victim is observed or reported to have submerged. We have learned the tremendous importance of a rapid search effort. We have learned some common aquatic search methods and patterns. We have learned how long an emergency search normally lasts and what happens after that time period. We have learned the importance of properly handling a recovered body and assisting relatives and families.

Credit: Eric Nurse

Advanced medical personnel prepare to give care as lifeguards perform an in water search.

DISCUSSION POINTS

- Explain the brief time frame for recovery and resuscitation of a submerged victim.
- Explain the need for backup when responding to a missing swimmer.
- Identify the methods for establishing a last seen point.

- List three commonly used search patterns.
- Select and describe a search pattern.
- Identify the steps in recovering a body when resuscitation is not appropriate.
- Describe why crisis intervention experts can assist as part of search protocols..

CHAPTER
21

Professionalism

In this chapter you will learn about the importance of maintaining a professional demeanor and the value of positive public relations. This includes all elements of lifeguard conduct, including public contact. You will learn about lifeguard uniforms, cultural diversity, and contacts with the media.

CHAPTER EXCERPT

Lifeguards are hired to protect and serve beach users. Tremendous courtesy and respect should therefore be paid to those asking questions, requesting assistance, or even filing a complaint.

Lifeguard operations are wide open to public view. It's often said that lifeguards work in a fishbowl, as they are constantly watched by beach visitors. On a busy day, just about every action of every lifeguard is probably observed by someone. Conversations are often overheard, despite assumptions to the contrary. Activities by lifeguards will be filmed by beachgoers and may appear in social media, on websites, and in the news. How lifeguards conduct themselves is critical to garnering the respect and cooperation of the public. If lifeguards project an image of dedicated public safety professionals with an essential role of taking action to protect the public, they are likely to engender great respect. On the other hand, if lifeguards project a cavalier image or fail to treat people fairly, public respect and support will be greatly diminished. An ongoing goal of lifeguards, in all activities, should be to enhance the image of lifesavers and the lifesaving profession. Each day and each public contact offers an opportunity to achieve this goal.

PRINCIPLES OF LIFEGUARD DEPORTMENT

Deportment is another word for behavior or manners. Lifeguards are hired to protect and serve beach users. Tremendous courtesy and respect should therefore be paid to those asking questions, requesting assistance, or even filing a complaint. The fact that a beach user may seem rude is no license for the lifeguard to respond in kind. Becoming angry or confrontational is both unprofessional and counterproductive. A professional demeanor involves an even temperament and a helpful approach regardless of how the lifeguard may be treated by others. Professional conduct ensures a better outcome for the lifeguard and the lifeguard agency.

Another important reason to promote a positive lifeguard image involves the public perception of lifeguard services in general. If lifeguards wish to engender the respect and support commonly enjoyed by other public safety providers, like police and fire-fighters, they must diligently project a professional image. Professional lifeguards have worked hard to promote the image of lifesaving and to put aside negative stereotypes. Each lifeguard has a responsibility to all lifeguards to help maintain and further this image by conducting themselves as professionals *at all times*, whether on duty or off.

There are two major areas of lifeguard deportment: professional conduct and public contact. The following are tips for maintaining ideal levels of lifeguard deportment in each instance.

Professional Conduct

- **Maintain a Professional Appearance**—An alert, well-groomed, physically fit life-guard in proper uniform inspires a sense of confidence and security in beach visitors. Male lifeguards are encouraged to report to work clean-shaven or with well-groomed facial hair, depending on agency requirements. The wearing of jew-elry should be avoided, both for safety reasons and to project a professional image.

- **Avoid Distractive Items**—Lifeguards should not keep items which create distrac-tions in lifeguard stands or towers. Such articles may include anything that distracts your attention from the water.

- **No Games On Duty**—Lifeguards should not participate in beach or water games while on duty. Workouts and lifesaving drills however, are encouraged in accor-dance with agency guidelines.

- **Don't Engage in Horseplay**—Horseplay and pranks constitute unprofessional conduct.

- **Keep Stations and Equipment Neat and Clean**—Vehicles should be regularly pol-ished. Assigned lockers should be tidy. Emergency equipment should always be in a ready condition and positioned in an obvious and highly visible place. Unneces-sary noise in and around the station should be eliminated. The public should not be permitted to use lifeguard stations as dressing rooms, checkrooms for valu-ables, or clubrooms. Only authorized personnel should be allowed in towers.

- **Keep the Area Clean**—Although lifeguards should not be assigned to general beach maintenance, when problems can be quickly and easily rectified, lifeguards should take reasonable steps to help clean up. The beach should be regularly checked for general cleanliness and any potentially dangerous debris. If a condition cannot be resolved easily, appropriate maintenance personnel should be notified through proper channels. Lifeguards should never litter. They should inform the public about regulations on littering and use appropriate means to ensure compliance.

- **Face the Water**—Lifeguards should always attempt to position themselves so that the beach and water is in full view and face the water. Turning away from the water risks not only criticism, but also missing cues of distress. Lifeguards should learn to accomplish all essential activities facing the water, including holding short conversations.

- **Avoid Congregating**—While lifeguards need occasional breaks, when several gather in one place for an extensive period of time it can create the appearance of having nothing productive to do. If time is available, routine tower straightening and cleaning are alternatives. Workouts may also be appropriate or patrols of the beach, which can enhance lifeguard image and performance. After a significant rescue or medical emergency, it's natural, sometimes essential for lifeguards to come together for a debriefing, but this should be accomplished expeditiously and lifeguards should quickly return to their assigned positions. In these situations, non-responding personnel are often spread thin and the system must be returned to normal status as quickly as possible.

- **Don't Appear to Leer**—Many people who come to the beach are proud of their physical fitness and appearance. They may seem to want to be viewed and appreciated. The skimpy covering provided by many bathing suits can easily attract attention. Lifeguards are not expected to completely ignore the appearance of others, but a glance is more than enough and any discussions about the appearance of a particular beach visitor are unprofessional. Such comments about the public or fellow lifeguards may constitute sexual harassment.

- **Use Binoculars for Lifesaving Duties**—Binoculars are an important lifeguard tool. It will be noticed however, if lifeguards use binoculars to view objects or people for reasons unrelated to their duties. Just as leering is inappropriate, using binoculars for this purpose only compounds the injury to a professional image.

- **Address Supervisors by Title**—Lifeguards should address lifeguard supervisors by their title (chief, captain, lieutenant, etc.) rather than by first names or nicknames, particularly when in the presence of beach visitors and other lifeguards.

- **Keep Disagreements Private**—Lifeguards should not engage in public disputes with fellow lifeguards or other emergency service providers. Problems should be worked out in a businesslike manner, with the assistance of supervisory personnel. If a dispute arises during an emergency, wait until afterward to work out differences of opinion, unless they must be resolved immediately in the interest of public safety. As Shakespeare wrote, the better part of valor is discretion.

- **Don't Pose for Unprofessional Photographs**—In the interest of public relations, many agencies will allow lifeguards to briefly assist with photography or pose for pictures. Lifeguards should always present a professional image in these cases, since they're likely to ultimately end up in somebody's slideshow. They may also show up in social or news media. A photograph, once taken, cannot be undone.

- **Enforce Rules Consistently**—Lifeguards should enforce all rules and regulations equally, with tact and diplomacy. Exceptions must sometimes be made, but they should never be made based on personal relationships or biases.

- **Keep Language Clean**—Lifeguards should never use foul language while on duty.

- **Show Respect for Other Lifeguards**—The best rule in any workplace is if you have nothing good to say about someone, don't say anything at all.

- **No Hazing**—Hazing has no place in a professional work environment.

Public Contact

- **Be Courteous and Polite**—Everyone should be addressed professionally and courteously. Use sir or ma'am. Whenever possible, visitors should be approached personally and spoken to individually. The use of public address systems, whistles, and signals is good for general announcements, but may embarrass individuals to which they are directed. Embarrassing people lessens the goal of compliance and respect.

- **Keep Electronic Communications Professional**—Public address systems and two-way radios should be used only for official matters. Lifeguards using them should realize that remarks made on these devices will be heard and judged by the public. Courteous language is particularly important when the message will be heard by large numbers of people.

- **Answer Questions Courteously**—Lifeguards should patiently and thoroughly answer all questions asked, unless it will interfere with public safety duties. When asked a question to which the lifeguard cannot supply an answer, the lifeguard should politely direct the visitor to a source where the information is available. When asked a question that seems to display ignorance on the part of the questioner, lifeguards should never display arrogance or disdain. Such questions offer the lifeguard an opportunity to educate the public. When speaking to a beach visitor, it's usually more polite to remove sunglasses.

- **Be Prepared with Answers**—Each day, beachgoers can be expected to ask similar questions. Examples are air and water temperature; times of tides; forecast weather; the correct time; and conditions for swimming, surfing, diving, and other activities. Be prepared with answers. If the station has a bulletin board containing this information, the board should be updated regularly and neatly.

- **Don't Flirt**—Lifeguards should keep social conversation with members of the public to a minimum. One negative stereotype of the lifeguard is of a person who uses the position to make social contacts. This appearance diminishes the public's perception of lifeguards. Conversations with beach visitors should be

Credit: Daphne Schwene

polite and businesslike. Reserve social conversation for after work.

- **Don't Reprimand Victims**—The person who has been rescued has likely already learned a lesson. If a lifeguard considers it important to say something to help the person learn about the reason they were rescued and ways to avoid it in the future, the contact should be private and diplomatic. The egos of those who have been rescued are often bruised. Lifeguards should be aware that the public will side with them if they remain professional. Conversely, they will side against the lifeguard if it appears that the lifeguard is using a position of power to embarrass a member of the public.

- **Identify Yourself**—On-duty lifeguards should immediately provide their full name, position, and employer to any person requesting the information. The lifeguard who refuses to provide such information suggests a need to hide from a complaint that may or may not be valid. It's good practice to inform a supervisor of all complaints. This procedure provides the lifeguard's record of what transpired and eliminates the possibility of a supervisor being blind-sided by a complaint.

UNIFORMS

Most beach visitors will never actually speak to a lifeguard or even observe a rescue in progress. Their image of a lifeguard will be based on what they see and hear. Uniforms are a major part of that image. Uniforms are an effective and inexpensive way to establish a professional image for a lifeguard agency. They are a valuable public relations tool which immediately identifies the wearer and shows authority. For example, when warning swimmers to move from one area to another due to a hazardous condition, the uniform itself lets people know that the lifeguard is someone who knows about these conditions and is authorized to move the public. Uniforms can be especially helpful in emergencies, since the public tends to defer to people in uniform. Properly designed uniforms also provide protection from the elements.

The most typical lifeguard uniforms are trunks for men and tank suits for women, who may also be permitted or required to wear trunks over the tank suits. Professional two-piece suits are also permitted for wear by female lifeguards at some agencies. The color is most often red. Usually an authorized patch, including the agency name and logo, is sewn on one thigh (always the same thigh) of the trunks or the lower side of the tank suit. A T-shirt or collared shirt of consistent color and design is also typical. The low cost of silk-screening and embroidering allows inexpensive creation of a uniform appearance.

Credit: Cary Epstein

Lifeguards are often seen from behind while watching the water or crouching over an injured victim. For this reason, some lifeguard agencies make a point of silk-screening the word "LIFEGUARD" in bold letters on the upper back of the shirt, along with the name of the agency. The large wording immediately identifies the lifeguard to the public and to other arriving emergency responders. Uniforms may also include patches that identify advanced training that the lifeguard has received, such as *Emergency Medical Technician*. Other uniform items include hats, jackets, wetsuits, and so forth. In general, the more uniform lifeguards are and the neater the uniforms, the more professional the lifeguard agency will appear.

Rescue flotation devices are not part of a uniform, but they have become symbolic insignias for lifeguards. Many agencies require that a lifeguard leaving a tower or stand carry a rescue device for identification and for ready use when needed. The USLA recommends this practice.

To be effective, uniforms should be identical or nearly so. Lifeguard agencies should issue policies to help in this regard. Few variations or changes from year to year should be permitted, so that uniformity is maintained and readily recognized by the public. In some agencies, lifeguards of different ranks may have different colored uniforms, but within ranks, they should be identical. Uniforms should always be neat and clean.

Credit: Nicholas Enns

Avila Beach, California lifeguards in uniform.

Uniforms, such as faded or "salty" trunks or hats that are clearly past their useful life should not be permitted to remain in use. While some lifeguards may resist uniformity of attire in favor of comfort, this is counterproductive to maintaining a professional image. Lifeguards are part of a public safety team and should take appropriate steps to promote the image of the team at all times.

The wearing of uniform items by off-duty lifeguards is no more professional than it would be for police or firefighters. The lifeguard image is perhaps more vulnerable to being tarnished. For this reason, most agencies issue policies restricting the wearing of official uniform components during off-duty time. This policy should be strongly enforced, especially since the design of lifeguard uniforms makes this clothing particularly attractive for casual wear by off-duty employees proud to be lifeguards. Lifeguards should recognize that the image of the entire lifeguard agency can be compromised by the indiscrete use of lifeguard uniforms while off-duty.

CULTURAL DIVERSITY

The United States is made up of people from myriad cultures, races, and ethnicities. Some are descendants of many generations of Americans. Others may be newer arrivals. Tourism draws people from around the world to U.S. beaches. Lifeguards must take great care to display evenhandedness and sensitivity to the users of their beaches.

From time to time disputes occur on the beach and lifeguards are placed in a position of being mediators. Nothing is more likely to incite anger than the appearance that one person's opinion is being valued over another's based purely on appearance, or for similar subjective reasons. If all people are treated with a strong degree of fairness and equality, the lifeguard's decision, recommendation, or direction is much more likely to be accepted by all. By treating situations involving people of different cultures and lifestyles as learning experiences, lifeguards can broaden their professional and personal knowledge.

MEDIA CONTACTS

Most lifeguards will not have direct communication with the news or entertainment media. This is typically a responsibility of supervisors. Nevertheless, the media has a high interest in beach activities and interviews of lifeguards are not uncommon. The media is generally very supportive of lifeguard services, but lifeguards can easily be unwittingly quoted in a newspaper report or on radio making a casual comment never intended for publication. Lifeguards should assume that anything they may say to or in earshot of a media representative may be quoted verbatim. This advice is particularly important in the aftermath of a death or other serious accident, or in regard to a controversial issue.

Lifeguard agencies should disseminate clear media policies that direct the media to designated contacts, whether supervisory personnel in general or specific media relations personnel. When being interviewed, lifeguards should take great care to state only facts, avoiding speculation. When being interviewed on-camera, it's particularly

The news media sometimes cover rescues in progress, as in the case of this cliff rescue in San Diego.

Credit: San Diego Lifeguards

important to have a professional appearance. Confidential matters related to issues such as personnel discipline or the medical status of a victim should not be divulged, unless specifically permitted by rules or regulations. By maintaining a professional demeanor appropriate for any public contact, most media contacts will be positive.

CHAPTER SUMMARY

In this chapter we have learned some principles of lifeguard deportment, including elements of professional conduct and appropriate public contact. We have learned about the benefits of uniforms in projecting a professional image and identifying lifeguards. We have learned about the importance of being sensitive to issues of cultural diversity. And we have learned about some issues related to media relations.

DISCUSSION POINTS

- Identify the importance of lifeguard deportment in public relations.
- List five guidelines for professional conduct.
- List five guidelines for public contact.
- Select three examples of ways lifeguards can demonstrate respect for cultural diversity.
- Identify three considerations in contacts with the media.

CHAPTER

22

Records & Reports

I n this chapter you will learn the basics of how to assemble and write professional reports. You will learn about some standardized reports commonly used by lifeguards. You will also learn about the importance of logbooks to record daily weather and activities.

CHAPTER EXCERPT

Lifeguard logbooks are legal documents, which may be publicly inspected or used in criminal or civil court cases. Lifeguards should limit their logbook entries only to information that is completely professional in nature and consistent with the information gathering needs of the lifeguard agency.

One important duty of a lifeguard is precise documentation of activities. Lifeguards, like other public safety providers, often view report routines as drudgery; but documentation helps justify appropriate levels of funding, staffing, and equipment. Documentation also provides the official records of an agency, which may be used in case of legal action. Few people can speak with certainty on the specifics of an incident which occurred in the distant past without referring to reports taken at the time. Reports can help improve lifeguard preparedness through a review of how incidents were handled and could be handled better in future.

Report forms and required records vary from agency to agency throughout the U.S., based on local or regional reporting requirements and laws. As a minimum requirement, however, most lifeguard agencies report on the topics covered in this chapter. The USLA offers a variety of report forms on our website at: www.usla.org/resources.

Lifeguard reports are legal documents which may be publicly inspected or used in criminal or civil court cases. They can contain sensitive information protected by state and federal law. They should be considered confidential agency material not to be released to others without approval of supervisory personnel. Care must be taken to safeguard these reports.

Nationally, the USLA works to gather and report statistics from all open water lifeguard agencies in the U.S. every year. These statistics are posted on the USLA website at: www.usla.org/statistics. You can check your own agency's reports going back to when the reports were first submitted. They are of critical value in helping inform the public about the important work of lifeguards. They are used for media reports and research. They also help demonstrate the need for lifeguards and the value they provide to public safety. All open water lifeguard agencies are strongly encouraged to report their annual statistics to the USLA. This is a requirement to maintain certification under the USLA *Lifeguard Agency Certification Program*. To report annual statistics, consult the USLA website, where they can be easily entered and submitted electronically.

REPORT WRITING

Well-written reports are a positive reflection on the lifeguard and the lifeguard's agency. Good reports "stand on their own," telling a full story. They need no further explanations from the writer. The report should be understandable to a lifeguard or to a person with no lifeguard background whatsoever. Effective reports are concise, easily understood, in clear and correct English, and legible. They are factual, accurate, objective, and comprehensive.

Credit: Eric Nurse

There are two types of reports about an incident—individual reports and comprehensive reports. Individual reports are first person. They primarily focus on what the writer saw, heard, and did. They are often used in creating comprehensive reports. For example, each lifeguard responding to a major incident might be asked to write a narrative about the incident from their perspective. Individual reports can be used to create fully detailed reports of the incident.

Comprehensive reports are typically created by interviewing witnesses (including lifeguards), observing the scene, taking measurements, and carrying out any other prudent actions needed to assemble pertinent information. During this information gathering process, the report writer takes notes as appropriate. Taking photographs may be valuable, depending on the circumstances. Once this is complete, the report is developed. While many reports are very simple and brief, perhaps using standardized forms detailed later in this chapter, the following are some considerations in writing professional reports.

Report Writing Tips

- **Start Right Away**—Complete the report as soon after the event as possible, so that facts are not forgotten.
- **Include Report Date and Time**

- **Include Incident Date and Time, and Key Elements**—Always record the time that key elements of the incident occurred, when that information is available. For example, "At 1030 hours, Lifeguard Duke Brown was on duty in tower #5. He states that he was contacted by a 35 year old female named Kara Harrison, who advised that her five year old son, Joey Harrison, was missing on the beach. Harrison states that she immediately contacted Lifeguard Lieutenant Jim McCrady. At 1035 hours, Lifeguard Kyle Maxwell made a general radio broadcast to all lifeguards, which was overheard by the writer of this report, including a full description of Joey."

- **Keep Witnesses Available**—Ask witnesses to wait nearby until you can interview them. Otherwise, they may leave. If this is not possible, ask them for contact information so that you can follow up later.

- **Interview Witnesses At-Scene**—It's usually easier for witnesses to remember and explain the circumstances and for you to understand them if you are at the scene of the incident.

- **Listen Carefully**—Within reason, let witnesses speak without interruption.

- **Don't Lead**—Witnesses should not be asked leading questions that imply a conclusion. Don't ask, "Is it true that this guy was showing off?" Ask, "What was he doing at the time this happened?"

- **Confirm Recollections**—Ask witnesses, "Did you see this happen?" You want to make sure they aren't speculating.

- **Avoid Second Person (hearsay) Reports**—Confirm that the person is telling you what they saw and experienced, not something they heard from others. If they heard things from others that are important to detail, be sure to note that these things were overheard.

- **Include Details**—The report should include details of participants, like physical description, clothing description, personal data, last seen location, swimming skills, etc.

- **Write in the Active Voice**—Use the name of the person before the action performed. For example, "Bob Ogoreuc stated that he ran into the water to make a rescue." Versus, "It was stated by Bob Ogoreuc that he ran into the water to make a rescue."

- **Companions**—Get information on any companions.

- **Medical Problems**—Ask whether the victim(s) had medical problems of any sort that might be pertinent. Don't speculate on their contribution to the event, but state their existence.

- **List All Responders**—Include the names of all officials (lifeguards, etc.) who responded to the incident. Include the rank of any referenced lifeguard, police, or fire official, and the agency for which they work.

- **Include Addresses**—Include the name, address, and telephone number of every person in your report, other than an official associated with a named agency.

- **Investigate Contradictions**—In cases where the circumstances of the event are uncertain, interview several witnesses, if available. Separate witnesses, so that they don't color their recollections (whether intentionally or unintentionally) with what they hear from someone else.

- **Take Verbatim Statements**—Try to write down key elements of witness statements verbatim to the greatest degree possible, using quotes where appropriate. Have the witness slow down if need be. Read the statement back to them to make sure you got it right.

- **Use Chronological Order**—Report facts in chronological order, whenever possible.
- **Attribute Information**—Never state something as fact unless you personally observed it or know it to be a fact. Instead, attribute statements to the person who told you the information. Instead of stating, "Matthew had been told to stay beside tower #4," state, "According to Valerie Due, Matthew had been told to stay beside tower #4."
- **Be Concise**—Keep sentences short and to the point.
- **Use Simple Words**—Reports are not intended to display the education level of the writer or to challenge the reader's comprehension.
- **Avoid Jargon**—Codes, abbreviations, and lifeguard shorthand will make reports difficult to understand, particularly for non-lifeguards
- **Use Proper Spelling and Grammar**—Use a dictionary if you are uncertain of words and ensure that grammar is correct. A report with misspellings or grammatical errors can embarrass both the writer and the agency.
- **Measure**—When distances are cited, use actual, measured distances wherever possible. If you must estimate, explain the basis of your estimation.
- **Don't Speculate**—Reports are intended to be factual. If you believe it important to state an opinion or conclusion, then make sure you state that it's your opinion and upon what facts that opinion is based.
- **Explain Conclusions**—If the report includes conclusions, explain how you arrived at them. Don't say, "Matthew had been sitting watching a volleyball game at tower #7 for over an hour." Say, "Information provided by witnesses Nikki Bowie and Peter Davis suggests that Matthew had been sitting and watching their volleyball game at tower #7 for over an hour."
- **Write Legibly**—If you are unable to type your report, write legibly. Printing is preferred.
- **Proofread**—Edit and proofread your report before submitting it.

STANDARD REPORTS

The following are some standard reports which lifeguards may be expected to complete. The forms may be generic or specifically designed for and by the agency. The USLA offers generic reports that agencies can use at: www.usla.org/resources.

Rescue Report

The USLA defines a water rescue of a swimmer as a case in which someone is judged to be in imminent peril and brought to safety by a lifeguard. This usually involves physical contact. It does not include cases where people are given oral instructions to move to a safer location. For reporting purposes, providing verbal commands or advice to swimmers in the water is considered to be an aspect of preventive lifeguarding, but not a rescue.

Even rescues considered routine by a lifeguard can represent the saving of a life which would otherwise be lost. This is a basic responsibility of lifeguards and should always be fully documented. The USLA has developed a simple *Incident Report Form* for use in documenting rescues, medical aids, and other activities. It may be used by any lifeguard agency.

Medical Aid Report

Medical aids include all incidents in which medical care is rendered to a beach visitor. All provisions of medical aid should be documented. The level of documentation appropriate depends on the severity of the injury and disposition of the victim. For minor medical aids and most moderate medical aids, a brief report should usually be adequate. The USLA *Incident Report Form*, for example, should suffice. Medical aids involving life-threatening injury or illness should be documented more thoroughly. The USLA

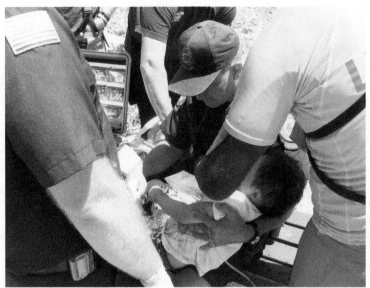

Credit: Ed Vodrazka

Major Injury Report is designed for this purpose. It's available at: www.usla.org/resources.

Another form valuable in medical aid cases is the *against medical advice* (AMA) form. In cases that a person refuses treatment when a lifeguard believes treatment is needed, it's prudent to have the person sign an AMA form indicating the person is knowingly refusing treatment against medical advice of the lifeguard. Against medical advice forms can greatly reduce liability and protect lifeguards if people later accuse lifeguards of refusing to provide treatment or downplaying the nature of their injury. Attorneys should be consulted in creating an AMA form. Local emergency medical services are often good sources for language which meets local legal requirements. Against medical advice forms are not appropriate for minors, unless signed by their legal guardian.

Boating Assistance Report

Boat rescues include all cases in which lifeguards provide physical assistance to a vessel in apparent distress. While some agencies will record the rescue of boats using the same format as for the rescue of swimmers, other agencies require that a special form be completed. Usually this report form will include a boat description, indicate the number of people rescued with the craft, and include the estimated value of the vessel before the rescue. Some states provide standardized boat accident report forms for responding agencies and for boaters. Some states require certain reports to be filed. The USLA *Incident Report Form* can be used for most routine boat rescues.

Missing Person Report

Missing person incidents include situations where people, usually children separated from their group or parents, require assistance from lifeguard staff in being reunited. Missing person incidents are common at beaches. Standardized report forms remind lifeguards to ask pertinent questions and allow ready dissemination of the information to others by reading from the report form.

Credit: GLC Aquatic Safety Department

A lifeguard prepares to take a report.

While missing person cases are often seen as routine by lifeguards, there are situations in which missing people are not found for days. In these cases, full documentation of the time and circumstances surrounding the initial report will be crucial to the continuing search. Since it can never be known upon the initial report whether the missing person will be quickly located, a thorough report should be taken in each instance. Taking a report also helps to demonstrate a sincere concern to anxious friends or relatives of the missing person. The USLA offers a sample *Missing Person Report* at: www.usla.org/resources.

Death Report

Thorough reports should be completed whenever a death occurs in a beach area under the responsibility of lifeguards. Death reports are of particular importance when they are the result of a drowning at or near a protected or unprotected beach. This report is usually required as part of a formal investigation into the drowning incident and may be required by law. Although police and medical examiners may also take reports, lifeguards should complete reports based on their information and involvement. The USLA *Major Injury Report Form* can be used to document deaths.

Public Safety Program Report

Many lifeguard agencies are actively involved with programs given to the public at or away from the beach as a means of public education. Most agencies require that these programs be reported using special report forms, which usually indicate the estimated number of program participants. These are valuable to the agency in demonstrating community commitment, but also to create a record that can be used to plan for the future. For example, if a local civic club or school requests a public safety program one year prior to summer, it may be prudent to put them on a calendar and inquire each year if they would like another.

Lost and Found Reports

Most lifeguard agencies offer lost and found services for the visiting public. People who have lost personal possessions can report their loss to lifeguards at stations or towers. People who have found items can turn them in. While operating a lost and found may sometimes be seen as routine, this service involves a significant degree of trust and responsibility. The person turning in the item(s) rightly expects honesty, integrity, and care on the part of the lifeguard, which must be fully satisfied.

Found items should be tagged and logged. Simple hang-tags may suffice. On them the receiving lifeguard should document the time the item was turned in, the place found, the name of the lifeguard, and the name and address of the person who turned it in. The item should then be logged on an appropriate form or in the logbook.

For cash, credit cards, or other valuables, a supervising lifeguard should take custody of the item and find an appropriate place to secure it. State or local laws, as well as agency protocols, may require that items of a certain value be turned over to police. In any case, it's important that these items be handled with great care and properly secured. When the property of others is entrusted to a lifeguard's care, the lifeguard and the agency immediately assume responsibility for its safekeeping and may be held legally responsible if the property is mishandled.

Narrative Reports

At times there is need for reports that don't fit into the standardized areas noted previously in this chapter. In other cases, there is a need to add further narrative descriptions or diagrams to detail the circumstances of an incident. The USLA offers a sample *Narrative Report* form and a form for creating a diagram on our website. Use of report forms such as these can present a more professional image and ensure that important information about the author and incident are included. Find this report at: www.usla .org/resources.

LIFEGUARD LOG

All lifeguard agencies should maintain a station or tower log, indicating, among other things, the weather and water conditions of the day, beach attendance, lifeguards on duty, workouts performed, rescues, and other key activities accomplished through the workday. Logs may be completed in simple hardbound datebooks, photocopied forms, or on electronic devices. The daily log is used to document statistics for the lifeguard agency's activities throughout the operational season or year. It also serves as a record of each day in case of inquiries at a later time. United States Lifesaving Association affiliated agencies also use lifeguard logs to collect data used to report lifeguard activity statistics throughout the U.S. Categories of lifeguard activities used for USLA statistics include:

USLA Statistics Data Areas

- Beach Attendance
- Rescues Performed
- Preventive Actions
- Boat Rescues
- Drowning Deaths – Guarded Areas
- Drowning Deaths – Unguarded Areas
- Other Fatalities
- Missing Persons

- Public Safety Lectures
- Attendance
- Rescues
  - Total
  - Rip
  - Surf
  - Swift
  - Scuba
- Cliff Rescue
- Boat Rescues
  - Passengers
  - Value
- Boat Assists
  - Passengers
  - Value
- Medical Aids
  - Total
  - Major
  - Minor
- Drowning Deaths (Unguarded)
  - Total
  - Rip
  - Surf
  - Scuba
  - Drop-Off
  - Alcohol/Drugs
  - Ability
  - Floatation
  - Other
- Drowning Deaths (Guarded)
  - Total
  - Rip
  - Surf
  - Scuba
  - Drop-Off
  - Alcohol/Drugs
  - Ability

- - Floatation
  - Other
- Other Fatalities
- Enforcements
    - Warnings
    - Boat/PWC
    - Citations
    - Arrests
- Lost/Found
- Public Education
    - Lectures
    - Students

Lifeguard logbook entries should be concise, professional, and consistent with the information gathering needs of the lifeguard agency. Each entry should be initialed by the lifeguard making the entry.

CHAPTER SUMMARY

In this chapter we have learned the steps required to develop a thorough and effective report. We have learned about standardized reports, including the rescue report, medical aid report, boating assistance report, missing person report, death report, public safety program report, lost and found report, and narrative report. We have learned about the value of a lifeguard logbook, what it should contain, and how it should be maintained.

DISCUSSION POINTS

- Explain some considerations for completing a useful and understandable report.
- Explain the value of a completed lifeguard report.
- Identify the importance in maintaining the confidentiality of reports and safeguarding them.
- List five examples of events that would be included in a lifeguard logbook.
- List three ways a properly completed lifeguard logbook can help the lifeguard agency.

CHAPTER
23

The Responsible Lifeguard

In this chapter you will learn about how responsible lifeguards do their work. You will learn about the influence of local laws, Good Samaritan laws, immunity, and liability. You will also learn about professional responsibility.

CHAPTER EXCERPT

There is a tendency in the United States to focus heavily on the civil liability system. Unfortunately, the emphasis on liability tends to overshadow the real issue, which is that lifeguards—like all other public safety providers—need to live up to the tremendous trust placed in them by the public, not because the law says they must, but because it is the responsible and right thing to do.

Many new lifeguards understandably have a great deal of pride at achieving their goal of working in the lifesaving profession. With that achievement comes a tremendous responsibility. Every day, people entrust their lives and those of their family and friends to lifeguards. Parents may still watch their children carefully, but they rely on a presumption that, if need be, a lifeguard will protect them from harm. This creates expectations, both professional and legal,

Credit: Asia Lee

that every lifeguard must meet. Each day, lifeguards have the opportunity to enhance our profession by rising to the level of trust placed in them by the public. One inadvertent lapse though, may mean the difference between a happy day at the beach and the most profound tragedy of all—untimely death.

GENERAL LEGAL CONSIDERATIONS

The expectation of the public and the legal system is that lifeguards will perform their job within the parameters of the training they have been provided. If another person or another person's property suffers injury due to failures on the part of the lifeguard to perform to appropriate standards, the lifeguard may be sued and found to be *liable* (responsible) for the injury. For example, the lifeguard who is distracted for no excusable reason when a preventable accident takes place may be successfully sued, along with the employing agency. Such a situation may also result in discipline and loss of employment. Lifeguards who do their job professionally, in accordance with their training, should have no inordinate fear of the civil liability system.

Discussions of legal points and case histories can fill an entire textbook on lifeguard management. The administrators of any well-organized lifeguard agency spend a considerable amount of time and effort studying the legal aspects of lifeguard services and developing appropriate protocols. These protocols are not only intended to protect and serve the public, but also to protect the lifeguard agency and its employees from allegations of malfeasance. The training program provided by each agency is intended to reflect the protocols that have been established.

Collectively, the protocols developed will help to establish the *standard of care* to be provided by a lifeguard agency. In legal terms, a safety provider found to have acted in accordance with a reasonable and accepted standard of care is without fault. This manual will not include extensive information on the various ways lifeguards may be held accountable for their actions. Instead, the following three generalizations are provided as yardsticks used to develop legal expectations:

- **Lifeguards Must Perform Their Duties**—Each lifeguard is given a special trust by the public as a guardian of safety at the beach. That trust requires constant vigilance during duty hours. Failure to act when actions are needed can be one of the most serious charges brought against a lifeguard; especially if that failure occurred because of distraction due to unprofessional conduct.

- **Lifeguards Must Perform Their Duties Consistently**—In addition to establishing policies and procedures for lifeguard duties, each agency establishes criteria for the performance of those duties (whether formally or informally) and a routine that lifeguards should follow during the workday. It is important to enforce rules and regulations, and to take preventive actions consistently, without making undue assumptions about conditions or abilities of beach visitors. Take for example the case of a beach where lifeguards consistently make a public address announcement at the end of each day to warn beach users that they are leaving the beach. One day, the announcement is forgotten and a swimmer dies by drowning soon after the lifeguard leaves. In addition to the tragedy of a death, this inconsistency of performance may cause a serious problem for the lifeguard and agency. Variations from normal protocol may be necessary in emergency work in special situations, but they should be considered carefully.

- **Lifeguards Must Perform Their Duties Properly**—During training, lifeguards are taught many procedures and techniques for use in rescuing and treating people who are the victims of aquatic accidents. These procedures and techniques are not advice to be considered, but rather directions and protocols to be followed. While judgment skills are important, lifeguards are expected to perform their duties following the established and authenticated procedures provided in training. Deviation may result in charges of malfeasance.

Conduct Checklist

The following checklist provides another way in which lifeguards can help ensure that their conduct is appropriate in a legal sense:

- Is it my intention to protect the health or safety of another person or property?
- In doing so, am I acting within the scope of my training and employment, either by handling the incident properly myself, or by handing it off to someone of equal or higher training?
- Am I exhibiting good faith as shown by behavior that the average, reasonable, trained person in my profession would exhibit under a scope of employment similar to mine?
- Am I providing medical care in accordance with my training and the recommended standard of care?
- If I must make a judgment call due to a circumstance that is not covered by my scope of employment, am I doing so in accordance with what the average, reasonable, trained person in my profession would do in same or similar circumstances?

Credit: Miami-Dade Ocean Rescue

Applicable Law

Each lifeguard agency falls under the jurisdiction of federal, state, and local laws that have been established to define the professional responsibility of employers and employees, or to define the limits of liability. Because these laws vary from region to region across the U.S., they cannot be covered thoroughly in this manual. Generally however, these laws fall into two categories:

Mandates

Laws and regulations can require that lifeguards and lifeguard agencies perform to certain standards. This may include required equipment, training, or behavior. Lifeguards and lifeguard agencies cannot hope to conform to required mandates unless they familiarize themselves with them and take steps to ensure they follow them. This requires careful review and consultation with appropriate authorities.

Immunities

Lifeguards and lifeguard agencies may enjoy immunities from laws and regulations that others must follow. For example, in most areas it is unlawful to drive a vehicle on the beach, but lifeguards and other public safety providers are typically exempted.

In some areas, certain government agencies are exempt from specific liabilities under governmental immunity laws or special provisions of constitutions. In other areas, there is a ceiling to the amount of damages an agency can be forced to pay if found liable for injuries. Some states have laws which specifically define types of recreation as hazardous and thereby regulate claims which may be made as a result of injuries sustained in this type of recreation. There can also be special tort claims laws which limit claims that may be made against agencies as a result of loss, damage, or injury.

In many areas of the U.S., good Samaritan laws have been established to protect people who happen upon an emergency scene and stop to render aid to injured or distressed people. These people may be shielded from liability as long as they act in good faith and to the best of their abilities. In most areas, these laws are limited to protecting lay people who provide assistance and professional emergency providers (physicians, paramedics, lifeguards, etc.) who stop to provide assistance during off-duty time. In other areas, good Samaritan laws also protect on-duty emergency personnel, but only under special stipulations and conditions. This varies significantly from state to state.

MEDICAL LAW

Providing medical care in the aquatic environment, like anywhere else, involves certain responsibilities on the part of those providing this care. They are expected to act in an appropriate manner. There are many laws, regulations, and legal precedents related to medical care.

Standard of Care

Standard of care is a legal term. In medicine, it generally refers to the care a person being treated has a right to expect based on common standards of medical practice. For example, a doctor who fails to provide a patient with important information about possible outcomes of a surgery the patient is considering might be found to have breached the accepted standard of care, particularly if most doctors in a similar situation would have provided this information. Since lifeguards provide medical care, they too must perform according to a standard of care.

In some cases, standard of care is set by law or regulation. In other cases, it is a concept based on common practice and reasonable expectation. Failure to meet the standard of care sometimes goes unnoticed. In other cases, particularly if the failure to perform to the accepted standard of care is believed to have resulted in unnecessary injury, legal liability may be found. People place great trust in the actions of emergency responders providing them with medical care. It's important, both for moral and legal reasons, for lifeguards to ensure that trust is well founded.

Each lifeguard agency should set limits on the emergency medical care that lifeguards are authorized to provide depending on local laws and policies. The provision and use of any special medical or rescue equipment should be restricted to those lifeguards who have received specific training in its use and who are specifically authorized.

Duty to Act and Abandonment

Because lifeguards are expected by the public to be knowledgeable in emergency medical care, visitors will look to lifeguards for advice and treatment. Lifeguards are considered to have a duty to act. Even when the lifeguard is confused or unsure about a particularly complicated injury or illness, it's important to follow through by carrying out the basic steps of care based on the lifeguard's level of training. In such situations, lifeguards should remember the medical credo, *do no harm*, as a reminder to be conservative and deliberate. Once treatment has begun for an injury, it should not be stopped until the situation is controlled, treatment is turned over to a higher medical authority, or consent to treat is lawfully denied (see following section).

One situation which can result in a charge of abandonment at a beach facility occurs when a bystander attempts to take over treatment and the lifeguard allows it, leaving the victim in the hands of the bystander. A lifeguard has no legal duty to relinquish control of a victim and should not do so until and unless it has been clearly established that the bystander is of equal or higher medical authority, and willing to accept medical responsibility. Identification and documentation of the bystander's medical training is critical. In a major medical emergency, lifeguard personnel should maintain control of the situation until it can be turned over to the responding emergency medical service.

Credit: California State Parks Lifeguards

Consent

An adult has the right to refuse medical treatment. Exceptions may include people who are obviously delirious or otherwise unable to make reasonable decisions. In general, an unconscious person of any age is considered to have given *implied consent* for emergency treatment. If an apparently coherent adult declines treatment, it is best to ask the person to sign a waiver of treatment to help indemnify the lifeguard and lifeguard agency. Witness names should also be included. See Chapter 22 (*Records and Reports*) for more information on forms for release *against medical advice*.

When treating minors, the most significant concern beyond treatment is gaining parental consent. Most lifeguard agencies establish strict policies regarding notification of parents before, during, or after medical treatment. In cases of life-threatening injuries, care should not be delayed for this purpose, but parents should be contacted as soon as reasonably possible. Parents and legal guardians may generally refuse treatment on behalf of minors, but at a certain point, this may border on child abuse or negligent care. If a parent refuses treatment for a minor in obvious and serious need, it is normally prudent to contact police. Some states require emergency medical personnel to make notifications in any case of suspected child abuse.

Medications

Lifeguards should not dispense medication of any kind unless certified to do so and authorized in writing by an appropriate medical authority. Most lifeguard agencies establish policies prohibiting lifeguards from dispensing medications, including non-prescription remedies. This may include over-the-counter medications such as aspirin and aspirin substitutes.

Confidentiality

A variety of laws and regulations protect the confidentiality of people who receive medical care. The most commonly cited of these is the Health Insurance Portability and Accountability Act of 1996 (HIPAA). This federal rule sets national standards for the protection of individually identifiable health information by three types of entities, including healthcare providers. The rule protects all "individually identifiable health information" held or transmitted, in any form or media, whether electronic, paper, or oral. This includes:

- The individual's past, present or future physical or mental health or condition
- The provision of health care to the individual
- The past, present, or future payment for the provision of health care to the individual

LEARN MORE

You can review the Health Insurance Portability and Accountability Act of 1996 (HIPAA) at: www.hhs.gov/hipaa.

Whether lifeguards and lifeguard agencies are specifically covered by this rule is not explicitly stated in the rule, but the best practice is to consider all materials you may gather regarding an individual's medical care or status to be confidential. You should never release any information regarding treatment provided to a victim or their medical status unless they specifically authorize (in writing) release of that information. Exceptions include people with a medical need and legal right to know.

A paramedic arriving at the beach to take over care of the victim has both a medical need and legal right to be updated on the victim's status, history, etc. The same is true of the treating physician or an emergency room nurse. On the other hand, a news reporter has no right to medical information about a victim. Releasing such information may result in liability to the lifeguard and lifeguard agency. Similarly, while parents normally have the right to complete information about their minor child's medical condition and treatment, an acquaintance of a victim, even a close friend, generally does not. Sometimes even a parent may have lost custody rights, and rights to information, due to court actions. When in doubt, release nothing and consult with a supervisor.

PROTECTING FROM LIABILITY

Most lifeguard agencies have access to the assistance of legal departments, corporate attorneys, district attorneys, city attorneys, or other legal experts in defending against lawsuits. Under some circumstances these legal departments may also represent or defend employees who are named in lawsuits as codefendants. Lifeguards should become aware of the level of protection which may be afforded them in a liability case. Even in frivolous lawsuits, where there is clearly no fault on the part of the lifeguard, significant costs may be incurred in mounting a legal defense.

Ultimately however, the best protection from liability is to perform all duties effectively within the guidelines provided by the hiring agency. A lifeguard who stays alert, responds expeditiously as needed, and provides aid which meets a reasonable standard of care should have few worries or incidents. After all, liability arises only if it is believed that errors have been made which could reasonably have been prevented by prudent action. By avoiding those errors in the first place, civil liability itself normally becomes a moot issue.

PROFESSIONAL RESPONSIBILITY

There is a tendency in the United States to focus heavily on the civil liability system. Unfortunately, the emphasis on liability tends to overshadow the real issue, which is that lifeguards—like all other public safety providers—need to live up to the tremendous trust placed in them by the public, not because the law says they must, but because it is the responsible and right thing to do.

When a father comes to the beach with his children, he is not thinking about suing the lifeguard or lifeguard service. He simply wants to enjoy the day and go home with his family at the end of the day with all of them safe and sound. He may never speak with a lifeguard, but he nevertheless entrusts the safety of his family to that lifeguard. When a lifeguard is assigned to water surveillance and is tired or distracted or otherwise less than fully attentive, the lifeguard would do well to remember that people are counting on that lifeguard—to protect their lives.

Credit: Sterling Foxcroft

This manual, along with a training program which meets the recommended standards of the USLA, is intended to provide all lifeguards with the knowledge, skills, and tools needed to ensure beach safety. All the training in the world however, will be to no avail if a lifeguard fails to maintain a vigilant and professional approach to the job at all times.

Lifeguards are given the gift of a job which can provide an extraordinarily high degree of personal satisfaction. The work environment is unmatched and hundreds of lifeguards go home each day having saved the lives of others. Those who choose to accept this gift should take the public trust that comes with it and protect that trust by doing the best job they can every day.

CHAPTER SUMMARY

In this chapter we have learned some of the elements of being a responsible lifeguard. We have learned about expectations of the public and the legal system, including local laws, good Samaritan laws, and immunities. We have learned about special requirements regarding medical aid and patient confidentiality. We have learned ways lifeguards can protect themselves from liability. And we have learned about the responsibilities of being a lifeguard.

DISCUSSION POINTS

- Explain some circumstances that might cause liability for a lifeguard or a lifeguard agency.
- Identify ways in which a lifeguard can limit exposure to liability.
- Explain a situation in which the Good Samaritan law would apply.
- List three examples of immunities.
- List three reasons why lifeguards should maintain the standard of care.
- List three examples of situations that might constitute failure to act or abandonment.
- Explain what constitutes consent to provide medical care to an adult and to a child.
- Explain the confidentiality requirements of the Health Insurance Portability and Accountability Act of 1996 (HIPAA).

CHAPTER

24

Lifeguard Facilities and Equipment

I n this chapter you will learn about lifeguard facilities, including stands, towers, and main stations. You will learn about lifesaving equipment that should be available at each beach area. You will also learn about daily tower preparation and maintenance.

CHAPTER EXCERPT

Like all emergency services, lifeguard agencies should have equipment available at a level adequate to allow a professional response to both the routine and major emergencies which can be reasonably anticipated.

Most emergency services operate from main stations—facilities designed to house the personnel, operations, and equipment of the agency. This is true of police, firefighting, and emergency medical services. Depending on agency size, some also maintain satellite stations. Along with providing a gathering point for personnel and materiel, these stations serve as contact points for people requesting service, whether in person or by phone.

Like the other emergency services, lifeguard agencies operate on the station concept by erecting lifeguard towers on beaches. Lifeguard towers serve as central points where lifeguard equipment is positioned for immediate use. Lifeguard towers are typically the most highly recognized features on a beach, often used by beach patrons as landmarks and gathering points. Beach patrons also look to lifeguard towers for assistance, making them focal points for summoning help.

Credit: Diana Schwene

LIFEGUARD TOWERS

Lifeguard towers are raised platforms that provide an enhanced view of the beach and water. Lifeguard tower design varies tremendously across the U.S., from small portable chairs to large, enclosed units. They may be known by other names, like stands or perches, according to local custom. While towers were once typically made locally of wood or similar materials, prefabricated fiberglass towers have become common. These towers can offer a variety of beneficial features including an enclosed area protected from the weather, room for secure storage of equipment, a degree of privacy, and portability. All enclosed towers should have windows with an unobstructed view of the water. Certain features of lifeguard towers are common:

- **Elevation**—Towers provide lifeguards with an elevated position from which they can observe the entire area of responsibility, from the water to the beach. This elevation allows the lifeguard to look down on the water, which aids in recognizing hazardous conditions and facilitates observation of swimmers in heavily crowded swimming areas. Elevation of the tower also helps to make the station highly recognizable to beach users, should they need the assistance of a lifeguard.

Credit: Adam Abajian

- **Identification**—To assist the public in determining the status of lifeguard protection, many agencies have developed signs or symbols which are attached to lifeguard towers, indicating when lifeguards are on duty. These signs may be locked in place when towers are closed, and include instructions for how emergency help can be summoned. It's a wise practice to devise and follow a system of notification to let beach users know when a tower is open and staffed, and when it is closed.

- **Numbers and Markings**—If there are several towers on a beach, it's recommended that they be numbered with large, easily readable numbers on all sides. This helps fix the location of reported emergencies, particularly those received by telephone. For example, "There's a person injured just south of Tower 4." Offshore rescue boats or helicopters responding to an emergency can be advised to work off a tower with a certain number. If helicopters are regularly used by police or other rescue agencies in the area, the tops of the towers (or seats of open stands) should also be numbered. Another advantage of numbering is that it can reduce the incidence of lost children. Since most towers on a beach look alike, visitors, particularly children, can easily become confused. By numbering towers, parents can advise their kids to "meet at Tower 5" if they become separated, for example. Some parents write the number of the tower on their child's hand when they arrive at the beach. When lost children are found on a beach with a public address system, parents can be advised to claim their children at a tower of a certain number. Use of a numbering system also helps in directing beach users to appropriate locations. For example, water or beach use areas can be more readily identified when associated with a numbered tower. For example, "Surfing is not permitted between Tower 7 and Tower 8." In addition to numbering, agencies may wish to consider unique symbols, colors, or icons to differentiate each tower. This adds to the ability of people, particularly small children, to remember where their group is located.

- **Equipment Storage**—Lifeguard equipment is normally kept at the lifeguard tower during duty hours. Tower design should therefore include places where equipment can be mounted or placed for immediate retrieval. While some towers require that lifeguards remove equipment for secure storage at the end of the day, other tower designs provide secure storage within.

- **Safety**—Lifeguard agencies commonly design towers with features to protect lifeguards from possible injury. Ramps or stairs have replaced ladders, since lifeguards have been injured climbing up to or jumping down from towers, but another approach is to mound sand in front of the tower and keep it high enough to lessen the chance of a sprain or strain when dismounting. Ideally, lifeguard towers are enclosed, to offer protection from the sun and weather. This provides two major safety benefits. First, as explained in Chapter 10 (*Water Surveillance*), lifeguards exposed to the elements for long periods of time, particularly heat and wind, experience a marked reduction in their level of alertness, which can adversely impact vigilance, as well as physical preparedness to respond to emergencies. Second, as explained in Chapter 16 (*Lifeguard Health and Safety*), sun and wind exposure pose very real physical hazards for lifeguards.

Credit: Leslie Schwene

- **Portability**—For lifeguard towers which are designed to be moved, the design should include features which allow movement without injury to lifeguards and protocols should be in place for movement in a manner that avoids injury. Back injuries are a major problem for lifeguards, partly due to efforts to move large objects.

MAIN STATIONS

While many smaller lifeguard agencies operate exclusively from moveable towers or stands, with storage facilities for equipment, many larger lifeguard agencies utilize permanent towers on their beaches, often referred to as main stations. These large, often multi-story structures are usually located at the waterfront. The primary feature of these stations is a commanding view of the entire beach area. Under the Tower Zero system, described in Chapter 10 (*Water Surveillance*), the main tower observation deck is the first observation point staffed on the beach and the last to close. This system provides considerable operational efficiency, since the Tower Zero station can have telephone or radio contact with other towers, vehicles, and boats, while the superior point

Credit: B. Chris Brewster

of observation allows lifeguards in the tower to both provide surveillance and coordinate backup to lifeguards in smaller, satellite towers. Main stations may also incorporate administrative staff offices, central communication and reception areas, first aid and recovery rooms, locker and shower facilities, training and apparatus rooms, maintenance shops, vehicle and equipment storage areas, meeting and training rooms, kitchen facilities, and areas to accommodate local police.

A main station that includes a garage, reception area, first aid area, offices and locker rooms on the second floor, an enclosed observation deck on the third floor, and sleeping facilities for lifeguards assigned to night response.

EQUIPMENT

At each beach where lifeguards will be assigned to the protection of swimmers, emergency equipment must be readily available. Like all emergency services, lifeguard agencies must provide emergency equipment at a level adequate to allow a professional response to both the routine and major emergencies which can be reasonably anticipated.

Credit: Kyle Maxwell

Minimum Equipment

The USLA has set minimum recommended equipment standards to be met by all open water lifeguard agencies. United States Lifesaving Association standards are modified from time to time. The latest can be found at: www.usla.org/certification.

Rescue

- **Rescue Flotation Devices**—At least one rescue flotation device (RFD) for each lifeguard on duty.

- **Masks and Snorkels**—Mask(s) and snorkel(s) readily accessible to mount an underwater search and rescue, as appropriate.

- **Binoculars**—Binoculars readily accessible in the beach area, as well as in each main tower and emergency vehicle.
- **Marker Buoys**—Marker buoy(s) readily accessible for submerged victim search and rescue.
- **Swim Fins**—Swim fins for rescue purposes readily accessible to lifeguards as appropriate according to local conditions.

Medical

- **First Aid Kits**—A first aid kit adequate to treat minor injuries at each staffed lifeguard tower and a first aid kit adequate to treat both minor and major medical emergencies at each beach area.
- **Personal Protective Equipment (PPE)**—Equipment to protect against bloodborne pathogens consistent with requirements of the U.S. Department of Labor, Occupational Safety and Health Administration (OSHA).
- **Spinal Stabilization Equipment**—Spinal stabilization equipment, including spineboard, head and neck immobilization devices, and fastening devices readily accessible at each beach area.
- **Oxygen**—Oxygen readily accessible at each staffed beach area, with all lifeguard personnel trained in its use.

Communications

- **Public Communication Equipment**—Equipment for lifeguards to communicate with the public at a distance (e.g. public address system, bullhorn, whistles, megaphone(s), air horn(s), etc.)
- **Lifeguard Communication Equipment**—Equipment for lifeguard to lifeguard communication and for lifeguards to immediately activate local emergency medical services (EMS).

Personnel Needs

- **Lifeguard Uniforms**—Lifeguards are required to wear an easily identifiable uniform, denoting the wearer as a trained rescuer (ex: "Lifeguard," "Beach Patrol," "Marine Safety") and denoting the employing agency.
- **Sunscreen**—Sunscreen for all lifeguard personnel.
- **Sun Protection Equipment**—Equipment to protect lifeguards from sun exposure.

Record Keeping And Reporting

- **Report Forms**—A system for documenting lifeguard activities, consistent with USLA standards, with annual statistical data reported to the USLA statistics coordinator by March 1 of each year.

Recommended Equipment

In addition to the minimum equipment standards, the USLA recommends the following:

- **Rescue Boards**—Rescue boards, readily available for use by lifeguards.
- **Rescue Boats**—Rescue boats, ideally motorized.

- **Boat Tow**—Boat tow for use by a swimming lifeguard in towing a boat offshore.
- **Positive Pressure Resuscitation Device**—An oxygen delivery device which provides positive pressure with 100% oxygen.
- **Automatic External Defibrillators (AED)**—Cardiac defibrillators readily accessible at each staffed beach area, with personnel trained in their use.
- **Blood Pressure Cuffs and Stethoscopes**—Blood pressure cuffs and stethoscopes for checking blood pressure and evaluating lung sounds.
- **Emergency Vehicles**—Emergency vehicles to transport lifeguards, equipment, and victims, in routine and emergency operations.
- **Posted Hours of Operation**—Hours of observation to inform the public of periods of lifeguard protection.
- **Public Information Board**—A board to inform the public of daily conditions, such as tides, currents, sunrise and sunset, etc.
- **Logbook**—An official logbook to record periods of operation, personnel assigned to water observation and periods of assignment, rescues, and other significant events.

TOWER PREPARATION

At the beginning of each workday or shift, it's important that lifeguards conduct a thorough check of all equipment. Each agency should develop its own checklist for setting up the tower, including the following recommended points:

Credit: Miami-Dade Ocean Rescue

- **Initial Area Scan**—As the lifeguard enters the beach area, an immediate scan of the water and beach is conducted for any signs of trouble. This scan is repeated once the tower is staffed.
- **Status Check**—The tower is checked for any damage or vandalism, which is reported immediately.
- **Tower Ready**—The tower is unlocked and equipment is readied. The first piece of equipment prepared for use is the lifeguard's RFD.
- **Open**—The tower is opened for service. Shutters may be removed or raised. Any *off-duty* signs are secured or stowed. Flags used by the agency are raised. (Any warning flags should be used in a manner consistent with flag warning guidelines detailed in Chapter 9: *Preventive Lifeguarding.*)
- **Communication Check**—Communication equipment is checked to ensure it is functioning properly. Radio checks are made. Calls are made to dispatch centers using radios or phones to notify that the tower is in service and ensure that communication works in both directions.

- **Rescue Equipment Ready**—Lifeguard equipment is carefully checked and deployed. Each piece of equipment should be inspected for damage, wear, and proper maintenance. Once any necessary needs are addressed, equipment is placed in predetermined positions for immediate retrieval and use when needed.

- **Medical Equipment Ready**—Medical aid gear and supplies are checked and deployed. Shortages of supplies are reported immediately so that supplies can be restocked. Oxygen tank pressures are checked.

- **Report Ready**—Supplies of report forms are checked. Completed forms that have not been turned in are submitted. Lifeguards ensure that there are suitable writing implements available. The lifeguard log is started for the day, including a listing of the time the station is opened and the personnel on duty.

- **Public Information Boards Updated**—Notice boards for public information are brought up to date with information such as tides and water/air temperature. Supplies of public education materials are checked.

- **Mobile Equipment Ready**—If boats or vehicles are used, they should be thoroughly inspected. Motorboats and vehicles should be checked for gas, oil, and other fluids, as well as any unusual wear and tear.

- **Accessways Marked**—As appropriate, runways formed of cones or rope may be placed to dissuade beach visitors from settling immediately in front of the tower. With respect to vehicle accessways, please see Chapter 14 (*Specialized Rescue Equipment*).

- **Cleanup**—The tower is checked for cleanliness. Personal gear is neatly stowed.

At some agencies, checklists for setting up the station are provided. In areas where lifeguards work in shifts, agencies may require that second shift employees complete the checklist even though the same checklist was completed by a lifeguard on a previous shift. This system of redundancy helps ensure that in an emergency, all necessary equipment is fully prepared and readily available.

TOWER MAINTENANCE

During the workday, lifeguards must remember that the lifeguard tower is a public safety facility and treat it as such. The maintenance of a lifeguard tower will reflect upon the professional image of the lifeguard agency. An agency that keeps well-organized and clean stations will be perceived by the public as an efficient, professional organization. Dirty, cluttered, and disorganized stations will leave a negative impression.

Lifeguards should work to keep their stations tidy throughout the workday. This may include sweeping and other tidying as needed. Clothes and other personal items should not be hung or draped on or about the tower. During periods of low beach attendance, maintenance may also include minor repairs to towers and rescue equipment. During all periods the station is open however, surveillance over the beach and water should continue without interruption.

CHAPTER SUMMARY

In this chapter we have learned about lifeguard towers, including main stations. We have learned about the minimum equipment standards recommended by the USLA, along with additional recommended equipment. We have learned about the process of tower preparation and about tower maintenance. We have been reminded that during duty hours, beach and water surveillance should be maintained at all times.

DISCUSSION POINTS

- Describe the benefits of an enclosed lifeguard tower.
- List five common features of a lifeguard tower.
- Explain the value of numbering lifeguard towers.
- Explain why the Tower Zero observation deck is the first to be opened and last to be closed.
- List ten examples of minimum equipment standards for lifeguard agencies.
- List five examples of additional recommended equipment for lifeguard stations.
- Explain the steps involved in opening a lifeguard tower.
- Explain why lifeguard stations are to be kept in a clean and tidy state at all times.

CHAPTER
25

Emergency Planning & Management

I n this chapter, you will learn about methods to ensure that responses to emergencies, both large and small, can be handled smoothly and efficiently, regardless of the number of responding personnel or agencies. You will learn about the *incident command system* and about pre-planning your emergency response. We will also present some tips about managing emergencies lifeguards commonly face.

CHAPTER EXCERPT

The incident command system (ICS) was created to promote effective coordination of diverse emergency resources. The incident commander is the person ultimately responsible for overall management of the incident.

THE INCIDENT COMMAND SYSTEM

Successful resolution of any emergency requires a cooperative and coordinated response by all appropriate emergency resources. A rescue of a single swimmer may be handled routinely by a single lifeguard. If there are multiple victims involved though, several lifeguards may respond. At the most elemental level in this example, each lifeguard is an emergency response resource (a single resource). These resources must work in a coordinated manner if the rescue is to be completed successfully. If they all respond to the same victim, other victims are left without assistance. While they may work intuitively, they may also work under the direction of a lifeguard in charge who directs each of the other lifeguards to the victims. In the language of emergency response, this rescue is an *incident* and the person directing resources is the *incident commander* (IC).

The *incident command system* (ICS) is a standardized approach to the command, control, and coordination of emergency response. As emergency incidents increase in complexity, additional resources (including both personnel and equipment) will be needed. Allied public safety agencies may be involved. For a lifeguard agency, this may involve summoning police officers, firefighters, ambulances, the U.S. Coast Guard, etc. Each will need to know what is expected of them.

Consider the example of a water rescue in which three victims suffer complications and need advanced medical treatment. Ambulances will be summoned, perhaps police for crowd control, patient information will need to be gathered, relatives will want to know to what hospital their family members will be going, and all the while there will be a need to ensure that those still recreating in the water and on the beach are protected. Coordination and direction are needed. The goal in these instances is to utilize all available and appropriate resources in the most efficient manner possible to successfully resolve the emergency.

The ICS was created to promote effective coordination of diverse emergency resources. The IC is the person ultimately responsible for overall management of the incident. The IC is usually a member of the agency most directly responsible for the emergency. The IC need not be the most senior member of a given agency. Initially the IC is the first emergency responder on-scene who is not directly involved as a rescuer and who is able to take charge. It could be the head lifeguard, a ranking police officer, or a fire department supervisor. Prearranged emergency operation plans will determine how the responsibilities of the IC are transferred as more senior ranking personnel and responders from allied agencies arrive at the scene of the emergency. If multiple agencies are involved, the ICS system calls for them to work under a *unified command*.

Regardless of who the IC may be, under the ICS, members from the IC's agency and those of all other responding agencies ultimately report to the IC for assignment. This requires that agency pride be put aside in favor of achieving a common goal. At major incidents, a liaison system is arranged which allows a representative (*liaison officer*) from participating agencies involved in the emergency to expeditiously communicate pertinent information to and from the IC.

The ICS is designed to begin developing from the time an incident occurs until the emergency is resolved. The incident command structure can be expanded or contracted depending upon the changing conditions of the incident. It can be seen as a pyramid with the IC at the top. In its most rudimentary form, if two lifeguards respond to a reported drowning, one will usually take charge and make the decisions. This person is in command of the incident—the IC—although that term would not normally be used in such a routine situation. At more complex emergency incidents, the IC may be ultimately responsible for hundreds of emergency responders.

Each lifeguard agency must have its own protocols, but under the ICS, the first lifeguard on-scene who is not directly involved as a rescuer is the IC until relieved by a higher authority from the lifeguard's own agency or a representative of another agency who has jurisdiction. This concept helps clarify the question of, "Who's in charge?" Even if you're not a supervisor, for a period of time, it may well be you.

LEARN MORE

The USLA offers a video on Code X, which provides a visual overview of the incident command system in practice in an actual emergency in the environment. You can acquire a copy at: www.usla.org/store.

LEARN MORE

You can take online classes in incident command at: www.firstrespondertraining.gov.

Credit: San Clemente Lifeguards

Incident command vests help identify those assigned to lead roles.

The basic principles of the ICS are easy to understand. They are an outgrowth of the concept of chain of command, wherein ever higher ranking people in an agency are in charge of those below, but applied more broadly. Incident command training is available online from the Federal Emergency Management Administration (FEMA)—www.firsrespondertraining.gov. Other possible sources of training include local colleges or fire and police organizations. The training is easily adapted to any public safety work, including lifeguarding. The USLA recommends that all lifeguard agency supervisors complete the courses numbered I-100, I-200, I-700, and I-800, which are available online. Intermediate (I-300) and advanced (I-400) courses are appropriate for lifeguard supervisors at agencies which regularly interact with allied public safety agencies at emergency scenes.

Incident Command Responsibilities

- Coordinate overall emergency activities
- Assess incident priorities and define objectives
- Determine strategic goals and tactics
- Develop or approve and implement the incident action plan
- Develop an incident command structure appropriate for the incident
- Assess resource needs
- Order, deploy and release needed resources
- Serve as the ultimate incident safety officer, responsible for preventing injuries
- Coordinate activities of outside agencies
- Direct information release to the media
- Coordinate safety plans or assign safety officer

EMERGENCY OPERATION PLAN DEVELOPMENT

Lifeguard agencies should have *emergency operation plans*. Effective emergency operation plans will assist lifeguards in dealing with a variety of emergencies, avoiding confusion and wasted time when emergencies develop. For example, a vessel grounds on a rock off the beach with 23 victims aboard, some with serious injuries. What emergency resources will be responded? A plane with three people aboard loses power and the pilot ditches in the water 100 yards from on-duty lifeguards. Who should be notified to respond? Five people are swept offshore in a rip current. They're rescued, but all have aspirated water and need immediate advanced medical care. How will they be treated and transported to the hospital; in what order; by whom?

Most emergency operations involving lifeguards are routine. In these cases, standard response methods should be very effective; but major emergencies, by their nature, are not routine. They may necessitate numerous responders from different agencies and specialized rescue equipment. Critical decisions will need to be made throughout the incident. Because of the complexities of major emergencies, important options and resources can easily be missed. For these reasons, professional public safety agencies prepare an emergency operation plan (EOP) for each type of emergency they expect to face.

LEARN MORE

The USLA offers example emergency operation plans at: www.usla.org/resources.

Effective EOPs should be developed in consultation with all agencies likely to be involved, considering all possible resources and courses of action for a given emergency. They usually include a menu of options to help ensure that no viable alternative will be missed in the heat of the moment. An EOP helps to harness all resources in the most appropriate way.

Emergency operation plans are based on worst case scenarios. They utilize the emergency personnel who can reasonably be expected to be available. They are designed to expand or contract depending on the extent of the emergency. Some subjects of lifeguard emergency operation plans are:

- Drowning victims
- Missing persons
- Major medical emergencies and mass casualty incidents (MCI)
- Scuba emergencies
- Fire
- Severe weather (e.g. coastal storms or flooding)
- High surf
- Landslides
- Air and sea disasters
- Law enforcement
- Dangerous marine life
- Environmental disasters
- After hours emergencies
- Automobile/aircraft crashes

Emergency operation plans are sometimes drafted in the wake of a major emergency for which the agency was unprepared. This approach should be avoided. Preventive lifesaving includes anticipating worst case scenarios and preparing to handle them professionally.

Creating the Plan

Development of an effective emergency operation plan is usually begun with thorough consultation among lifeguard staff members, particularly those with experience in major emergencies and those with special skills. Various emergency scenarios are considered with best possible response modes and alternatives considered. If it becomes clear that a given type of emergency will require members of other agencies, they should be consulted and asked to provide input during the planning process. This not only provides expertise, but hopefully a buy-in to the plan which is ultimately devised. Once goals are set, representatives of each affected agency should be designated. They should then meet to prepare a draft plan. In doing so, they should consider the following list of items to facilitate an effective, coordinated response.

- **Skills Assessment**—What skills do members of each agency have that might contribute to successful management of the emergency? A skills list should be developed by each agency and shared among the planners.

- **Rescue Resources and Assets**—What resources and assets do each agency have that might contribute to successful management of the emergency? A list of rescue resources and assets should be developed by each agency and shared among the planners.

- **Identify Standard Operating Procedures**—Each agency will have *standard operating procedures* (SOP) in place, whether formal or informal, that may have an impact on the plan. For example, might the area where one agency's vehicles typically park conflict with access of responding vehicles of another agency? Creating a plan includes reducing the potential for actions by one agency that might impact response of another.

- **Lead Agency**—What agency should be the lead agency and assume incident command for the type of emergency covered by the plan?

- **Communication**—How will the various agencies communicate during the response? Are there shared radio frequencies that can be used? If so, what will the protocols be to ensure that radio traffic is organized? Can a dispatcher from one agency handle communication among all agencies? If radio communication is not practical, what alternatives are there? How will primary agency representatives be identified on-scene?

- **Command Post**—Depending on the length of the emergency, it may be valuable to have an on-scene command post. This could be an office, a mobile command post, or simply a designated location for the respective agency representatives. Agreeing upon this in advance avoids the problem of trying to find representatives of the agencies at the scene.

- **Crowd Control**—Major incidents draw crowds. These crowds must be managed to prevent interference with emergency responders and to prevent spectators from becoming victims. Who will handle this responsibility?

- **Staging Areas**—Staging areas are places that personnel and equipment gather before being committed to specific tasks, or in between those assignments. By designating staging areas, you can prevent the problem of having all emergency responders show up at the same location, which can create congestion and confusion. For example, ambulances could be directed to stage a block from the incident so that until they are needed they leave room for other responders.

- **Safety Officer**—The intense pressure on emergency responders, particularly at major emergency scenes with spectators involved, can cause agency supervisors to lose focus on personnel safety. Emergency response carries inherent risks, but those risks should be managed to ensure that all involved are protected to the greatest extent possible. Designating a *safety officer* who stands aside and observes with a role of making recommendations to the IC about safety, helps reduce unnecessary risk and lessens the chance of injury to personnel.

- **Witness Statements**—In major emergencies it's always a good idea to gather witness statements. These statements can help explain what happened, which may help in emergency response, and help create a record of the incident later. Responsibility for gathering witness statements should be designated.

- **Family Liaison**—Whenever someone is imperiled or injured, friends and family are inevitably concerned. They may have many questions. Part of an effective emergency response involves ensuring that someone is made available to answer their questions and address their concerns. This demonstrates concern for the affected parties, but also helps ensure that they do not interfere with the emergency responders and incident managers.

- **Public Information Officer**—Major incidents inevitably draw attention of the news media. They have a desire to garner factual information about the incident. By designating a *public information officer* (PIO), the media can be provided with necessary information while rescuers handle immediate needs of victims without undue interference. For long-term incidents, briefings should be planned and an area designated for the media to gather.

Once the plan is developed in draft form, it should be circulated to staff members and leaders of allied agencies included in the plan for comment. Comments should be incorporated as appropriate and the final plan produced. It should then be provided to all involved parties. Each agency will have a responsibility to ensure that the plan is immediately available to key personnel who will be primarily responsible for its implementation.

Developing Checklists

Checklists are valuable adjuncts to emergency plans. A checklist helps ensure that basic steps are not forgotten when an emergency occurs. Checklists should include all of the likely sequence of procedures required, worst case, in a specific emergency. The IC can select which steps in the sequence will be taken depending on the circumstances of the emergency, but the checklist helps to ensure that major options are considered. An example search and recovery checklist for a submerged swimmer scenario (Code X) can be found at: www.usla.org/resources.

LEARN MORE

The USLA example checklists at:
www.usla.org/resources.

Checklists are particularly valuable for dispatchers and scene commanders. For example, in a submerged swimmer emergency the dispatcher can simply be advised via radio to follow the submerged swimmer checklist, which may include summoning of an ambulance, arranging dispatch of a dive team, requesting police for crowd control, summoning additional personnel for the search, and so forth. In this way, the on-scene supervisor doesn't have to remember to advise the dispatcher of each step to take or tie up radio traffic. In addition, the task is accomplished sooner. Checklists for dispatchers can be written in such a way as to require clearance prior to taking a particular step, but they still help to remind all involved of the need to consider certain actions.

Training

Once emergency action plans are developed, all personnel who will be expected to implement them must be trained. Initially, this will include senior staff members likely to take charge or to play key roles. Since the most senior staff members may be off duty the day of a major emergency, training should also include any staff members likely to have a lead role in an emergency. Once people at this level are trained, remaining staff should be familiarized with the plan. Although most lifeguard agencies operate under a chain of command system, in which subordinate lifeguards are expected to execute directions quickly and without unnecessary questioning, when employees have an understanding of the reasons for their actions and are able to anticipate likely roles they will assume, they are more likely to be prepared to act in accordance with expectations.

Conducting Drills

Once an EOP has been developed and training has been provided, drills should be conducted to test the integrity of the plan, to provide practice to those involved, and to identify areas that may require modification. This begins with the tabletop drill. An example scenario is developed and designated representatives of all agencies involved in the plan discuss their roles. Example scenarios might be a water rescue with missing victims and a search underway or a nearshore boat collision with multiple trauma victims.

Credit: Joel Gitelson

Lifeguards preparing for an emergency drill.

How many personnel would be sent? Where would they go? To whom would they report? Each agency representative explains what they would do on a step-by-step basis. A good tabletop drill includes a few unexpected elements. For example, if the scenario involves a boat collision offshore with multiple trauma victims, partway through the tabletop drill, it may be stated that one of the boats is now sinking or has caught fire. How would things change? This process is intended to get everyone thinking about their roles and how they can best contribute to the collaboration.

The next step is a walkthrough drill. This is a preplanned practice operation utilizing members of the responsible lifeguard agency to literally walk through a rescue scenario in coordination with members of assisting agencies who would be expected to be called to the scene. The focus is on having those involved develop a familiarity and trust with members of other responding agencies, as well as with their own roles.

The final step is a live drill. This involves an actual run-through of the designated scenario, with the goal of having the rescue operation seem as real as possible, albeit with an understanding that it will not mirror the real thing. A live drill happens only after the EOP has been finalized and personnel from each agency have received training in the plan. This step is intended to reinforce proper response protocols among all responders, and to prepare them for their roles when the inevitable happens. Live drills should not be a one-time event. Rather, they should be scheduled with a frequency that avoids unnecessary disruption, but that helps responders keep a fresh sense in their mind of what their roles will be.

MANAGING COMMON LIFEGUARD EMERGENCIES

Missing persons

Large crowds and an abundance of activity make reports of missing persons very common in the beach environment. Once a person is discovered to be missing, family and friends, particularly if a small child is involved, often fear the worst. At the beach, drowning is the primary fear. A crucial question in these cases is, *"Did you see the person submerge?"* Usually the answer is that the person wandered off or was last seen swimming. In the vast majority of cases the missing person is later found on the beach.

If a credible person reports witnessing a submersion, a water search should be initiated immediately. On the other hand, if a person is simply reported to be missing and last known to be going swimming, a full water search may be inappropriate. In this case there is no *last seen point* at which to initiate the search, nor any certainty that the missing person is even in the water. Consideration should be given to the fact that committing lifeguard personnel to an extensive water search in this instance could unduly detract from safety protection provided to other water users.

LEARN MORE

The USLA offers example forms at: www.usla.org/resources.

The most difficult decision for a lifeguard in charge of a beach comes when the report of a missing person falls into the gray area between a witnessed submersion and a simple loss of a person on the beach. For example, how should the case be handled if a mother last saw her teenage son in the water, but turned away for a minute and upon trying to find him again couldn't do so? In this case the son may well have left the water or be lost in the swim crowd. On the other hand, he may have submerged.

It's essential that lifeguard agencies develop procedures for such cases to assist lifeguards and to protect the agency from criticism for a failed response. Emergency action plans and checklists can help. Ultimately though, judgment decisions will have to be made based on the unique facts in each case.

In-water search procedures are covered in Chapter 20 (*Underwater Search and Recovery*). General management of shore searches for missing persons should include the following:

1. Elicit a full description of the missing person including:
   - name
   - age
   - height
   - weight
   - hair color
   - skin color
   - clothing description
   - distinguishing characteristics
   - swimming skills
   - medical problems
   - likely beach hangouts
2. Find out the last seen location and direction of travel.
3. Notify all agency staff in the area.
4. Check likely locations, such as bathrooms, snack bars, arcades, and so forth.
5. If available, a public address system may be used to summon the missing person or to broadcast a description to elicit assistance in the search from beach patrons.
6. Regularly check the "towel area" (i.e. where the group located themselves on the beach). The missing person may return while you are searching elsewhere.
7. Check the car if the group drove to the beach.
8. If they have one, call the person's mobile phone, home phone, and hotel phone. Use mobile phone tracking apps if available.

During a check of beach facilities, the reporting person should be kept at the lifeguard facility until the incident is resolved or should be allowed to join in land-based searches only in the company of a lifeguard with communications gear. This policy ensures reunification once the lost person is located. It also prevents situations where the reporting party locates the lost person and disappears into the crowd without telling lifeguards that the problem has been resolved. This could cause lifeguards to search endlessly. All other witnesses should be isolated from the general population and interviewed as soon as possible.

Credit: San Diego Lifeguard Service

A leader of the San Diego Lifeguard Service Dive Team briefs allied agencies on a non-emergency search and recovery operation to locate a missing swimmer.

Any local law enforcement or maintenance crews who happen to be on the beach should be notified. If a missing person is not located expeditiously, a formal notification to police should be made. The actual timeframe for this notification should be set by agency protocol. A missing person report form, which may be helpful in missing person cases, can be found at: www.usla.org/resources.

Major Medical Emergencies

Depending on beach activity, some lifeguard agencies must summon ambulances daily for transportation of ill or injured people to the hospital. At other agencies, this may happen only once or twice in a season. Regardless of volume, lifeguards should be prepared to expeditiously summon needed assistance in a medical emergency. This includes having proper telephone numbers and radio frequencies readily available. Since street addresses can be unavailable or confusing for some beach locations, it's valuable to work with the local EMS provider to predesignate specific meeting points to which EMS can be summoned.

Depending on remoteness of the beach area and availability, helicopter evacuation may be necessary in some cases. Pre-planning will involve consultation with the helicopter provider to determine the cases to which they will respond. It will also involve considerations for appropriate landing areas.

Medical emergencies on the beach can draw crowds which tend to obstruct efforts of emergency medical personnel and make the patient very anxious. Some agency protocols call for summoning police assistance for crowd control in any serious medical emergency.

Multiple trauma victims are a tremendous challenge to any medical aid provider. Boating accidents and car accidents are typical causes. Lifeguard agencies should be

Credit: Eric Nurse

Law enforcement can be a great resource to aid in crowd control.

prepared to triage and treat several injured people at the same incident. This includes knowing how to summon additional ambulances and other emergency resources for backup as necessary.

Law Enforcement Emergencies

Law enforcement emergency action plans may be initiated whenever the assistance of police is needed on the beach. In the case of a simple property crime, lifeguards may respond by calling for a police officer, while keeping the victim nearby to await the officer's arrival. More serious incidents however, may require additional emergency action.

Some lifeguards are trained and authorized to enforce the law. They may carry firearms or other weapons and act as primary sources of law enforcement for the beaches they serve. Lifeguards without special training, authority, or equipment should avoid attempting to diffuse or confront violent activity. Instead, the agencies they serve will usually advise them to react to violence by calling for emergency police assistance and taking steps to protect themselves and others. All lifeguards should make reasonable attempts to protect beach visitors by helping to move them away from scenes of violent criminal activity and to rescue and treat injured beach visitors, if it can be done with a reasonable degree of safety.

Credit: California State Parks Lifeguards

California State Parks lifeguard on a traffic stop.

One area in which all lifeguards can provide invaluable assistance to law enforcement is through observation and documentation. Criminals often forget that lifeguards have a commanding view of the beach and may attempt to hide in plain view of lifeguards. Lifeguards should inform police of criminal activity and update them as the circumstances change. For example, police are understandably anxious to know if they are being summoned to an incident in which weapons are involved, as well as the type of weapons.

An impediment to law enforcement is that witnesses often forget details of the description of those involved in criminal activity. This information can be critical to capture of the perpetrator(s) and ultimate prosecution. Lifeguards should attempt to thoroughly document the descriptions of those observed to be involved in criminal activity and a description of their actions. Any object used in criminal activity observed by the lifeguard should be documented, including location and description, but not touched or moved by the lifeguard. Witnesses to a crime or victims should be contacted when it is safe to do so and asked to wait for police. Their names, addresses, and contact information should be documented so that if they leave the scene, it can be provided to police upon arrival.

Severe Weather

In Chapter 7 (*Weather*) we explained that lifeguards assist beach visitors by monitoring weather conditions, by warning beach visitors of approaching severe weather conditions, and by assisting beach visitors in the event of sudden, severe weather. When such weather conditions approach beach areas, emergency operation plans for severe weather are implemented. At small beach facilities, these plans may be initiated by the tower lifeguard after recognizing threatening weather patterns. At larger facilities, EOPs may be initiated by a supervisor.

The goals of any severe weather EOP are to:

- Ensure the safety of lifeguard staff
- Alert the public and emergency staff to threatening weather conditions
- Warn beach visitors who may be reacting to threatening weather conditions with unwise actions
- Protect beach facilities
- Assist with protection of adjacent beach property

Severe weather warnings are best made using public address systems. Alerts can also be sounded using long blasts from whistles or other alarm devices. Gestures can be used to call people in from the water and warn them. Flags can be flown if their meaning is widely understood in the area. An important goal is to avoid issuing warnings in a manner that could cause panic.

Most people will recognize threatening weather and move toward reasonable shelter on their own. Some visitors, however, may react to threatening weather by attempting to wait the storm out on the beach or may gather in the unsafe shelter of tree groves or other areas. Lifeguards can watch for this behavior and warn visitors to move to adequate shelter, offering suggestions of areas or facilities that have been determined or established as storm shelters. Since beach patrons may attempt to return to the beach before it is safe, stay alert after providing a severe weather warning.

Lifeguards themselves should also take safe shelter. In many areas, lifeguards are ordered out of towers during lightning activity, since certain tower designs may not offer adequate protection from lightning strikes. These policies are to be taken seriously, since lifeguards have been killed during electrical storms at beach facilities.

At some agencies, lifeguards are recognized and trained as special rescue responders during times of severe weather incidents. Lifeguards may be called to stand by and respond to rescues in floods, hurricanes, tornadoes, and other storms. That type of rescue response requires special training beyond the scope of this manual.

Sand Hole Collapse

Sand hole collapse is an unusual, but immediate life threatening emergency. Lifeguard agencies should have emergency operation plans in place to respond to these incidents. Chapter 15 (*Special Rescues*) provides some insights into responses to sand hole collapse.

Hazardous Materials

Hazardous materials are sometimes found in the beach area by lifeguards or citizens. They can pose a danger to humans and the environment. Lifeguard agencies should have emergency operation plans in place regarding appropriate response and handling of hazardous material incidents.

Death

In case of a death in the beach area where lifeguards are first on-scene, it's important to preplan the steps to be taken, who should be notified, and how the body should be handled.

Fire

Emergency operation plans for fire usually involve the summoning of fire services and the establishment of crowd control measures to protect beach visitors. Lifeguards can also establish and maintain access for incoming firefighting equipment. In the case of injuries, lifeguards should be prepared to provide medical aid to people injured by the fire. At beaches in wooded areas, lifeguard EOPs should include evacuation procedures for personnel and the public if a wildfire should threaten beach areas or public access routes.

CHAPTER SUMMARY

In this chapter we have learned about the incident command system and how all lifeguards play a part in this system. We have learned about the importance of emergency operation plans to help prepare lifeguards, lifeguard agencies, and allied agencies to work effectively in major emergencies. We have also learned about some common emergency situations lifeguards face and how they can be effectively resolved.

DISCUSSION POINTS

- List five circumstances in which the incident command system should be utilized.
- Name the responsibilities of an incident commander.
- Describe the value of having developed emergency operation plans.
- List the key individuals who are involved in developing an emergency operation plan.
- List three benefits of using drills in emergency action plan development.
- Explain why it is important to retain the reporting party in cases of a lost person at the beach.
- Explain what roles a lifeguard may have in a law enforcement incident.
- Identify important considerations when there is a need for issuing severe weather warnings.

CHAPTER
26

Junior Lifeguard Programs

In this chapter you will learn the history and purpose of junior lifeguard programs. You will also learn about the components of typical junior lifeguard programs.

CHAPTER EXCERPT

It is estimated that there are approximately 35,000 participants in junior lifeguard programs in the U.S. each year. Many current open water lifeguards were themselves junior lifeguard participants at one time.

Junior lifeguard programs have become an important component of the services of open water lifeguard agencies. These programs help train youth about safe ways to enjoy the aquatic environment, serve as a recruiting tool, and offer a meaningful summer activity. Junior lifeguard programs also benefit a community by teaching water safety and survival skills to participants and ultimately their friends and families through exchange of information. Additionally, they improve community support for lifeguard programs and water safety. Junior lifeguard programs combine the fun of a summer camp with the physical and mental challenges of a lifeguard training program. In the course of a typical five to ten week program, participants can be introduced to the beach environment, educated about how to identify and avoid possible dangers, and grow in their confidence and ability to enjoy the beach. Most programs charge a fee intended to partially or fully offset program costs. Some agencies have policies to waive fees based on need in an effort to ensure that all children have access.

HISTORY

During World War I, Chicago beaches faced a triple threat. The budget was tight, the war had caused a decline in lifeguard candidates, and the influenza epidemic made things even worse. Chicago was lacking in money for lifeguards and in people who could assume the responsibility. As one solution, the head of the city's beaches, Thomas R. Daly, decided to develop a junior lifeguard corps. Initially, this group was composed of boys who would add to the eyes of the regular lifeguards, notifying them of problems.

In exchange they received T-shirts and the opportunity to practice with lifeguard equipment. Although they weren't supposed to be involved in rescue work, in 1924 six junior lifeguards rescued the 35-foot sailing vessel *Casmere*, which had run aground on a sandbar. As the Chicago program evolved, the numbers increased and the training became much more thorough. In 1926 there were 40 junior lifeguards. By 1939, there were 160.[1]

In 1927 the Los Angeles City lifeguards established the first junior lifeguard program in California. This was followed in 1942 by the Los Angeles County lifeguards at Hermosa Beach. Eventually, most of the major lifeguard agencies on the West Coast had junior lifeguard programs and with information sharing as a result of the expansion of the USLA, East Coast lifeguard agencies began these programs during the early 1970s.[2]

In some areas junior lifeguard programs evolved as a means for creating a pool of candidates for lifeguard jobs. Potential lifeguard candidates who showed promise, but were either too young or were not selected for a job, were placed into a junior lifeguard program. In this case they would undergo a training process similar to that of a new lifeguard recruit, but without pay or assurance of future employment.

Lifeguard agencies came to recognize that these summer training programs not only produced strong lifeguard recruits, but also provided a valuable public safety education opportunity and youth activity. The goal was to offer a fun, safe way for children to become oriented to the beach, as well as to learn lifesaving fundamentals, including CPR and first aid. This public education model had very positive results.

The first junior lifeguard programs were small by today's standards, but in some areas they have grown tremendously. For example Los Angeles County, California enrolls about 3,500 junior lifeguards each summer; the East Bay Regional Park District in Northern California about 800; and Volusia County, Florida about 600.

It is estimated that there are approximately 35,000 participants in junior lifeguard programs in the U.S. each year.[2] Many current open water lifeguards were themselves junior lifeguard participants at one time. Other junior lifeguards go on to take jobs outside lifesaving, but benefit greatly by the instruction they have received.

Credit: California State Parks Lifeguards

In the 1990s the USLA decided to accept junior lifeguards as members and in 1996 membership was required to compete in the USLA National Junior Lifeguard Championships. Junior lifeguards are now a major membership group within the USLA, receiving membership cards, a subscription to American Lifeguard Magazine, and other benefits. Many junior lifeguard programs enroll all of their junior lifeguards as USLA members as part of the registration fee to ensure that they all receive the benefits of USLA membership.

JUNIOR LIFEGUARD PROGRAM COMPONENTS

The content of junior lifeguard programs varies somewhat, depending on local needs and interests. This section covers some of the typical elements of these programs.

Beach Orientation

Over the course of a summer session, a junior lifeguard is introduced to the beach environment. Depending on location, this may include information on subjects such as surf, piers, jetties, and aquatic life. Junior lifeguard programs also offer participants the opportunity to become acquainted with several areas to which the public does not readily have access, such as lifeguard towers, emergency response vehicles, and rescue boats. An emphasis is on providing an understanding of the hazards present in the aquatic environment and how to enjoy the area safely. For example, junior lifeguards are taught about inshore holes, currents, and sandbars. They learn to read the water to determine the hazards that exist. They are taught how to react if they should find themselves in a dangerous position.

At surf beaches, junior lifeguards may learn the basics of bodysurfing and use of bodyboards. Many programs teach participants about the wealth of aquatic life in and around the waterfront area, as well as instructing them how to avoid injuries caused by aquatic life. They are taught to respect the beach as a precious and fragile resource.

In addition to learning how to enjoy the beach and avoid potential dangers, junior lifeguards are introduced to the tools of the lifeguard trade. They are taught the purpose of lifeguard towers, the meaning of warning flags, how lifeguards work together as a team, how lifeguards use emergency vehicles and rescue boats, and how lifeguards use tools like RFDs and rescue boards.

The most important instruction involves teaching junior lifeguards how they can utilize these existing lifesaving resources when they visit the beach on their own. One of the golden rules for all junior lifeguards is the USLA admonition to *always swim near a lifeguard*. Though they may emerge from their junior lifeguard program feeling stronger, smarter, and more capable of enjoying the beach on their own, they will also be more aware of the fact that accidents can and often do happen, so they should use appropriate caution and select a beach with on-duty lifeguards.

Skills Training

Junior lifeguards should be constantly reminded that in case of an emergency, the best assistance

Credit: Alec Eng

Junior guards practice entering the water with buoy and fins.

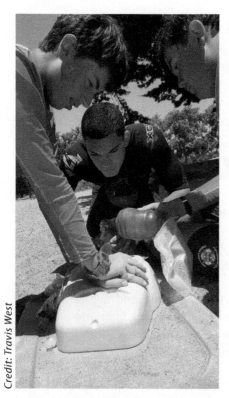

Credit: Travis West

Junior guards practice CPR skills.

they can offer is to call for help. However, many junior guard programs also attempt to provide their participants with skills training so that they will have additional options in the event of an emergency. The lifesaving skill most universally provided in junior lifeguard courses involves medical aid. Depending on the program and age of the participants, this may be simple orientation to the basics of maintaining airway, breathing, and circulation. Some programs go well beyond, teaching recognized courses in CPR and first aid, and issuing appropriate completion certificates.

Junior lifeguard programs may also offer training in use of swim fins, mask and snorkel, RFD, and rescue boards. They may perform mock rescues or learn to spot victims in distress. They are usually provided sun protection tips, the importance of keeping themselves hydrated, and how to read a tide book.

The purpose of skills training is to prepare program participants to respond to the most common dangers or accidents that present themselves in a beach environment. It is not, however, intended to make these junior guards into self-sufficient lifeguards. In fact, one of the very first rules that junior guards are taught is *when in doubt, get help.* Junior lifeguard program instructors should ensure that the confidence instilled in program participants will not cause them to over-extend themselves. A goal of any junior guard program is to prepare each participant to face every dangerous situation with a level head and calm rational thinking. This will help alleviate panic, which so often makes matters worse.

Physical Training

A valuable benefit that junior lifeguard programs boast over most conventional summer day-camp programs is physical training. While many teens and preteens may spend their summer in front of a television or computer screen, junior lifeguard participants engage in a number of physically challenging events and competitions. Junior lifeguards participate in activities such as mock rescues, sand runs, rescue board paddling, and buoy swims.

Every event has a practical purpose for preparing a junior lifeguard to safely enjoy the beach or see what it takes to be a lifeguard. Beach runs and swims improve stamina as well as

Credit: Alfredo Hernandez

Junior guards practicing mock rescue scenarios.

helping participants become more comfortable in and around the ocean. Games like beach flags and surf balls help a junior lifeguard understand what it's like to locate and reach a potential victim. Ultimately, the goal of these events is to make junior lifeguard participants stronger, faster, and more confident in their physical ability.

Credit: Travis West

Competition

Most junior lifeguard programs designate a competition day, on which junior lifeguards compete against one another. Competition events not only encourage each participant to push themselves physically, but also prepare them for the types of physical events that they might encounter in a lifeguard tryout or throughout lifeguard training. Although there are a number of universal events that most junior lifeguard programs run (e.g. soft or hard sand runs, swims, run-swim-runs, paddleboard races, rescue relays), each junior lifeguard program also offers its own unique, fun, and challenging events.

Credit: Alec Eng

USLA Mid-Atlantic Region junior lifesaving championships, Asbury Park, NJ.

Local competitions may be intersquad, among the junior lifeguards or include programs from several agencies. Some USLA regions offer annual regional competitions. Each year the National Junior Lifeguard Championships are hosted by the USLA in August, bringing junior lifeguards together from throughout the USA.

The primary requirements are USLA membership and participation in a junior lifeguard program provided by a USLA affiliated agency. Competitors are divided into divisions by their age:

> A—14–15 years old
>
> B—12–13 years old
>
> C—9–11 years old

LEARN MORE

You can find information on upcoming junior lifeguard events and download a copy of the rules for USLA competition at: www.usla.org

USLA sanctioned competition events include: Distance Run, Distance Swim, Rescue Board Race, Rescue Race, Swim Relay, Beach Flags, Run-Swim-Run, and Junior Ironguard. Winners of each event can earn medals for themselves as well as competition points for their team.

Credit: Jo Wagenhals

CHAPTER SUMMARY

In this chapter we have discussed how and why junior lifeguard programs exist, as well as some of the physical training and lifesaving skills that a typical junior lifeguard program will offer. Junior lifeguard programs are fun programs focused on the aquatic environment that also teach valuable lifesaving skills, medical aid, and personal safety.

Credit: Alec Eng

DISCUSSION POINTS

- List five ways junior lifeguard programs can help improve public safety in a community.
- List three overall benefits of a junior lifeguard program.
- Identify some examples of age appropriate activities for junior lifeguards.
- Examine some important limitations that should be instilled in junior lifeguards.

USLA Approved Arm Signals

All Clear (OK)

All Clear (OK)

Assistance Needed

Resuscitation Case or Oxygen Needed

Submerged Swimmer

APPENDIX
B

Knots and Splicing

The rope work described and illustrated in this appendix will meet most ordinary needs in lifesaving. Lifeguards must learn these knots and practice them until they can be tied with speed and certainty. Supervisors should regularly test these skills. It is better to know these few knots expertly than to have superficial knowledge of many.

A knot or splice is never as strong as the rope itself. The average efficiency of knots varies from 50-60% of the rope's strength. However, a well-made splice has about 85-95% of this strength. Splices are therefore preferred for heavy loads.

The strength of a rope is derived largely from the friction that exists between the individual fibers, yarn, and strands of which the rope is made. The twisting of these fibers into yarn, then into strands, and finally into cables is done in such a manner as to increase the amount and effectiveness of the friction between the rope elements.

KNOTS

Knots use friction to keep two or more pieces of line together. Properly tied knots create a level of friction adequate to keep the end of a line secure (fastened) when a load is placed on the line. Knots that can be tied and untied swiftly can make the difference between life and death, or the saving and destruction of property.

The square or reef knot (Figure B-1) is perhaps the most useful knot known. It should not be used to tie together lines of different sizes, as it will slip. The square knot is used for tying light lines together, not for tying heavy hawsers. Although simple and effective, the square knot has one serious flaw—it jams and is difficult to untie after being heavily stressed.

The sheet or becket bend (Figure B-2) is used for tying two lines of different sizes together. It will not slip, even if there are great differences in the size of the lines.

The bowline (Figure B-3) will not slip, does not pinch or kink the rope as much as some other knots, and does not jam and become difficult to untie. This knot is the most desirable knot for carrying heavy loads and is the most useful and important knot for lifeguarding purposes.

The clove hitch (Figure B-4) is actually composed of two half hitches, tied in such a way that they work together. This knot is used for making line fast temporarily to a piling or bollard.

Figure. B-1   Square Knot

Figure. B-2   Sheet Bend

Figure. B-3   Bowline

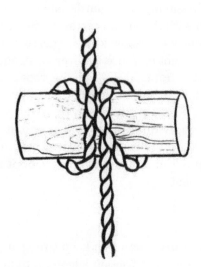

Figure. B-4   Clove Hitch

Figure. B-5   Fisherman's Bend

Figure. B-6   Tying to a Cleat

The fisherman's bend (Figure B-5), also called the anchor bend, is handy for making fast to a buoy or the ring of an anchor.

Cleats (Figure B-6) are found on most boat docks, on flagpoles, and in other places. They allow the free end of a line to be quickly and securely fastened, and detached with equal ease. Tying a line to a cleat involves running the line around the base of the cleat, and then tying a half hitch around one of the horns. Usually, an additional half hitch is tied to the other horn in such a way that the line falls together on the cleat.

SPLICING

Splicing essentially involves weaving a rope back into itself. It is stronger than a knot and cleaner, without a large bulge that might catch on something as the line plays out. Splicing is usually done to create a loop in the line (eye splice), or to join the ends of two lines. The following explanations cover the splicing of twisted, not braided, line. For purposes of explaining splicing and knots rope is said to have a *standing portion* and a *free end*. The free end is the end of the rope in which the knot is tied or the splice is made. The standing part is the remainder of the rope, away from the free end.

END SPLICE

An end splice (Figure B-7) is used to permanently join the ends of two lines to create a single line. The splice will be much stronger than any knot and much cleaner. This enlarges the rope's diameter at the splice, but much less so than would a knot.

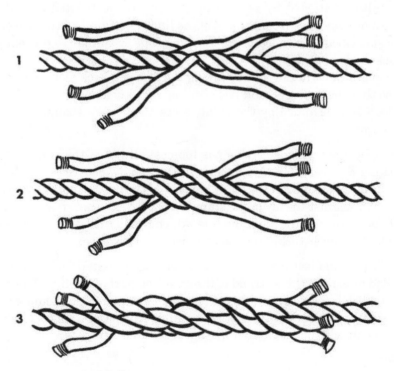

Figure. B-7   End Splice

Step 1—To start the end splice, the splicer first unlays the strands of both rope ends for a short distance as described for the eye splice. The six strand ends are taped to prevent unraveling. In this type of splice, it may also be helpful to wind a small piece of tape or string around the standing end of each line at the junction where unlaying of the strands was started. Next, the ends are married together so that the strands of each rope lie alternately between strands of the other.

Step 2—Working with any one of the three free strands on one line, it is tucked under a strand on the other line just above where the unlaying was done and past the tape or string. Then the next strand is tucked under the next adjacent strand in the standing line, and finally the third. It may be easiest to fully splice one line into the other in one direction, until the ends are fully tucked, before beginning the splice in the other direction.

Step 3—Once the splice has continued in both directions until all six strands are fully tucked, the splice is complete. For adequate strength, there should be at least five tucks per strand. After the splice is finished, it can be rolled under foot to smooth it up, then a strain put on it, and finally the excess ends cut off.

EYE SPLICE

The eye splice (Figure B-8) creates a permanent loop in the end of a line. The loop can be spliced around a fixed object, such as the end of a rescue buoy, to create a permanent attachment or simply left in the end of a line for other purposes. One end of a boat tow, for example, is a spliced loop.

The eye splice is started by separating (unlaying) the twisted strands about six inches to a foot or more back from the end of the line, depending on the size of rope being spliced. The ends should be taped using masking tape or similar to prevent unraveling of the strands during splicing.

Next a loop is formed in the rope by laying the free end back along the standing portion of line so that the center strand lies over and directly along the standing part. The size of the loop is determined by the point where the opened strands are first tucked back into the line.

Step 1—The splicer starts by selecting the topmost strand of the standing part of the line and tucking B under it. It should be pulled up snugly, but not so tight as to distort the natural lay of the strands in the standing part of the line. Note that the tuck is made from right to left, against the lay of the standing part. Next, the left strand (A) is tucked under a different strand of the standing line, which lies to the left of strand under which B was pulled. The splicer tucks from right to left in every case.

Step 2—The loop should be turned over as has been done in Step 2 of Figure B-8. Strand C is now pulled under the third strand of the standing part of the line. The greatest risk of starting a splice incorrectly is in the first tuck of strand C. It should go under from right to left. If the first tuck of each of the strands A, B, and C, is correctly made, the splice at this point will look as shown in Step 2.

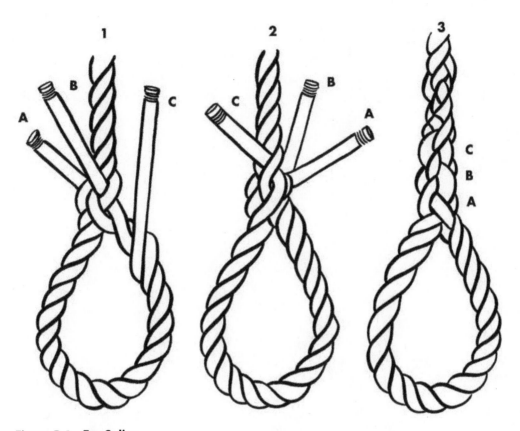

Figure. B-8   Eye Splice

Step 3—The splicer then returns to strand A, lays it over the next strand up the standing part of the line, and then tucks it under the one after that. The same is then done with B and C in order. This process is repeated, one tuck at a time, until the ends have been woven (spliced) fully into the standing part of the line with no significant end left. When complete, the splice should appear as in Step 3 of Figure B-8.

Glossary

abaft—aft of, to the rear of

abeam—on the side of the vessel, amidships, or at right angles

about—to go on the opposite tack, change directions

abyss—an extraordinarily deep part of the ocean

accretion—gradual build-up of sand or shoreline due to current or tidal action

adrift—floating at the mercy of wind or current

aft—toward the stern of a vessel

aground—a vessel which has struck bottom; also known as grounded, beached

air embolism—in scuba diving, a serious disorder caused by rapid expansion of air in the lungs during a fast ascent

all-terrain vehicle (ATV)—a small three or four wheel vehicle with oversized tires or treads designed for use on rough terrain

alveoli—small sacs in the lungs where exchange of carbon dioxide and oxygen takes place

amidships—middle point of a vessel between bow and stern

anoxia (also anoxemia)—absence of oxygen

antifouling paint—a substance applied to a the hull of a vessel which is intended to chemically resist attachment of marine organisms

antimicrobial—a substance which is capable of destroying or inhibiting growth of microorganisms

artificial respiration—inflating the lungs of a person by mechanical means or by blowing into the airway of the victim

aspirate—to inhale a substance into the lungs; a typical finding in a near drowning incident is *water aspiration*

aspirator—tool used to clear fluid or food regurgitation from the air passages of an asphyxiated or non-breathing patient

astern—behind a vessel

atmosphere—(physics) a unit of pressure equal to the air pressure at sea level; pressure at sea level (one atmosphere) is 14.7 pounds per square inch (psi), but it doubles at 33 feet in water depth (two atmospheres), triples at 66 feet in depth (three atmospheres), and so on

awash—covered by water; usually the state of a vessel overcome by waves or tide

backboard—see spineboard

backrush—seaward return of water following the uprush of a wave on the beach

backup—safety personnel who respond to assist the primary rescuer(s) to assist or stand-by a rescue operation

backwash—see backrush

backwater—(1) water turned back by an obstruction, opposing current, or the like; (2) to propel a rowboat or dory in a stern first direction using a reverse rowing or boating stroke

bag-valve-mask resuscitator (BVM)—a hand-held ventilation device used for artificial respiration consisting of a self-inflating bag, a one-way valve, and a face mask; used with or without oxygen

bailout bottle—a small scuba tank with limited air supply that can be strapped to the waist and used for a rapid underwater search (also known as a pony tank)

ballast—broken stone, gravel, or other heavy material used in a vessel to improve stability or control the draft

bar—a submerged or emerged embankment of sand, gravel, or mud built on the sea floor in shallow water by waves and currents

barometer—an instrument for measuring atmospheric pressure and generally used for predicting changes in the weather

bar port—a harbor that can be entered only when the tide rises sufficiently to permit passage of vessels over a bar

bather—(dated term) a swimmer or wader

bathymetric chart—a map delineating the form of the bottom of a body of water, usually by means of depth contours

BC, BCD—see buoyancy compensator

beach break—waves breaking hard on a sharply sloping sand beach (shorebreak)

beach erosion—the carrying away of beach material by wave action, tidal currents, littoral currents, or wind

beam—(1) a vessel's maximum width (2) the side of a vessel

beam sea—wind at right angles to a vessel's keel

bearings—the position of one location with respect to another; for example, lifeguards may get their bearings by noting their location in the water as compared to several fixed points on shore

becalm—a sailing vessel is becalmed when there is no wind adequate to propel the vessel forward; also known as being "in irons"

belly board—see bodyboard

bends—see decompression sickness

berm—a narrow shelf, path, or ledge created by wave action on the sand

bilge—lower internal part of vessel's hull

bitt—a vertical post (usually one of a pair) fitted into a vessel's deck for securing lines for towing, mooring, or other purposes

blind rollers—long, high swells that have increased in height almost to the breaking point as they pass over shoals or run in shoaling water

bloodborne pathogen—an agent carried in the blood, particularly a living microorganism, capable of causing disease

boardsurfing—any activity that involves riding waves with the use of a surfboard; also known as surfing, riding

boat tow—a short length of line with a loop at one end and a fastener at the other that enables a swimming lifeguard to tow a boat in distress

bodyboard—a short, hard foam board for riding waves while lying prone on the board

bodysurfing—riding a wave without the aid of a floating device

boil—upwelling of water caused by a swell riding or striking shallow water or rock formations, causing a visual disturbance on the water surface; also known as upswelling, swirls

Boogie Board®—see bodyboard

bow—the forward part of a vessel

breaking wave—a wave breaking on the shore, over shoal water or reef; a wave which makes an audible noise as it spills over; also known as a breaker or crasher

breakwater—a structure protecting a shore area, harbor, anchorage, or basin from waves or current; also known as seawall, jetty

broach—to veer sideways to the wind or swell; a vessel which broaches in the surf is in great danger

buddy system—two persons, usually divers, swimming together for mutual support and safety

bulkhead—(1) any upright partition separating compartments on a vessel; (2) a wall or embankment for holding back earth and protecting a shoreline from erosion due to wave action

buoy line—(1) a line supported by buoys, used to delineate a boundary in the water; (2) separated buoys placed in a line to delineate a water boundary

buoyancy compensator (BC)—an inflatable vest-like device used by divers to compensate for changing buoyancy when descending and ascending; also known as a buoyancy compensator device (BCD)

Burnside buoy—a variation of the term *rescue buoy*, which refers in this case to the primary inventor (Robert Burnside)

can rack—storage rack for rescue buoys

cataracts—a clouding of the lens of the eye, associated with long term exposure to sunlight

cat's paw—a puff of wind; a light breeze affecting a small area, as one that causes patches of ripples on the surface of a water area

Certification Officer—person appointed by the USLA to evaluate whether an applying agency adheres to the recommended USLA open water lifeguard guidelines

chafe—to rub or damage by rubbing

chafing gear—anything used to prevent chafing

channel—(1) a natural or artificial waterway that periodically or continuously contains moving water, or that forms a connecting link between two bodies of water; (2) the part of a body of water deep enough to be used for navigation through an area otherwise too shallow for navigation; (3) the deepest portion of a stream, bay, or rip current through which the main volume or current of water flows

chop—disturbed surface of water usually caused by strong wind or after-effects of waves; whitecaps

cleat—a metal fitting with two horns pointing in opposite directions and used for temporarily fastening a line; usually attached to a dock, pier, or vessel

Code III—the code in many states for an expedited emergency response; requires emergency lights and siren for an emergency vehicle

Code X—(1) the USLA approved term which signifies a missing (submerged) swimmer, causes implementation of an emergency plan for locating and retrieving a missing swimmer; (2) the USLA approved signal for a missing (submerged) swimmer formed by crossing the arms overhead in the form of an X

coral—(1) a rocklike structure or reef formed of the hard calcareous skeleton of various anthozoans; (2) a polyp of the family Anthozoa

coral head—a mushroom or pillar-shaped coral growth

countercurrent—a current flowing adjacent to the main current but in an opposing direction

crest—the highest part of a wave

critical incident stress debriefing—a meeting of those involved in a life-threatening incident to help workers cope with related stress, usually led by a mental health professional,

curl—curved portion of a wave which tumbles forward

current—a stream of flowing water

davit—a small crane-like device on a vessel used for launching a small boat over the side or hoisting cargo; usually used in tandem with one holding the bow and the other the stern of the small boat

dead reckoning—a method of navigation utilizing only the speed and heading of the craft, without reference to astronomical observations or mechanical positioning devices

decompression illness—a scuba diving affliction which occurs when compressed gases in the body produce bubbles which form in the cells or circulatory system

defibrillator—a device that sends an electric shock through the chest to the heart to attempt to change the rhythm of an ineffectively beating heart to a productive rhythm

degree—(1) a unit of temperature; (2) a unit of angular distance; 1/360 of a circle

demand valve—a valve attached to a mask that delivers 100% oxygen to a breathing person on demand

diver's flag—a flag generally flown on a floating device, intended to warm boaters of submerged scuba divers; standard appearance of the diver's flag is either square red with a white diagonal bar running across from one corner to other or alpha flag (burgee) with inner half blue, outer half white

dive tables—chart of rules for scuba divers to use in avoiding decompression sickness; also known as decompression tables

documented vessel—vessel registered with the U. S. Bureau of Customs or the U. S. Coast Guard

dorsal fin—the main fin located along the back of many fish and marine mammals

draft—the depth of a vessel below the water line

drowning—the process of experiencing respiratory impairment from submersion/immersion in liquid. Drowning may result in injury or death, or may be interrupted by timely rescue and effective medical care. Drowning outcomes include death, injury, and non-injury.

dry suit—diver's suit designed to protect and retain body heat without allowing water to permeate

ebb current—outgoing tidal current associated with a decrease in the height of a tide

ebb tide—outgoing tide

eddy—a circular movement of water, usually formed where currents pass obstructions between two adjacent currents flowing counter to each other, or along the edge of a permanent current

eight plate—descent device shaped like the number 8 which, when properly used, exerts friction on line passing through it and allows control of line with a load placed on it; used in cliff rescue

electrolysis—(nautical) chemical decomposition of metals or alloys by the action of an electric current caused by contact with salt water

embayment—an indentation in a shoreline forming an open bay

emergency medical system (EMS)—network of community resources and medical personnel to provide emergency care to victims of sudden illness or injury

emergency operation plan—a plan for efficient response to an anticipated emergency situation

equalize—to bring air pressure in the sinuses to a point equal to ambient air pressure; necessary primarily in scuba diving and flying; also known as clearing

erosion—a natural process by which sand, soil, or rock is broken up and transported, usually by wind and water

estuary—the area where a river meets a tidal bay; also known as drowned river mouth, branching bay, firth, forth

exostosis—an abnormal bony growth on the surface of a bone or tooth (sometimes a complication in the ear canal of swimmers due to long term exposure to cold water)

fake—(n) one coil of a rope; (v) to lay out line in such a way that it will easily play out when one end is thrown or otherwise pulled

fathom—six-foot measure of water depth

fathometer—device used to measure the depth of the water; also known as depth gauge, depth finder, depth sounder

feeder channels—channels parallel to shore along which feeder currents flow before converging to form the neck of a rip-current

feeder—current of water moving along the shore providing water to a rip current; usually created by wave action and gravity

feeling bottom—the action of a deep water wave on running into shallow water and beginning to be influenced by the bottom

fender—cushion to protect a boat from bumping against a dock or another boat; also, bumper

ferry angle—an upstream angle against a current taken in an effort to reach a specific point ashore

fetch—(1) an area of the sea surface over which seas are generated by a wind having constant direction and speed; (2) the length of the fetch area, measured in the direction of the wind in which the seas are generated

first responder—(1) a medical aid provider first to the scene of a medical emergency; (2) an emergency medical aid course offered by the National Highway Traffic Safety Administration

flag system—consistently colored flags used to designate certain water activity or surf conditions

flotation device—(also: floatation device) any device that a person uses for support on the water surface

flood tide—the incoming tide

flotsam—floating debris, driftwood, etc.

free ascent—an emergency ascent by a scuba diver in reaching the surface when air supply is unexpectedly available; a free ascent is likely to result in decompression illness

free diver—a diver operating without the benefit of scuba equipment; skin diver

freeboard—the vertical distance from the water to the gunwale of a vessel

full time lifeguard—lifeguard appointed to a full-time, year-round position

fully developed sea—the maximum height to which ocean waves can be generated by a given wind force

gang grapnel—A series of hooks set in a parallel pattern and used in the same fashion as a grappling hook

glassy—smooth, unrippled sea surface caused by absence of wind

grappling hook—a device with four, five, or more flukes or claws used to drag on the bottom to snag corpses or other objects

groin—a small jetty, extending at roughly right angles to the shore, usually designed to trap lateral drift and/or retard erosion of the shoreline

ground swell—a long, high ocean swell

guarded area—water recreational area with lifeguards on duty; a guarded beach

guide lines—lines secured to an object to prevent it from being damaged; lines attached to aid in control of a floating or suspended object

guidelines—(USLA) the Guidelines for Open Water Lifeguard Training & Standards promulgated by the USLA for use in the national Lifeguard Agency Certification Program or Aquatic Rescue Response Team program

gully—a relatively narrow ravine in the ocean bed

gunwale (gun-el)—the upper edge of the side of a vessel; also known as the rail

gutter rip—a short, powerful, fast-moving rip current found on a scalloped, steep, sloping beachfront; gutter rips can sweep people off their feet by surprise and into the next wave; the sweeping underwater current action is often confused with the misnomer "undertow"

harbor—an area of water affording natural or manufactured protection for vessels

hawser—a heavy line used to moor or tow a vessel

head (of a rip)—area where the neck of a rip widens and disperses and the power of the rip disperses

heavy sea—severe water disturbance caused by winds or swell; also known as rough sea

heavy surf—large breaking waves; also known as heavies, surf's up, crashers, blue birds on the horizon

helm—wheel or tiller by which a vessel is steered

helmsman—one who steers a vessel; also known as skipper, captain, operator, pilot

high siding—leaning body weight toward that side of a boat that is broadside and being pushed by a wave in an effort to avoid capsizing

high water mark—the highest point that water reaches during a tidal phase

hyperventilation—excessive breathing in and out; hyperventilation purges the breathing stimulant, carbon dioxide, out of the respiratory system and to a minor degree increases the percentage of oxygen in the lungs; hyperventilation can cause unconsciousness and drowning

hypoxia—lack of oxygen in the tissues of the body

incident command system (ICS)—a system used to control and direct resources at the scene of an emergency; commonly used by emergency providers

incident commander (IC)—the person in charge of an emergency incident; most often used when the incident command system has been formally implemented

inflatable rescue boat (IRB)—an inflatable soft hulled boat powered by an outboard engine capable of carrying several lifeguards and rescue equipment; also known as an inshore rescue boat

in irons—a condition that prevents a sailing vessel to move forward; the operator of a sailing vessel that is in irons is unable to change the position of the vessel to allow the sails to fill

inlet—a short, narrow waterway connecting a bay or lagoon with the sea

inside—area between the breaking waves and the shoreline; usage: "the vessel was caught inside by large surf"

intersecting waves—one of the component waves that, when superimposed on others, produces cross-swells; also known as sugarloaf sea, pyramidal sea

intertidal zone—that portion of the shoreline lying between the high and low tide marks

intramuscular—within a muscle (e.g. an intramuscular injection involves first inserting a needle into the muscle)

intravenous—within a vein or administered into a vein (e.g. intravenous fluids are administered by first inserting a needle into a blood vein)

invertebrate—an organism that lacks a spine, such as a sea urchin or mollusk

isthmus—a narrow strip of land, bordered on both sides by water, which connects two larger bodies of land

jettison—to throw objects overboard, especially to lighten a craft in distress; to remove articles from a person to allow more buoyancy, such as the weight belt from a scuba diver

jetty—a structure, usually of rock, extending into a body of water to protect a harbor or shoreline from erosion and storm activity; also known as a groin

junior lifeguard—adolescent or younger person involved in a program taught by professional lifeguards to learn lifeguarding techniques; also known as nipper, J.G., junior guard

keel—a longitudinal structure extending along the center of the bottom of a vessel that gives main support to the vessel's hull bottom; the keel often projects below the bottom; also known as center line, skeg

kelp—the general name for large species of seaweeds; kelp forests are common along the West Coast with single plants extending 60 or more feet from the bottom; also known as seaweed

Kimball, Sumner Increase—first and only leader of the U.S. Lifesaving Service during its existence from 1878 to 1915; formerly chief of the Revenue Marine Division which (included lifesaving services) from 1871 to 1878

knee board—a type of bodyboard designed and used to surf in a kneeling position

knot—one nautical mile per hour (a nautical mile is 1.15 times a statute mile)

landline—line swum out to a victim or victims in distress and used to pull them back to shore; also known as reel, line, lifeline

landmarks—a conspicuous object on land or sea that marks a locality; a visual line-up of two or more fixed objects on the beach to obtain a precise location on the water surface; also known as marks

last seen point—the last place a victim was observed before submerging

lead line—(1) a line, wire, or cord used in sounding; (2) a light line which is thrown, shot, or swim to make a connection between two points and to then pull a larger line, such as a hawser, between them (usually for towing purposes)

leash—a short line used to secure a surfboard, bodyboard, or similar flotation device to the user's wrist or ankle; also known as a tether, surf leash

leeward—the side (usually of a vessel) away from the wind

life car—a device used by the first lifesavers in conjunction with the breeches buoy apparatus to evacuate several victims at a time from a distressed ship

lifeguard stand—a primitive elevated observation post used by lifeguards, lacking first aid or storage facilities; usually staffed only in the busy season; also known as seasonal tower, bird cage, supplementary tower, perch, bench

life ring—a floating ring which can be thrown to a person in distress, often including rope around the edges

littoral transport—the movements of material along the shore in the littoral zone by waves and currents

littoral zone—the nearshore zone

logbook—book kept at main stations, on rescue boats, and in emergency vehicles listing pertinent daily activities and times; used as a record of lifeguard activity

low water—the lowest limit of the surface water level reached by the lowering or outgoing tide

lull—period of lower waves between sets of unusually large waves

Lyle, David—originator of the Lyle gun used by early lifesavers to deploy the breeches buoy apparatus

macular degeneration—loss of central vision, associated with long term exposure to sunlight

main tower—a lifeguard station, usually staffed all year, that supplies assistance to other lifeguard facilities in a given area; also known as tower zero, main station

make fast—to secure the end of a line by tying it to a fixed point

mass rescue—a rescue involving multiple victims, usually more than two or three; also known as multiple victim rescue

mat surf—surfing waves with the aid of an air-filled, semi-flexible object; also known as air mattress, rubber raft, float

mechanical resuscitation—resuscitation done with the aid of a mechanical device, as opposed to mouth-to-mouth

mooring—an anchored buoy to which a boat is secured when not in use

mouth-to-mouth—resuscitation of a non-breathing victim by blowing air from the lungs of the rescuer into a nonbreathing victim's airway; also known as rescue breathing

narcosis (nitrogen narcosis)—a sense of stupor or drunkenness felt by scuba divers due to increased levels of dissolved nitrogen in the blood; also known as rapture of the deep

neck—portion of a rip where most drownings and rescues take place

nematocyst—stingers, found in jellyfish and Portuguese man-of-war, which are intended to paralyze prey and ward off attackers

offshore wind—a wind blowing seaward from the land in a coastal area; also known as land breeze, opposing wind

off-gassing—in scuba diving, the release of nitrogen from body tissues upon ascending, which must be done gradually to avoid decompression sickness (DCS)

one-feeder rip—rip current fed by a current coming from only one direction

onshore wind—a wind blowing landward from the sea in a coastal area; also known as a sea breeze

open water—any natural body of water such as a lake, river, ocean or bay

OSHA—acronym for the Occupational Safety and Health Administration of the U.S. Department of Labor, charged with ensuring that workplaces are safe

outflow—the flow of water from a river or its estuary to the sea

outside—anything on the offshore side of the surfline; also known as back side, out back

over the falls—object or person falling without control from wave peak to the wave bottom; also known as a wipeout

painter—a short line attached to bow of a small boat primarily for purposes of fastening to a dock or towing

passage—a narrow navigable pass or channel between two land masses or shoals

pathogen—an agent, particularly a living microorganism, which causes disease

patrol—walking or driving in an emergency vehicle or rescue boat, with ready rescue gear, to observe and inspect a beach and water area; also known as a beach check, beach run, down to the line

peak—the top of a wave at the maximum point before breaking

pendulum technique—a rescue technique in swiftwater that involves throwing a line to a victim who is then pulled to shore in an arc by the natural flow of the current

permanent lifeguard—(see full-time lifeguard)

personal flotation device (PFD)—a buoyant device designed to be held or worn to keep a person afloat; a life jacket

Peterson tube—a variation of the term *rescue tube*, which refers in this case to the primary inventor (Pete Peterson)

photokeratitis—damage to the cornea of the eye from exposure to intense light

plunging wave—wave that tends to curl over and break with a crash; also known as crasher, breaker

pod—a school of marine mammals, such as seals or whales

porpoise—(lifeguarding) an action taken by a lifeguard to move through water, particularly incoming surf, during the transition from high stepping through shallow water to swimming; the arcing motion of repeatedly diving forward in a surface dive, grabbing the sand, crouching, and then diving forward again

port—side of a vessel to left when facing the bow

posted area—area that has signs, flags, or signals regulating water and beach activities; also known as designated area, signed area

pothole—a hole in the ocean floor in the surf line a few feet or yards in diameter; also known as hole, inshore hole

prevailing current—the flow most frequently observed during a given period, usually a month, season, or year; also known as prevailing drag

preventive action—providing verbal commands or taking other actions to help people avoid or extricate themselves from a dangerous area; note: a preventive action is not a rescue; see rescue

primary zone—a lifeguard's assigned water zone of responsibility

psi—acronym for pounds per square inch

pterygium—a callous-like growth that can spread over the white of the eye, caused by exposure to sunlight, wind, and dust or blowing sand; requires surgery to remove

radio code—numbers used in place of often used words or phrases for purposes of abbreviating radio conversations and masking their meaning; also known as code list, codes, code

rail—the edge of a rescue board or surfboard running lengthwise

recompression—the treatment of decompression sickness or air embolism in a recompression chamber, which simulates returning the injured diver to an underwater depth

recurring training—training conducted cyclically to maintain proficiency in rescue, physical, and EMS skills

red tide—rust-coloring in the ocean caused by a natural dinoflagellate plankton bloom

reef—any hard geographical structure that is underwater at high tide

reef break—waves breaking over shallow waters of a reef

refraction—a phenomenon by which wave trains approaching a beach from an acute angle tend to wrap to a direct, perpendicular angle prior to striking the shoreline

regulator—a mechanical device for adjusting the high pressure flow of air from a compressed air cylinder to the current atmospheric pressure so that it can be comfortably breathed

rescue—any case in which a person who is judged to be in imminent peril is brought to safety by a lifeguard; usually involves physical control; does not include oral instructions

rescue board—a large, wide surfboard, usually over ten feet long, typically with handles, used to make rescues; also known as a paddle board

rescue boat—a boat used in the observation and rescue of swimmers, surfers, or boats; may be motorized or manually powered; some rescue boats are used in firefighting and related functions; also known as a patrol boat or lifeguard boat

rescue breathing—resuscitation of a non-breathing victim by blowing air from the lungs of the rescuer into a nonbreathing victim's airway; also known as mouth-to-mouth

rescue buoy—cylindrical flotation device with handles, secured by a line and harness to a lifeguard and used to effect a swimming rescue or an assist; also known as: Burnside buoy, torpedo buoy, torp, can, or can buoy

rescue flotation device (RFD)—a rescue buoy or rescue tube

rescue tube—a flexible foam rubber flotation device which can be wrapped around a victim's chest, fastened, and used by a lifeguard to tow the victim to safety; also known as a Peterson tube

resting stroke—swimming stroke used to rest the body without losing buoyancy or forward motion; may indicate fatigue; common resting strokes are: sidestroke, breaststroke

resurgence—the continued rising and falling of a bay or semi-enclosed water body many hours after the passage of a severe storm

resuscitation—process of rhythmically inflating the lungs of an asphyxiated victim with oxygen or air

resuscitator—machine used to rhythmically inflate the lungs of an asphyxiated victim with oxygen from a tank

RFD—acronym for "rescue flotation device"

rip current—current of water traveling away from shore, generated by wave action; also known as: rip, hole, seaward current, run, runout; note: the rip current is commonly misnamed a "rip tide"

roller—(1) one of a series of waves, usually a long-crested wave that rolls up a beach; (2) an air-filled fabric cylinder used to facilitate moving small boats on the land

rudder—the device used for steering and maneuvering a boat, particularly a sailboat or a large motorized boat

runback—a colloquial term for backwash

sandbar—a ridge of sand in the sea bottom, normally submerged depending upon tides and other factors; also known as bar, shoal

scuba—self-contained underwater breathing apparatus which involves the use of a tank of compressed air and a regulator which reduces the pressure of the air to a breathable pressure

sea level—the height of the surface of the sea at a given point in time; also known as: water level

seawall—a manufactured structure of rock, concrete, or wood built along a portion of coast to prevent wave erosion of the beach

seasonal current—a current that changes with seasonal winds or swell direction

seasonal lifeguard—lifeguard employed during the summer months, vacations, weekends, and holidays, usually an hourly employee; also known as recurrent guard, weekend guard, part-time guard, guard as needed, temporary guard, summer guard

seaward—the direction away from shore and toward the sea

seaweed—any macroscopic marine algae, such as seagrass or kelp

sediment—any natural material carried in suspension by water which causes underwater visibility obstruction

seiche—an occasional and sudden oscillation of the water of a lake, bay, or estuary resulting in dramatic changes in the water level caused by wind or change in barometric pressure; may result in sudden shoreline flooding

senior guard—a lifeguard who by virtue of experience, knowledge, and/or maturity has been assigned to a key station, tower, area, or function that carries with it added responsibility and/or supervisory duties

set—series of waves larger than the norm

shallow water wave—a wave moving from sea toward shore, influenced by the decreasing water depth of the shoreline

shelf—a rock ledge, reef, or sandbank in the sea

shoal—a submerged ridge, bank, or bar consisting of or covered by mud, sand, or gravel that is at or near enough to the water surface and constitutes a danger to navigation; if composed of rock or coral, it is called a reef

shoaling effect—the alteration of a wave as it passes over a shoal

shorebreak—waves which quickly peak and break onshore to a sharply sloping beach; also known as: inside break, insiders

side current—body of water traveling parallel to shore, generated by wave action, wind, or tide; also known as drag, parallel drag, feeder, trough, lateral drift, long shore current

skeg—the fin on the bottom of a surfboard or bodyboard which helps provide stability in the water; a timber that connects the keel and sternpost of a ship; also known as a keel

skim board—a flat, thin board, usually round, ridden standing up after being thrown into very shallow water over a flat sand beach

skindiver—see free diver

slack water—the interval when the speed of the tidal current is very weak or zero; usually refers to the period of reversal between ebb and flood currents; also known as: slack tide

slough—a marshy or reedy pool, pond, inlet, backwater, etc.

small craft warning—storm signal warning pleasure craft vessels of dangerous water surface conditions caused by strong wind

snorkel—a J-shaped tube held in the mouth and used in conjunction with a mask that permits breathing when a person's face is just at water level or just under the surface

snub—to quickly secure a rope by wrapping it around a cleat, post, etc.; also known as make fast, secure

sounding—the measurement of the depth of water beneath a ship

spilling wave—wave breaking gradually over a considerable distance; also known as a slider

spineboard—a rigid board used to immobilize and transport victims suspected of having suffered spinal injury; also known as a backboard

stand-by—a state of readiness during which a lifeguard prepares for an imminent emergency response; a stand-by may proceed to an emergency response or be canceled if the emergency is resolved

starboard—side of vessel to right when standing on the vessel and facing the bow

stern—the rear end of a vessel; also known as transom, aft

Stokes Basket®—a contour stretcher constructed of tubular frame woven with wire mesh; also known as: litter, litter basket, Stokes stretcher

storm surge—increased water level due to storm activity and resultant surf

storm tide—a regular tide exaggerated by storm surge

stretcher—portable platform or body contour platform used to transport any injured or deceased person in a lying position; also known as gurney, litter

surf (noun)—breaking waves; (verb) to be propelled or gain momentum using the forward motion of a swell or wave with or without the aid of a floating device; to board surf; to bodysurf

surface dive—the act of submerging underwater in a forward motion, usually a forward rolling motion

surface wave—a wave on the surface of the water; most often formed by wind, but may be formed by seismic activity or the gravitational pull of the moon and sun

surfboard—any rigid, inflexible device upon which or with the use of aid which a person can ride waves or be carried along or propelled by the action of waves; also known as: board, stick

surfline—the offshore point along a beach where waves are breaking at a given time, bordered on the outside by the most offshore break and on the inside by the most shoreward break; the distance of the surfline from shore varies with the size of the waves since larger waves break further offshore than smaller waves

surf zone—area between the furthest outside waves that are just beginning to break and the edge of the water on the beach

surf's down—waves are breaking smaller than normal; no surf at all

surf's up—waves are breaking larger than normal

surfing area—area open to surfboarding only, no swimming unless incidental to surfboarding

surfing—riding or being propelled by the action of a wave with the aid of a surfboard; also known as: board surfing, surfboarding

surge—a swelling or sweeping rush of water, a violent rising and falling of water

swell—a surface wave in open water before it strikes a beach

swim fins—flat, webbed rubber footwear worn by swimmers to gain power and speed out of their kick by artificially elongating the feet; also known as fins, flippers

swimming area—water area open to swimming only

tertiary zone—area of responsibility checked by a lifeguard in less frequent pattern than primary and secondary zones

tether—a short line used to secure a surfboard, belly board or similar flotation device to the user; also known as a leash, surf leash

thermocline—a layer of water in a lake or similar body of water that is of distinctly different temperature than the layer above or below; most often used to refer to a sudden and dramatic lowering in temperature when descending in a lake; most likely in still water, since current tends to adversely affect formation

three points of a rescue—the three components of every water rescue as identified by the USLA: 1) recognize and respond; 2) contact and control; and 3) signal and save

thwart—a seat that runs across the beam of a boat or vessel

tidal flat—a marsh or sandy or muddy coastal flatland covered and uncovered by the rise and fall of the tide; a mud flat

tidal wave—a disfavored term for a tsunami

tide mark—(1) a high water mark left by tidal water; (2) the highest point reached by a high tide; (3) a visual mark indicating any specified state of tide

tide pool—a pool of water remaining in the intertidal area after recession of the tide

tide race—a very rapid tidal current in a narrow channel or passage

tide tables—tables that give daily predictions, of the times and heights of the tide

tideway—a channel through which a tidal current flows

tiller—bar or handle for turning a vessel's rudder

topside—upon the upper deck of a vessel; also known as above deck

transverse bars—slightly submerged sand ridges that extend at right angles to the shoreline

treading water—maintaining a stationary position on the surface of the water by using the legs and arms

trough—parallel inshore channel in the ocean floor running a few to many yards in length which may help foster development of a rip current; also known as hole, feeder, trench, drop-off, channel

tsunami—very large wave created by events that cause a sudden shift in the sea, such as earthquakes, volcanoes, landslides, or the crash of a meteorite; tsunamis generally have extraordinarily long periods which make them almost invisible in the open ocean, but deadly when they arrive onshore and break; also known as a tidal wave or seismic wave

two-feeder rip—rip current generated by two currents which merge, feeding the neck of the rip current

undertow—a misnomer which suggests a current pattern (not known to exist) that drags a person under the water; this word is not used by knowledgeable lifeguards except to correct others; usage note: this term may have been coined to refer to a combination of phenomena involving a person being knocked down by a wave, pulled offshore by a backrush or rip current, and submerging due to lack of swimming ability

underway—vessel in motion

universal precaution—an approach to infection control which assumes that all blood and human bodily fluids are infectious

uprush—the rush of water up onto the beach following the breaking of a wave

up-welling—bottom water reaching the surface because of disturbance caused by swells, waves, or current

victim—any person who is imperiled or injured and (usually) requires the assistance of a lifeguard; a person caught in a rip current is considered to be a victim; depending on circumstances; a victim may also be known as a casualty, accident victim, or patient

wake—path of disturbed water left behind a moving vessel or moving object in water

warning—verbal contact by voice or electronic equipment explaining an existing danger

water ability—personal performance and endurance in all types of water conditions, such as surfing, diving, swimming, paddling, etc.

waterspout—a tornado occurring over water

wave—a ridge or swell, representing a force of energy, moving through water; surface waves are most often caused by wind on the water

wave crest—The highest part of a wave

wave generation—the creation of waves by natural or mechanical means

wave train—a continual series of water waves moving in the same direction and generated by the same source

wave trough—the lowest part of a wave; the area between two ocean swells

weight belt—belt containing varying weights worn by a diver to compensate for surface buoyancy

wetsuit—foam neoprene rubber suit that fits snugly to the body, allows some water inside, and helps insulate a swimmer, surfer, or diver from cold water

white cap—wind-blown surface chop that has white froth or foam appearance

whitewater—in the surf zone, water that is mixed with air causing it to turn white; also known as: soup, surge, slop, fizz, foam

wind-driven current—a current fed by the force of a wind

wind-mixing—mechanical stirring of water due to motion induced by the surface wind

windward—the direction from which the wind is blowing

wind wave—a wave formed by wind

References

CHAPTER 1

[1] *Annual Report to Congress*, United States Life-Saving Service. 1884.

[2] Quinn, W.P., *Shipwrecks around Cape Cod; a collection of photographs and data covering the period from the late 1800's to 1973 on Cape Cod*. 1st ed. 1973, Farmington, Me.,: Printed by Knowlton & McLeary. 239 p.

[3] Shanks, R.C., W. York, and L.W. Shanks, *The U.S. Life-Saving Service : heroes, rescues, and architecture of the early Coast Guard*. 1996, Petaluma, CA: Costaño Books. 262 p.

[4] Tipton, M. and A. Wooler, eds. *The Science of Beach Lifeguarding*. 2016, CRC Press: Boca Raton, Florida.

[5] Johnson, R.E., *Guardians of the sea : history of the United States Coast Guard, 1915 to the present*. 1987, Annapolis, Md.: Naval Institute Press. x, 412 p.

[6] Ryder, R.G., *Old Harbor Station, Cape Cod*. 1st ed. 1990, Norwich, Conn. (29 Cuprak Rd., Norwich 06360): Ram Island Press. vii, 128 p.

[7] Merryman, J.H., *United States Life-Saving Service: 1880*. 1989, Grand Junction, Colorado: Vistabooks.

[8] Dalton, J.W., *The life savers of Cape Cod*. 1991, Orleans, Mass.: Parnassus Imprints. 152 p.

[9] *Annual Report to Congress*, United States Life-Saving Service. 1880.

[10] Kimball, S., *Rescuing flood victims in the middle western states*, United States Life-Saving Service. 1913: Congressional Record.

[11] Methot, J., *Up & down the beach*. 1988, New Jersey: J. Methot. 208 p.

[12] Talese, G., *And now, another spin of the wheel for Atlantic City*, in *The New York Times*. September 8, 1996.

[13] Fowler, M., B.A. Olsen, and E.B. Olsen, *Lifeguards of the Jersey shore : a story of ocean rescue in New Jersey*. 2010, Atglen, Pa.: Schiffer Pub. 129 p.

[14] Talese, G., *Century by the sea*, in *The New York Times*. August 25, 1956.

[15] Jaggard, E., *Between the flags : one hundred summers of Australian surf lifesaving*. 2006, Sydney, NSW: University of New South Wales Press.

[16] *Single handed rescues seven from drowning*, in *Los Angeles Herald*. December 17, 1908.

[17] United States Department of the Treasury, *Record of Medals Issued 1910*. National Records and Archives Administration.

[18] United States Lifesaving Association., *Lifesaving and marine safety*. 1981, Piscataway, NJ: Association Press : New Century Publishers. ix, 256 p.

[19] Kucher, K.A., *A century of lifesaving for city lifeguards*, in *UT San Diego*. January 2, 2015.

[20] *Life-Saver is held for endangering life*, in *The New York Times*. August 13, 1938.

[21] National Research Council (U.S.). Committee on Trauma. and National Research Council (U.S.). Committee on Shock., *Accidental death and disability: the neglected disease of modern society*. Public Health Service publication. 1971, Rockville, Md.: Reprinted by the U.S. Division of Emergency Health Services. 38 p.

[22] Sheffield, C.T.W., *First Aid in Water Accidents - Life Saving Methods of American Red Cross*. Undated.

[23] *Kahanamoku helps save 13 in launch*, in *The New York Times*. June 15, 1925.

[24] *Beach lifeguards make real difference in safety*, in *Pensacola News Journal*. September 25, 2005.

CHAPTER 2

[1] Houston, J.R., *The economic value of beaches—a 2013 update*. Shore & Beach, Winter 2013. **81**(1).

[2] TripAdvisor. *Vacation rental stays on the rise in 2015, according to TripAdvisor survey*. 2015 [cited 2016 April 6]; Available from: https://www.tripadvisor.com/PressCenter-i7181-c1-Press_Releases.html.

[3] Shillinglaw, J., *Expedia Releases Results of 2012 Vacation Deprivation Study*, in *Travel Pulse*. November 15, 2012.

[4] Cicin-Sain, B. and R.W. Knecht, *The future of U.S. ocean policy : choices for the new century*. 2000, Washington, D.C.: Island Press. xv, 398 p.

[5] Environmental Protection Agency. *Frequently asked questions (beaches)*. Available from: http://www.epa.gov/waterscience/beaches/faq.html#public.

CHAPTER 3

[1] Mael, F., M. Seck, and D. Russell, *A work behavior-oriented job analysis for lifeguards*. 1998: Washington, D.C.

[2] Branche, C.M. and S. Stewart, *Lifeguard effectiveness: A report of the working group*, Centers for Disease Control and Prevention, Editor. 2001: Atlanta, Georgia.

CHAPTER 4

[1] *Guidelines for establishing opern-water recreational beach standards—proceedings of a conference*, J.D. McCloy and J.A. Dodson, Editors. 1981, Texas A&M Sea Grant College Program: Galveston, Texas.

[2] United States Department of Labor, *Fact Sheet #43: Youth Employment Provisions of the Fair Labor Standards Act (FLSA) for Nonagricultural Occupations*. 2010.

[3] U.S. Department of Transportation. *National EMS Education Standards and Instructional Guidelines*. Available from: http://www.ems.gov/EducationStandards.htm.

CHAPTER 6

[1] Bascom, W., *Waves and beaches : the dynamics of the ocean surface*. Rev. and updated, 1st rev. ed. 1980, Garden City, N.Y.: Anchor Press. xvii, 366 p., 24 leaves of plates.

[2] National Oceanic and Atmospheric Administration. *Wind, Swell and Rogue Waves*. [cited 2016 April 7]; Available from: http://www.srh.noaa.gov/jetstream/ocean/waves.html.

[3] Lascody, R.L., *East central Florida rip current program*. National Weather Digest, 1998. **22**(2): p. 25–30.

[4] National Weather Service. *Natural Hazard Statistics*. [cited 2016 April 8]; Available from: http://www.nws.noaa.gov/om/hazstats.shtml.

[5] MacMahan, J.H., E.B. Thornton, and J.H.M. Reniers, *Rip current review*. Coastal Engineering, 2006. **53**: p. 191–208.

[6] Open University. Oceanography Course Team., *Waves, tides, and shallow-water processes*. 1st ed. 1989, Oxford ; New York: Pergamon Press, in association with the Open University, Milton Keynes, England. 187 p.

[7] National Oceanic and Atmospheric Administration. *Tsunami*. [cited 2016 April 8]; Available from: http://www.tsunami.noaa.gov/.

[8] National Hurricane Center. *Storm Surge Overview*. Available from: http://www.nhc.noaa.gov/surge/.

[9] National Hurricane Center. *Storm Surge Overview*. [cited 2016 April 8]; Available from: http://www.nhc.noaa.gov/surge/.

CHAPTER 7

[1] National Weather Service. *Natural Hazard Statistics*. [cited 2016 April 8]; Available from: http://www.nws.noaa.gov/om/hazstats.shtml.

[2] Jensenius, J., John S., *A Detailed Analysis of Lightning Deaths in the United States from 2006 through 2015*, N.W. Service, Editor. 2016.

[3] National Oceanic and Atmospheric Administration. *Lightning fatalities by state 2005 - 2014*. [cited 2016 April 16]; Available from: http://www.lightningsafety.noaa.gov/stats/05-14deaths_by_state_maps.pdf.

[4] Golden, F. and M. Tipton, *Essentials of sea survival*. 2002, Champaign, Ill.; Leeds: Human Kinetics.

[5] Tipton, M., et al., *Immersion deaths and deterioration in swimming performance in cold water*. Lancet, 1999. **354**(9179): p. 626–9.

[6] Krause, K., et al., *[Cold-induced urticaria and angioedema. Classification, diagnosis and therapy]*. Hautarzt, 2010. **61**(9): p. 743–9.

[7] The Skin Cancer Foundation. *Skin cancer facts & statistics*. [cited 2016 April 15]; Available from: http://www.skincancer.org.

CHAPTER 8

[1] van Beeck, E.F., et al., *A new definition of drowning: towards documentation and prevention of a global public health problem*. Bulletin of the World Health Organization, 2005. **83**(11): p. 853–857.

[2] Laosee, O.C. and J. Gilchrist, *Drowning — United States, 2005–2009*. Morbidity and Mortality, 2012. **61**(19): p. 344–347.

[3] Centers for Disease Control and Prevention. *Unintentional drowning: get the facts*. [cited 2016 April 8]; Available from: http://www.cdc.gov/HomeandRecreational-Safety/Water-Safety/waterinjuries-factsheet.html.

[4] Mael, F., M. Seck, and D. Russell, *A work behavior-oriented job analysis for lifeguards*. 1998: Washington, D.C.

[5] Brenner, R.A., et al., *Where children drown, United States, 1995*. Pediatrics, 2001. **108**(1): p. 85–9.

[6] *Statistical abstract of the United States: 2012. Arts, recreation, and travel: Participation in selected sports activities 2009*, U.S. Census Bureau, Editor. 2012.

[7] Cordell, H., et al., *Outdoor recreation activity trends: what's growing, what's slowing?*, U.S. Forest Service, Editor. 2008.

[8] *National Recreational Boating Survey 2012*, U.S. Coast Guard, Editor.

[9] U.S. Department of Transportation, *Recreational boating safety, alcohol involvement, and property damage data*. 2012.

[10] U.S. Coast Guard, *2012 Recreational boating statistics*.

[11] Smith, G.S., et al., *Drinking and recreational boating fatalities: a population-based case-control study*. JAMA, 2001. **286**(23): p. 2974–80.

[12] NSCISC National Spinal Cord Injury Statistical Center, *2014 annual report*.

[13] *DAN annual diving report, 2012-2015 edition* P.M. Buzzacott, PhD, Editor., Divers Alert Network.

[14] Epilepsy Foundation. *Safety at camp*. [cited 2016 April 9].

[15] Orlowski, J.P. and D. Szpilman, *Drowning. Rescue, resuscitation, and reanimation*. Pediatr Clin North Am, 2001. **48**(3): p. 627–46.

[16] Plueckhahn, V.D., *Drowning: community aspects*. Med J Aust, 1979. **2**(5): p. 226–8.

[17] Morley, P., *Resuscitation: Unusual circumstances of drowning*, in *Handbook on Drowning*, J. Bierens, Editor. 2005.

[18] Davide, C., C. Eleonora, and G. Luciano, *Ventilatory management of ARDS after drowning*, in *Drowning*, J. Bierens, Editor. 2014.

CHAPTER 10

[1] Driscoll, T.R., J.A. Harrison, and M. Steenka.m.p, *Review of the role of alcohol in drowning associated with recreational aquatic activity*. Inj Prev, 2004. **10**(2): p. 107-13.

[2] United States Lifeguard Standards Coalition, *United States lifeguard standards, an evidence-based review and report by the United States Lifeguard Standards Coalition*. 2011.

[3] Smith, J., *Recognition, vigilance and surveillance techniques*, in *The science of beach lifeguarding*, M. Tipton and A. Wooler, Editors. 2016, CRC Press: Boca Raton.

[4] Fenner, P., et al., *Prevention of drowning: visual scanning and attention span in lifeguards.* The Journal of Occupational Health and Safety Australia and New Zealand, 1999. **15**(1).

CHAPTER 16

[1] Ludcke, J.A., et al., *Impact data for the investigation of injuries in inflatable rescue boats (IRBS).* Australas Phys Eng Sci Med, 2001. **24**(2): p. 95–101.

[2] American Academy of Dermatology. *Skin cancer.* [cited 2016 April 15]; Available from: www.aad.org.

[3] The Skin Cancer Foundation. *Skin cancer facts & statistics.* [cited 2016 March 15]; Available from: http://www.skincancer.org.

[4] Green, A.C., et al., *Reduced melanoma after regular sunscreen use: randomized trial follow-up.* J Clin Oncol, 2011. **29**(3): p. 257–63.

[5] Hughes, M.C., et al., *Sunscreen and prevention of skin aging: a randomized trial.* Ann Intern Med, 2013. 158(11): p. 781–90.

[6] U.S. Food and Drug Administration. *Tips to Stay Safe in the Sun: From Sunscreen to Sunglasses.* [cited 2017 April 3]; Available from: https://www.fda.gov/ForConsumers/ConsumerUpdates/ucm049090.htm#2.

[7] Consumer Reports. *Testing sun protective clothing.* [cited 2016 April 15]; Available from: www.consumerreports.org.

[8] Brewster, B.C., *Lifeguard skin cancer protection, an approach to protecting health and promoting image*, in *International Life Saving Federation Medical-Rescue Conference Proceedings.* 1997: San Diego, California.

[9] Dahl, A.M. and D.I. Miller, *Body contact swimming rescues--what are the risks?* Am J Public Health, 1979. **69**(2): p. 150–2.

[10] U.S. Centers for Disease Control and Prevention. *Vaccine Information for Adults - Recommended Vaccines for Healthcare Workers.* [cited 2016 April 15]; Available from: www.cdc.gov.

[11] United States Lifeguard Standards Coalition, *United States lifeguard standards, an evidence-based review and report by the United States Lifeguard Standards Coalition.* 2011.

CHAPTER 17

[1] International Shark Attack File. [cited 2016 April 16]; Available from: https://www.flmnh.ufl.edu/fish/isaf.

[2] Williamson, J.A., P. Fenner, and J.W. Burnett, *Venomous and poisonous marine animals: a medical and biological handbook.* 1996, Sydney, Australia: University of New South Wales Press.

CHAPTER 18

[1] American Heart Association. *2015 American Heart Association Guidelines for CPR & ECC*. [cited 2016 April 16]; Available from: eccguidelines.heart.org.

[2] Mejicano, G.C. and D.G. Maki, *Infections acquired during cardiopulmonary resuscitation: estimating the risk and defining strategies for prevention*. Ann Intern Med, 1998. **129**(10): p. 813–28.

[3] International Life Saving Federation, *Medical Position Statement: In water resuscitation*. 2001.

[4] Manolios, N. and I. Mackie, *Drowning and near-drowning on Australian beaches patrolled by life-savers: a 10-year study, 1973-1983*. Med J Aust, 1988. **148**(4): p. 165-7, 170–1.

[5] International Life Saving Federation, *Medical Position Statement: Positioning a statement on a sloping beach*. 2003.

[6] Orlowski, J.P. and D. Szpilman, *Drowning. Rescue, resuscitation, and reanimation*. Pediatr Clin North Am, 2001. **48**(3): p. 627–46.

[7] International Life Saving Federation, *Medical Position Statement: Who needs further medical help after rescue from water*. 2000.

[8] International Life Saving Federation, *Medical Position Statement: Marine Envenomation*. 2000.

[9] Atkinson, P.R., et al., *Is hot water immersion an effective treatment for marine envenomation?* Emerg Med J, 2006. **23**(7): p. 503–8.

[10] Loten, C., et al., *A randomised controlled trial of hot water (45 degrees C) immersion versus ice packs for pain relief in bluebottle stings*. Med J Aust, 2006. **184**(7): p. 329–33.

[11] Thomas, C.S., et al., *Box jellyfish (Carybdea alata) in Waikiki. The analgesic effect of sting-aid, Adolph's meat tenderizer and fresh water on their stings: a double-blinded, randomized, placebo-controlled clinical trial*. Hawaii Med J, 2001. **60**(8): p. 205–7, 210.

[12] Williamson, J.A., P. Fenner, and J.W. Burnett, *Venomous and poisonous marine animals : a medical and biological handbook*. 1996, Sydney, Australia: University of New South Wales Press.

[13] Rathjen, W.F. and B.W. Halstead, *Report on two fatalities due to stingrays*. Toxicon, 1969. **6**(4): p. 301–2.

[14] Golden, F.S., G.R. Hervey, and M.J. Tipton, *Circum-rescue collapse: collapse, sometimes fatal, associated with rescue of immersion victims*. J R Nav Med Serv, 1991. **77**(3): p. 139–49.

[15] Bolte, R.G., et al., *The use of extracorporeal rewarming in a child submerged for 66 minutes*. JAMA, 1988. **260**(3): p. 377–9.

[16] Bentley, B., *Cold-induced urticaria and angioedema: diagnosis and management*. Am J Emerg Med, 1993. **11**(1): p. 43–6.

[17] Mathelier-Fusade, P., et al., *Clinical predictive factors of severity in cold urticaria*. Arch Dermatol, 1998. **134**(1): p. 106–7.

CHAPTER 19

[1] Divers Alert Network, *Annual Diving Report, 2012 - 2015 edition*.

[2] Morgan, W.P., *Anxiety and panic in recreational scuba divers*. Sports Med, 1995. **20**(6): p. 398–421.

[3] *Report on decompression illness, diving fatalities, and project dive exploration*, P. Vann, R. and M.S. Uguccioni, D., Editors., Divers Alert Network: Durham, NC.

[4] Kizer, K.D., *Undersea emergencies: treating barotrauma and the bends*. The Physician and Sportsmedicine, 1992. **20**(8).

CHAPTER 26

[1] Serb, C., *Sam's boys : the history of Chicago's Leone Beach and legendary lifeguard Sam Leone*. 2000, Chicago, Ill.: Leone Beach Advisory Council. 169 p.

[2] Burnside, R., *The origin and history of junior lifeguard programs*. American Lifeguard Magazine, 2014. **31**(2).

Index

Note: Page numbers followed by *f* indicate figures.